Psychiatric Social Work

Psychiatric Social Work:

A Transactional Case Book

ROY R. GRINKER, SR.

HELEN MACGREGOR

KATE SELAN

ANNETTE KLEIN

JANET KOHRMAN

From the Institute for Psychosomatic and Psychiatric

Research and Training of the Michael Reese

Hospital and Medical Center, Chicago

BASIC BOOKS, INC. · NEW YORK

PERMISSIONS

The authors extend grateful thanks to the following publishers and individuals for permission to quote from the indicated materials:

Family Service Association of America: Gordon Hamilton, "A Theory of Personality: Freud's Contribution to Social Work," in H. J. Parad (Ed.), *Ego Psychology and Dynamic Casework*, 1958.

W. W. Norton & Company: F. Alexander and H. Ross (Eds.), *Twenty Years of Psychoanalysis*, 1953.

The Ronald Press Company: T. M. French, "The Transference Phenomenon," in F. Alexander and T. M. French, *Psychoanalytic Therapy*, 1946.

© 1961 by Basic Books, Inc.
Library of Congress Catalog Card Number: 61-6401
PRINTED IN THE UNITED STATES OF AMERICA
Designed by Guy Fleming

Preface

SINCE WORLD WAR II psychiatry has been on the move and its practitioners have shaken off their complacency. The newly formed *Group for the Advancement of Psychiatry* (GAP) has played an important role in activating change, but it could not have been effective were it not for the recent ferment of excitement in the field. Many scientific developments from physiology, biochemistry, and pharmacology promise impending breakthroughs into greater knowledge of the etiology of the psychoses. Clinically new methods of management of hospital patients, new forms of psychiatric treatment, and new roles for psychiatric personnel bear witness to profound changes during the last decade.

Scientific progress, however, is not synonymous with improvement in understanding or increased effectiveness in *therapy*. Continuous scrutiny of the validity of various therapeutic procedures has fortunately replaced the self-complacency responsible for maintaining traditional attitudes and techniques. Today we are asking searching questions about what kinds of therapies are suitable for whom and whether these procedures are really effective. Such scrutiny has naturally extended to analyses of the operations of outpatient clinics, the functions of various members of the psychiatric team, and vigorous investigations of psychotherapy.

In 1950 Dr. John P. Spiegel, who was then chief of our outpatient clinic, organized a seminar with several psychiatric social workers for the purpose of answering the question: What are the functions of the psychiatric social worker? We knew at the time that, with pressure and approval from psychiatrists, they were doing more than what had been traditionally conceived as social service or casework. The time had come to know what the psychiatric social worker actually did and how he did it.

For two years Dr. Spiegel worked as the leader of the seminar which developed an outline for a method of analysis of social work functions. When he left our Institute for another post, he asked me to "carry on for a bit." This "bit" turned out to be more than six years.

During these years the goals of the seminar changed somewhat. We became interested in the historical evolution of psychiatric social work from the "friendly visitor" to the psychotherapist of today. We studied the current dilemma of the social worker-therapist and how this dilemma could be relieved. We developed theoretical concepts and operational approaches and subjected them to preliminary testing.

Shortly after the war Spiegel and I had continued our collaborative work begun during our military service (*War Neuroses*[1] and *Men Under Stress*[2]) by attempting to write a treatise on dynamic psychiatatry. Although this work was never completed, it led us to great interest in the transactional approach adapted from the philosophy of Dewey and Bentley.[3] We have since utilized their concepts in our own research—Spiegel[4] for the family, myself[5] in the psychosomatic field—and have written about them in our publications.

It was only natural that Spiegel should have applied the transactional approach to the task of defining and refining psychiatric social work functions and that I should have applied it to social work operations and finally to psychotherapy. A by-product of this research was the application of transactional concepts to psychotherapy conducted by all disciplines, and especially to the teaching of psychiatric residents. As a result, the major portion of this book is suitable for study by all disciplines involved in psychotherapy.

From time to time several psychiatric social workers participated in our seminar but for various reasons could not continue. During their stay they contributed extensively to our work. Among these collaborators were Prudence Hanford, M.S.S., Grace Slocum, M.A., Joy Simon, M.A., and Winifred Walsh, M.A. A great deal of credit and our gratitude belong to June Miller, our efficient, effective, and loyal secretary.

The research was supported by funds from the State of Illinois, Department of Public Welfare—Mental Health Fund.

ROY R. GRINKER, SR.

References

1. Grinker, R. R., and Spiegel, J. P.: *War Neuroses*. Philadelphia: Blakiston, 1945.
2. Grinker, R. R., and Spiegel, J. P.: *Men Under Stress*. Philadelphia: Blakiston, 1945.
3. Dewey, J., and Bentley, A. F.: *Knowing and the Known*. Boston: Beacon, 1949.
4. Spiegel, J. P.: The Resolution of Role Conflict Within the Family. *Psychiatry, 20*:1, 1957.
5. Grinker, R. R.: *Psychosomatic Research*. New York: Norton, 1953.

Introduction

THE RESEARCHES REPORTED in this volume were carried out in the Outpatient Clinic of the Division of Psychiatry at the Michael Reese Hospital and Medical Center. They were initiated in order to resolve what we felt to be a pressing need to evaluate the current functions of social workers in general and of psychiatric social workers in particular. For a long time their operations in the Clinic were taken for granted as necessary and valuable, but the operations eluded definition because of profound and rapid changes in emphasis which began about the time of World War II. Because current social work functions are syntonic with psychiatric needs—in fact, the therapeutic roles of social workers were induced by psychiatrists—the underlying confusions, doubts, and uncertainties in the social work field for the most part have been unrecognized or at least neglected.

At Michael Reese psychiatry was initiated in 1921 with the establishment of a child guidance clinic whose leadership gradually evolved an early form of psychodynamically oriented diagnosis and treatment. By the time an adult psychiatric clinic was opened in 1936, dynamic psychiatry was practiced by a team composed of psychiatrists, psychologists, and psychiatric social workers, each member having his own specific function. Serious efforts during those early days were made to increase the specific skills of each team member and to facilitate integration into a cohesive group.

Gradually changes occurred in these specialized approaches, so that now each member of the psychiatric team functions in a somewhat similar interpersonal relationship with client or patient. The learning and perfecting of special skills have been disturbed by this realignment of functions. For example, the social worker does less casework, but more direct therapy. The psychologist relies less completely on objective tests, but includes as evidence for diagnosis his personal transactions with the patient, which often becomes therapeutic. Furthermore, the directing social work theories of interpersonal relationships changed in rapid succession from "passivity" to "relationship therapy" of the functional school, to "attitude therapy" to "dynamic passivity," and finally to psychoanalytic "psychodynamics." Today the question as to what each discipline does differently from the other has become difficult to answer.

For this reason we set up a seminar for psychiatric social workers led by a psychiatrist with the goal of finding out what the social worker actually does. We first listed the traditional levels of functioning from so-called "steering" to "psychotherapy" but found them empty of meaning except as indicating expectations of certain goal achievements. We then set up parallel lists indicating social service functional counterparts to the needs of the usual client or patient population. Here the essence of what went on consisted only of the empty spaces between the parallel lists.

The next obvious step was to study what went on between the client-patient and the social worker-therapist. This, however, could not be understood adequately by observing and describing the verbal and nonverbal behavior of one of the pair as if it were some sort of self-action. Describing the impact of the behavior of one on the other as an interaction was a limited view of cause and effect. We were forced to enlarge our temporal and spatial perspective to create what is known as a transactional approach.

In the transactional approach the setting or field of operations must be known not as a fixed state but as an ever changing matrix which affects the persons involved and is altered by them. The behavior of each participant can be viewed as portrayed through explicit instrumental social roles and by implicit roles expressing affective or emotionally meaningful messages. Through these rapidly changing roles within slowly moving fields, information is exchanged by means of verbal, nonverbal, and paralingual communications. Finally the cyclical reverberating influence of one on the other, back to the first, and back again, eventually reaches closure when information becomes repetitive and explicit role-complementarity has been achieved. At this point the implicit meaning of the transaction is communicated, and a new focus of communication is opened up.

The transactional approach is operational; it requires an understanding of the tactics of skilled relationships. Its underlying basic theories involve field-, role-, and communication-theories. It restricts the use of psychodynamic theory to the understanding of underlying motivations, conflicts, and defenses without the confusing use of modified psychoanalytic techniques.

The transactional approach furthers the understanding of human beings in relationships with one or more other persons. Thus, it is a means for understanding social workers in relationship to colleagues, to staff, to members of other disciplines in the psychiatric teams, and primarily to patients, but this approach as we have used it is applicable to the understanding of persons in trouble by all therapists of any discipline. It is essentially the most adequate frame of reference from which to understand what people try to say in any relationship, especially when the role relationship is structured as that between the need-requesting client or patient and the helping social worker or therapist.

We present our transactional approach as we have developed it in a research seminar after many years' study and illustrate it with case reports from various areas of social work functioning. We have extended its use, after further study, for supervision of psychiatric residents and in the treatment of patients by all staff members of the psychiatric clinic and hospital. As a report of this extended piece of group research, our experiments and conclusions have been organized in monograph form. However, by the fact that our conclusions can be broadly applied, this volume may be utilized as a textbook for social work students, graduates, and teachers.

Contents

xiii

PART. IV • The Transaction

I

The Setting

1

A Theoretical Framework
for Social Work

T HE EVOLUTION OF SOCIAL WORK from the "friendly visitor" to the professional specialist was slow and tortuous. At each phase of the specialty's growth its practitioners were doubtful and insecure, constantly searching for certainty. Contrary advice from academic teachers of social work theory and practical chiefs of psychiatric services, who needed as much therapeutic time as possible for their overwhelming case loads, resulted in a victory for the latter. Social workers gradually moved from casework to depth psychology and psychotherapy. But the "pied pipers" of psychodynamics and psychotherapy led them into dangerously deep waters and more confusion and uncertainty!

Since no one was sure what the social worker was supposed to do or for that matter what he actually did, our studies began with two basic questions oriented toward defining social work operations: (1) What does the psychiatric social worker do with his time in the psychiatric clinic and hospital? (2) How does he use his knowledge and technical skill in serving his patient's needs?

Previously, in annual reports, the above questions had been answered in terms of number and kind of interviews and conferences held, and number of patients or relatives served. Caseworkers' activities were broadly and vaguely reported in terms of "history-taking" or "planning" or "treatment" with either patients or relatives. These statistical analyses, although useful in some ways, were of little value in reflecting

3

specifically either what the social worker did or how he did it. We felt perhaps that this was true not only because of our particular methods of reporting but also because we ourselves were unclear as to how to describe, classify, and report this work. Professional schools and other agencies and we, too, were troubled and confused when we tried to differentiate some aspects of social work functioning from those of the psychiatric residents and staff psychiatrists.

Bowers culled 34 definitions of social casework from the literature, beginning with Mary Richmond in 1915 and ending with Charlotte Towle in 1947. The integrated conclusion is as follows: "Social case work is an art in which knowledge of the science of human relations and skill in relationship are used to mobilize capacities in the individual and resources in the community appropriate for better adjustment between the client and all or any part of his total environment." [1] However, such generalities are no longer sufficient for those actively engaged in the practice of social work.

Concepts or theories of social work in a psychiatric clinic, if extracted from their operations, may be ordered into three levels of abstractions. The most abstract are similar or even identical to the formulation made by Bowers. Here adjustment between the client and his environment is the ultimate goal, even *all* his environment. This determines, in *a priori* fashion, a set of operations designed to achieve the intended result. A glance at Table 2 (see page 288) shows that social work operations are heavily loaded with goals and purposes of the worker, but with little consideration of the patient and his needs.

A less abstract set of theories is demonstrated operationally in Table 3 (see page 290). These are collateral concepts in that the functions of the social worker are listed in hierarchical order parallel to needs of unidentified patients. There is no indication of the relationship between patient and worker within the specific setting of the clinic or the special changing needs of the patient.

A more operational theory of social work emphasizes the changing aspects of the transactions reverberating between patient and worker as a system. Such a dynamic model formulates an operational and understandable approach to processes of human relationships directly applicable to all psychiatric social work functions (see Table 1, page 22).

In searching for a more fruitful way to understand the functions of social workers, especially those specializing in psychiatric clinics, we first studied the historical background of the field and its evolutionary changes during the last half century. The term *social* early became structuralized to emphasize a traditional emphasis on knowledge and skills relative to relationships among people. It indicated a change from emphasis on material supplies and environmental conditions, as the sources of misery, to a concern with *interpersonal* processes. With the development of dynamic psychiatry, *internal* feelings, attitudes, and concerns, as expressed in social relations, became dominant and significant indices of mental health and illness.

Although the social worker currently strives to understand the individual with whom he is working, his transactions within the nuclear family, his role in the family's equilibrium, and the costs to him should still be of utmost importance. Not only the other members of the family and how they relate to the patient but also the extended social, economic, and cultural environments with their assets, strains, and stresses contribute to the adaptations and illness of the patient. His social matrix influences the patient's well-being and is affected by him. It contributes to the cause, course, and prognosis of all psychiatric illness.

Despite the influx of social scientists into mental hospitals and psychiatric clinics and the increasing interest in family and group dynamics, the concepts of "social psychiatry" are still nebulous.[2] Cultural anthropologists and sociologists under the influence of psychoanalysis are attempting to explain the reciprocal processes among culture, society, personality, and mental illness. At the present time there is still considerable confusion in these efforts, and theoretical formulations are less than tentative. Correspondingly, techniques for effecting change in the social matrix of any one patient directly are entirely lacking, with the exception of some beginning approaches to treatment of the family.[3] Should theory and operations in "social psychiatry" develop, they will probably stem from the social scientists who will then extend their roles from investigators to therapists. The social worker today can only be aware of the social matrix of psychiatry, obtain and transmit information about its processes in specific cases, and return information and advice about specific patients to significant representatives of the family or other small groups.

To help people in trouble the social worker acquires knowledge and facility in utilizing the resources of social agencies, many of which are highly specialized for particular purposes, both for information and action. In addition, he needs to know much about economic processes, social institutions, many subcultures within the framework of the total American culture, the characteristics and relations among social classes,[4] and the larger institutions of armed services, churches, and schools.

Because of the primary emphasis on the *individual* as a focus around which family and society were considered at one time to radiate as passive environments extending to infinity, it was inevitable that the social worker should be fascinated by psychodynamics and interested in the internal personality establishment of the psychologically ill. To understand psychodynamics the social worker needs to know some aspects of psychodynamic theory. For its application the processes of *communication of information* at various levels or degrees of awareness are essential tools. The behavior of the patient and of the therapist as participant-observer requires a knowledge of *role behavior*. Finally, relating this two-person microcosm to environments is a function of *field theory*. No one is expected to know all about these theories or the operations that they induce, but knowing a great deal about each may enable social workers to synthesize them and perhaps in the future to develop an operational approach for themselves. This synthesis in brief is what we shall now call the *transactional approach*.

FIELD THEORY

Ordinarily part-whole relationships among systems of living organizations are represented by *levels,* with hierarchies of increasing complexity of organization and corresponding greater flexibility of function and looser integration. Such an analysis attempts to view larger units as composed of many simpler inner parts as in a "Chinese box nest." One way of viewing such a model of systems is to proceed from the physicochemical structure of the body, to organs and organ systems (digestive, respiratory, etc.), to the psyche (personality), to groups of psyches (persons), to society, to culture, etc. Various scientific disciplines place dominance or greater complexity at different points in the evolutionary hierarchy. The danger of this method is to reduce all functions to their basic physicochemical limitations (reductionism) or to extend biological concepts directly to psychology (extensionism).

According to field theory, however, each organization is in process with its environment and with other organizations; none can be fractionated from the total field except artificially for the purpose of analysis or because of language difficulties. Altogether they compose a field whose size and contents depend on the frame of reference of the observer, the tools he uses, and the biases he carries with him. Within this field are systems (soma, psyche, society, culture, etc.) with a varying degree of stability or integration, and each with a structure in space and a function in time.[5] The structure-function of any part or focus in the field affects the structure-function of all other parts of the field, making for a diffuse interdependence of activity, requiring no either/or choice but, instead, equal value for any consideration of each part. Yet each system maintains its own steady state and resists disintegration. As a primary focus of observation it has multiple integrated parts dominated by a specific gradient. It functions as a whole, but only as a part within the total field in relation to other systems of organization. Within the field a system can be studied only in process with another system by the observer who constitutes a third system. In interviewing, the two systems are represented by client and participating therapist; the third system is the observing part of the therapist.

Translating this into specific practical considerations, the narrow field of therapeutic action is the interviewing room in which the worker and client communicate. Yet beyond this is the total clinic setting and its explicit and implicit meaning to both worker and client. Still larger are the social, cultural, economic, and ethnic environments of the past and present of both persons. All of these extensions have important influences on the behavior of worker and client as they relate to each other, and all influence the type, degree, and success of their communications.

To illuminate these statements, we diagram below an example that occurred in an eastern city over a period of time. The first decision started a process that moved slowly in time to the final dilemma.

FIELD = COMMUNITY CLINIC AND HOSPITAL WITH ITS PARTS
AND ENVIRONMENT

1. Prosperity increasing—more patients over budgetary limits apply for clinic help.
2. Young voluntary physicians request placement on list for referral of above as private patients.
3. Environment of hospital becomes an extension of Negro ghetto.
4. Increased number of Negroes apply at clinic—increased number of Negroes in private office practice.
5. Demand for private hospital beds for Negro patients from private physicians.
6. Increasing discontent of white supporters of hospital budget and white users of hospital.
7. Private instructions to physicians to limit Negro hospital patients to certain percentage.
8. Negro community reacts to other hospitals admitting practically no Negro patients, although denying this (never have a vacant bed when Negro applies), by threatening to make public attack on original, most liberal hospital.

According to this example we have in this community clinic and hospital field the following systems: clinic, physician, hospital, Negro patient, clinic-hospital administration, hospital-supporting community, Negro public, and other hospitals. Note that the extended field is composed of many systems; the reverberating and eventual feedback effect of the initial decision occurs over an extended period of time. The transactional processes seem markedly different depending on the frame of reference—*i.e.*, whether the observer is Negro, physician, head of hospital, or philanthropist.

Field theory postulates that all systems within the field form a continuum which in itself has a basic relative stability.[6] But since all parts are in relationship to one another, change in one will affect all others; the one originally affected will respond to the resultant change in the others. The rate and degree of change determine the extent of effect. Sources of change, although far distant (in both space and time), are significant; they may be unobserved, however, if the suitable frames of reference are not utilized. Furthermore, change can be recognized only by observing a system in action through time, for the longitudinal view reveals its alterations in structure, integration, or function.

The social worker today seems to be the only professional person concerned with the extended field within which the disturbed or troubled person operates. Psychiatrists have become more and more myopic as their interest in psychodynamics and individual psychotherapy has increased. Imitating the psychoanalytic model even in clinic practice, they not only neglect the immediate social matrix of their patients (family, work, recreation, etc.) but often refuse to see, interview, receive information from, or enlighten close members of the family. Actually, the modern generation of psychiatrists is not really neglectful but has never been taught the importance of environmental influences.

Pollak [7] points out that the social worker historically was the first to counteract such trends toward narrowing specialization in medicine and the resultant fractionation of the total field. Contrary to his statement, we see no evidence that the psychiatrists have taken over the field concepts and endangered the special positions of the social worker. Rather, the social worker could still assume an important pedagogical role in disseminating information regarding the significance of the social matrix and utilizing this information himself for therapeutic social action. The psychiatric social worker, however, has yet to assume the necessary leadership on the job for this purpose and to develop the appropriate techniques. In this field much research is needed.

To return now to the actual relationship between worker and patient, we recognize that in this two-person situation as in any other, both rational and irrational elements are involved. Our first attempts to formulate the workers' functions on a goal-directed rational basis were ineffective as long as we structuralized them in terms of levels, areas, etc., in relation to equally structuralized needs of the patients. A concept of fluid, moving, changing relationships between two people in all areas of social service work was missing. This brings us to psychoanalytic theory and transference-countertransference problems which are concerned with the irrational or emotional elements in human relationships.

TRANSFERENCE AND COUNTERTRANSFERENCE

Among the difficulties encountered by the psychiatric social worker in using psychoanalytic concepts and techniques in his own work are the problems arising from transference and countertransference. These imply unconscious relationships between therapist and patient which are repetitive of old patterns developed in formative periods of psychological growth. Much as they may facilitate progress in treatment, they are often evidence of resistance and, as such, are detrimental to therapy.

We are indebted to Orr [8] for making a historical survey of the literature concerned with the unconscious transference attitudes of the patient, and those of the therapist, the countertransference. Transference in its widest sense is a universal phenomenon in interpersonal relationships, but between patient and therapist it connotes a specific type of relationship. Freud defined transference as a special class of mental processes, for the most part unconscious. "They are new editions or facsimiles of the tendencies and fantasies which are aroused and made conscious during the progress of the analysis, but they have this peculiarity which is characteristic for their species, that they replace some earlier person by the person of the physician." [9]

Transference as an emotional relationship to the therapist has the characteristics of a repetition compulsion in that the unconscious feelings avoid the recognition that the treatment demands. Instead they are reproduced, which is a form of resistance; they are "acted out" in a defense against remembering. Transference, as Freud states it, is uncovered and isolated by analysis, but it is a universal phenomenon and defies the success of all medical influence. Analysts attempt to resolve the transference by consistently translating its unconscious attributes in all of its expressions, not only according to the meaning of the patient-doctor relationship in the therapeutic situation but also according to the infantile past which is antecedent to it.

In analytic circles there has been a change in attitude toward the transference. As French [10] says, not all of the patients' reactions to the therapist are transference reactions. Some are appropriate to the therapist's actual personality characteristics and to his behavior. Schilder [11] emphasizes that the current situation in analysis is of greater importance than the past. He states that conflict can never be completely understood on the basis of past facts because of the persistence of irreducible elements. Strachey [12] points out that the interpretations and their effects not only throw light on the past that is projected in the transference but at the same time refer to an immediate situation, the interpretation of which facilitates the separation of the real and present from the fantasied and old. Horney [13] also shifted her focus to a greater concentration on transference in the current interpersonal situation. Wolstein [14] in his discussions of transference and countertransference clearly demonstrates that patient and therapist in the "here and now" operate in a mutually experiential field and are not isolated in two self-enclosed systems of forces.

In quoting from French, the following is of significance.

> The more we keep our attention focused on the patient's immediate problem in life, the more clearly do we come to realize that the patient's neurosis is an unsuccessful attempt to solve a problem in the present by means of behavior patterns that failed to solve it in the past. We are interested in the past as the source of these stereotyped behavior patterns, but our primary interest is in helping the patient find a solution for his present problems by correcting these unsuccessful patterns, helping him take account of the differences between present and past, and giving him repeated opportunity for actual efforts at readjustment within the transference situation. Then, when the patient attempts to put his new attitudes into practice in his outside life, he will find that they have become second nature. Thus does psychotherapy indeed become a process of emotional re-education.[10]

Let us now consider countertransference, which is the unconscious emotional attitude of the therapist in the therapeutic situation with his patient. These need not be so-called blind spots or unanalyzed neuroses but are part of his life processes which are based upon his capacity for relationship. Mabel Cohen states:

> We see that the recent studies on countertransference have included in their concepts attitudes of the therapist which are both conscious and unconscious, attitudes which are responses both to the real and to the fantasied attributes of the patient, attitudes which are stimulated by the unconscious needs of the analyst, and attitudes which are stimulated by sudden outbursts of affect on the part of the patient, attitudes which arise from responding to the patient as if he were some previously important person in the analyst's life, and attitudes which do not use the patient as a real object but, rather, as a tool for the gratification of some unconscious need.[15]

Understanding the countertransference—that is, the emotional attitudes of the therapist—supposedly protects him from entering as a co-actor in the scene which the patient re-enacts in the analytic situation and from exploiting it for his own needs. Fromm-Reichmann [16] states that every psychiatrist now knows that there must be a fluctuating interplay between doctor and patient. This inevitably follows from the interpersonal character of the psychotherapeutic process. The psychiatrist who is trained in the observation and is at least partially aware of the inner realization of his own reactions to patients' messages can frequently utilize these impacts to understand better what the patient really means. Thus, the therapist's share in the reciprocal transference reactions of doctor and patient in the wider sense of the term may furnish important clues in conducting the psychotherapeutic interview.

Benedek [17] states that the therapist is a real person and evokes in the patient both explicit and implicit reactions. This holds equally true for the patient's effect on the therapist. The psychotherapist, even more than a psychoanalyst (who sits behind the couch and has his features hidden), is exposed to the patient. The psychotherapist, then, is known and observed, and his real person is a stimulus for responses on the part of the patient along with those attitudes which the patient repeats in the current situation from the past.

We go further than the above-quoted authors in that for us countertransference feelings, when recognized, are not to be considered as interfering with treatment. Rather, as we shall demonstrate later, they represent impacts of the patient's messages on the therapist's most important perceptive instrument. Giving credence to the aroused feelings enables him to interpret more adequately the meaning of the patient's messages and thus to respond better to them.

COMMUNICATIONS AND INFORMATION THEORY

Although psychotherapy has been viewed as a process of communication by Sullivan,[18] Moreno,[19] and Frieda Fromm-Reichmann,[16] it was Ruesch and Bateson [20] who viewed communication as the social matrix of psychiatry as a whole. Recently Ruesch [21] has discussed in great detail the operations utilized in defining disturbed communications. He indicates that human problems may be viewed in terms of quantitative alterations of communications or as forms of exchange not fitting the social situation. There is no need to view personality in action as a conglomerate of several instinctual forces and defenses, since all are contained in communicated messages which express the total person with his memories of the past and anticipations of the future. To understand communications of the patient, the therapist must be a subjective participant in the communication process as well as an objective observer. As a therapist dealing in verbal and nonverbal communication he needs to be an expert in understanding language as it is related to thinking and behavior and is, therefore, facilitated or handicapped by the language, often characteristic of his social class,[4] with which he thinks, speaks, and understands.

Two people relate to each other as parts of an adaptive system by means of various types of communication. These may be verbal in the form of words, sentences, paragraphs, or in the paralingual form of ejaculations and other abbreviated syllables. The flow of communication may be nonverbal in the form of gestures, overt movements of parts of the body, of the eyes, changes in the color (blushing or pallor) of the face, etc.

Successful communication is associated with recognition between two persons of messages received and understood to fit the situation at hand. This gives rise to mutual pleasure and often agreement. Disturbed communication is part of psychopathology. It may take the form of too much, too little, too early, or too late and causes considerable frustration in the persons involved. Such failures of communication are derived from types of inappropriate learning at various ages of predilection in life. Various forms of disturbed communication have enabled Ruesch to postulate profiles of personalities. Psychotherapy aims essentially at normalized systems of internal and external communications.

Ruesch [22] demonstrated that the internal communication system may be divided into three parts: reception, evaluation, and transmission. The reception aspect is derived from the outside world via the sense organs, from the inner or proprioceptive senses registering bodily changes, and from memories of past events. Evaluation is accomplished in hypothetical communication centers through which the many codings of messages are accomplished, resulting in the loss of much detail.

Both Bateson and Ruesch indicate that most communications are accompanied with supraordinate implicit commands as to how to interpret the message, often thus negating or denying their explicit meanings. It is these *metacommunications* to which the therapist needs to be sensitive. In fact, Bateson indicates that there is often a network of messages about messages about messages *ad infinitum* but usually limited to only three orders. These require careful decoding. What has been called "double bind" is observed particularly in schizophrenics who transmit incongruent messages as a result of having learned this form of communication in family life.[23]

Haley [24] states: "As an illustration, suppose that a mother said to her child, 'Come and sit on my lap,' in a tone of voice which indicated she wished the child would keep away from her. The child would be faced with the message 'come near me,' qualified incongruently by the message 'get away from me.' The child could not satisfy these incongruent demands by any congruent response." Response to either would be wrong, and he can only meet the incongruent demands in an incongruent way: by coming near her but denying it, for example, by stating it was for another purpose.

Haley says that "communication between people consists of (1) the context in which it takes place, (2) verbal messages, (3) vocal and linguistic patterns, and (4) bodily movement." All of these should be part of the therapist's observational field if he wishes to decode his patient's messages accurately and fully.

About thirty years ago Whorf [25] developed a new concept of linguistics which for him expresses modes of thinking and corresponds with inner psychic processes. We think according to the ways we have learned to speak. Likewise, behavioral manifestations are associated with different language phenomena. Thus the relation of behavior and thought to language is the science of linguistic relativity. Differences in language structure are associated with different ways of perceiving and conceiving the world. Whorf pointed out that English, as one of the standard average European languages (SAE), differs from some primitive languages, such as the Hopi, in ways which restrict our view of the world. In this context primitive languages are sometimes superior.

Processes that occur between objects, extensions of self in transaction with others, and time relationships are very poorly differentiated by analogies and metaphors as contrasted with more adequate representations in the Hopi language. Thus, in English, psychological processes involving circular transaction between two or more persons are as difficult to grasp as they are poorly represented in our language. For example, in his so-called Kennetic inquiry, Bentley [26] states, "This is a name proposed for organized investigation into the problem of knowings and knowns, where this is so conducted that the full range of subject matters—all the knowings and the knowns—form a common field."

We are compelled to use terms referable to physical relations such as: feeling close to a person, warm or cool toward him, feel for him, move toward or away from him. We talk about contents of a professional interview as material. We feel low or high. Many other examples could be given to illustrate the poverty of our language (and thoughts) for expressing relationships. When we come to feelings or reactions in which mutual participation within the same setting occurs—the "knowings and the knowns"—we are literally without syntax and have to draw diagrams or use mathematical symbols.

Communications function as carriers of information which in most cases elicit adaptive responses within the two-person system. Most healthy biological systems are open, regulative, or adaptive, and the two-person system is no exception. The inputs or perceptions make an impact which in itself involves energy transmitted through the sensory nervous system. At some unknown point a sensing device acts as a transducer converting nervous energy into information which passes through error detectors, steering signals, and controlling devices. At this point appropriate quantities of available energy effect action which innervates effector portions of the nervous system to influence the original controlled system receiving the input.

This chain of events either augments, by positive feedback, or decreases, by negative feedback, the activity of the primary system. In a psychological system with deficient controlling devices, a high level of anxiety will produce a positive feedback or increased activity which spirals in the direction of extinction of function. A compulsive system associated with overcontrol will result in negative feedback and decrease in function, or lessened reactivity to stimuli.

Granted that the therapist has some control devices that will not be disturbed in either direction beyond normative levels, it is his task to help his patient effect appropriate changes in control so that his psychological system responds appropriately and adaptively to messages. It is not necessary to speak of the "illusive" unquantifiable myth of "psychic energy." The entire process may be conceptualized according to information theory, proven so successful in viewing biological systems. That the parts of this functioning system cannot yet be analogized according to the topological aspects of psychoanalytic theory is beside the point.

ROLE THEORY

Let us first consider what role theory means to the social scientist and the advantage of using such theory in dealing with a small group of two persons in transaction within the therapeutic system. In contrast to psychiatrists who by the very nature of their interests usually focus on the internal psychological aspects of personality, Parsons and Shils [27] have developed the concept of personality as a system of action. Personality within a social structure or a cultural system is not reducible to a collection of organs, the brain, a triad of topological, psychological entities such as id, ego, and superego, nor a composite of conflicts and defenses. Personalities within the social system behave in action in relationship to other personalities. For the sake of description Parsons applies the term *ego* to the subject considered in any process of transaction, and the object with which the subject transacts is termed *alter*. Thus, ego and alter constitute a two-person system. It becomes quite obvious that there could be many alters with which the ego transacts at various times.

The personality, or ego, assumes various types of roles with various people at various times for a variety of purposes. Thus, social role theory indicates a way to study and describe the interaction of two members of a social group as they adjust to each other within a social system. Spiegel states: "A role is a goal-directed pattern or sequence of acts tailored by the cultural process for the transactions a person may carry out in a social group or situation. . . ."[5] Most roles are acquired behavior and represent the effect of culture and society on the developing individual.

Any small social group, of which the nuclear family composed of father, mother, and siblings is only one example, achieves some level of stability or equilibrium. Each actor or person in the group has his allocated roles in relation to each other member of the group. Complementarity, that is, the fit of the roles of ego and alter, is desirable. For every speaker there should be a listener, for every parent a child, and for every teacher a pupil. Complementarity of roles means that each personality automatically acts in conformity with the role that he is expected to assume, and, since few decisions are required, energy is conserved and there is little strain. When such strains are more severe, they stem from one or more transacting members whose role relations are disturbed in some manner. What may be a functional equilibrium for the family as a system may be disturbing for one of its members and vice versa.

Often the equilibrium maintained by role-complementarity is disturbed, and disequilibrium occurs. People's expectations from others are disappointed, and tension, anxiety, and self-consciousness develop. The result may be disruptions of interpersonal relations and breakdowns in group living. There are many reasons why role-complementarity becomes disturbed, but they all lead to more or less, shorter or longer disequilibrium followed by attempts at re-equilibrium.

Spiegel[5] points out five main causes for failure in complementarity. The first is a cognitive discrepancy in which one or both parties are not familiar with the roles which they are expected to assume, and thus miss their cues. The second cause for failure is a discrepancy of roles— when ego or alter requires roles that the other does not possess. Third, there is an allocative discrepancy, which means that roles are not accepted for one reason or another.

How are roles allocated? They may be *ascribed* automatically by age, sex, etc. They may be *achieved* by virtue of occupation, domestic situation, etc. In addition, they may be *adopted* because they satisfy some need. And finally they may be *assumed* in a playful way, in a "let's pretend" kind of attitude. When there is an allocative discrepancy there is a failure in complementarity. This arises because of the use of invalid or inappropriate allocation, with one of the parties withholding cues or presenting misleading cues.

The fourth reason for failure of complementarity is the absence of the instrumental means. For example, a person who is requested to be generous may be unable to accede because of the lack of money. A teacher may not be able to satisfy a student because he has not the necessary knowledge, or a therapist may not know how to handle a particular situation or problem. The fifth item is a discrepancy in cultural value orientations, as for example in mixed marriages or in rapid shift of social mobility.

After disequilibrium has occurred there is an effort to establish equilibrium again—which Spiegel calls requilibration. The first five of the eleven steps of requilibration constitute unilateral decisions on the part of ego, who attempts to *induce* alter into the appropriate role. The second five steps are bilateral decisions and include the *mutual modification* of roles. The sixth step is a connecting link between the two and may be stated here as a role reversal in which each party attempts to put himself in the other's place.

Under role induction we have the processes of coercing, coaxing, evaluating, masking, and postponing, against which alter has a series of defenses that he can use in order to avoid being inducted into the role which ego desires. Thus, he may defy, refuse, deny, unmask the pretensiveness, or provoke ego.

Under role modification the two participants in the transaction may resort bilaterally to joking, referring the matter to the third party, exploring or re-exploring the issues, compromising, and consolidating their positions in their transaction.

These roles are largely *explicit;* that is, they are conscious, describable and classifiable in general terms, and communicable by rational verbalizations and standard behavioral performances. They are explicit, for they refer to consciously motivated behavior, and, insofar as they contribute to solving problems, they are instrumental. Explicit roles are conscious and exposed to observation and awareness of both participants in transaction. A person who comes into a therapeutic situation as a patient says he is a patient and knows it and acts the role.

On the other hand, there are *implicit* roles which the person may not be aware of and, as a matter of fact, is usually unconscious of. They often express complex preconscious feelings and hence are termed expressive (emotional) in contrast to explicit or instrumental roles. These roles present certain personal attitudes and needs of the patient aside from his role as a patient, and sometimes conflicting with it. For example, a patient, by virtue of his *explicit* role structure, comes for help and treatment, with a desire to get well; nevertheless, he may *implicitly* behave like a little child searching for gratification of his dependent needs, who is not interested in achieving any independence or change from the satisfying dependence on the therapist. It is obvious that the therapist himself has many implicit as well as explicit roles which become expressed within the transaction.

There has crept into descriptions of psychiatric techniques the concept of *role-playing*. Some psychiatrists have adopted this term from the social sciences, but have given it a significantly different meaning. The psychiatric usage implies a manipulation and artificiality of attitudes and participation. For example, Alexander [28] states that one should keep the intensity of the patient's emotional participation in therapy at an optimal level. This is accomplished by thwarting his dependency desires by frequent changes in scheduling and interruptions in therapy. The psychotherapist consciously modifies the emotional climate and manipulates the therapeutic situation by assuming certain roles which he believes the patient needs. In this sense, role-playing is as artificial as an actor playing a part and is often performed with much less skill.

Dollard [29] indicates that the therapist should create a warm and permissive atmosphere in which the patient is allowed free expression. The therapist does not judge such free expression. He focuses on conflicts in present situations and on one single conflict at a time. The therapist should play a role of being puzzled or doubtful in an effort to elicit more data. In this way, says Dollard, movement in therapy proceeds from the outside environment to the inside psychological structure. Said in other ways, the progression is from projection to self-blame.

There are other therapists who express their concept of role-playing in psychotherapy as artificially assumed roles which they consider necessary for particular patients or on particular occasions. The main and most obvious criticism against this kind of operation in psychotherapy is that the artificiality cannot escape the patient's notice. The spontaneity of the relationship becomes diminished to the point where confidence and trust must suffer. Furthermore, those of us who know therapists who have advocated such artificial role-playing are aware of the fact that these people can be nothing other than themselves and any acting of a part would obviously be unsuccessful.

It must be re-emphasized that role-playing, in the sense that one plays social roles, does not imply artificiality such as occurs on the stage when actors play their parts. Roles refer to automatic patterns of behavior, well-learned through the influence of persons who represent society and who impart to the developing child a repertoire of expected behavior patterns.

We shall study the role processes in psychotherapy in greater detail later, but, as a general statement, we may say that reality interpretation, reassurance, or ego support are procedures in which the therapist accepts the explicit role assigned to him by the patient. Ultimately the patient may be able to take a new view of himself in the transaction with his therapist at the current time. However, it does not lead the patient to a discovery of his underlying motivation or to a clearer realization of what his implicit roles are.

Actually, as we shall see later, movement within the transactional process, although it deals with the current reality and starts with well-defined explicit roles, often exposes the repetitive nature of the patient's unadaptive behavior in the implicit roles and stimulates his recall of past experiences. Some of these are preconscious, and some are unconscious. They become apparent even though the orientation of the therapist is in the present transaction within the field in which both members of the transaction find themselves.

It can be stated quite emphatically that this transactional *approach* can evoke implicit, expressive, or emotional roles; it incites repetition of old patterns and illuminates the genetic sources of the current behavior. In considering the relationship of therapist and patient as a system of transactions between ego and alter, we may apply what has been learned in general about small groups. Therapy as a system consists of the behavior of a patient in terms of his role in transaction with the therapist as a role partner. When established, complementarity of roles represents stability and harmony and is conducive to obtaining information—especially by the worker in his intake explorations and by the patient in his listening to recommendations. Disequilibrium because of noncomplementarity, eventually resulting in re-equilibrium, represents the disruption of an old repetitive process and the establishment of a new system. This can produce learning, change, and a therapeutic result.

Social psychiatrists and sociologists have considered social roles as bridges between personality and social behavior. They constitute a description gross enough to be defined through a period of time but limited to what may be available or permitted in a specific social system. They are derived from unconscious attitudes based on past learning and are governed by motivations which have their origin in a multiplicity of internal identifications which may never be revealed or at least not directly in behavior.[30] Although the regulative mechanism of role systems is concerned with complementarity between actors in any social system, without which there is tension, those roles that are assumed, assigned, accepted, or declined are determined by multilevel internal processes of thinking and feeling, all of which as mentation are richer, more complicated, and faster moving than the available social roles.

Identifications that determine characteristics of the component parts of personality and delineate the self are expressed not only in role performance—that is, in the dimensions of words or action—but also internally in conscious or unconscious communications among the various processes of the mental apparatus. Some are then expressed in whatever social ways are available after filtering ego functions have been passed through. Others in conflict with each other are neutralized or locked in or delayed for later expression. The formalized content of social roles represents but a small part of the internal action system, much of which is antagonistic or at least not in conformity with the main or observable stream of the self.

Identifications are achieved through internalization of many previous transactions with significant human objects of the past. Early experiences with successes and failures in achieving complementarity for biological and psychological needs remain as memories, not of isolated experiences or individual objects but of the patterns of the experienced transactions. Parsons [31] postulates that parents who gratify, teach role patterns, and participate in the child's socialization must participate in terms of the child's needs. By entering in such transactions the parent may induce conditions for future more mature roles in the process of development. The formula is permissiveness, support in spite of failure, gradual increasing denial of reciprocity, and reward for achievement on a more advanced level of behavior. This then is Parsons and Bales' definition of the process of social maturation of the child by means of multiple transactional internalizations. It obviously is as adequate for therapy as for development, both as aspects of learning.

It becomes clear that many problems arise in the transaction between therapist and patient during which various explicit and implicit roles are played by each and the current reality situation is under focus. Some of these are: How do the internalizations and identifications become clearer, and how do they become amenable to change? How may one achieve a structural and functional change within the personality by experiences contained within a two-person therapeutic situation? How it occurs, why it occurs, and what is the nature of the change are questions which will be posed as we proceed.

TRANSACTIONAL THEORY

For our purposes we decided to abandon the psychoanalytic terminology now endowed with so many shades of meaning by different people and to utilize another terminology to describe concepts applicable to psychotherapy—in fact, to all psychiatric social work functions. We have indicated that the relationship between the worker and the patient is transactional within the current life situation.[32] Let us further describe what we mean by transactional. It is not self-action, for this indicates some wound-up process which is unwound or released and comes to an end after its energy has been expended. A clock that is wound up has self-action. An infant in its first hours after birth is a self-acting organism, but, like the clock, it soon winds down if it does not obtain food, liquid, and maternal attention. We do not mean interactional in the sense that one person acts on another and produces some effect on him like the impact of a billiard cue ball on the target ball. The interactional only tells us about a unidirectional effect, the influence of one person on another, without regard to the situation or setting of the process.

Transactional, on the other hand, implies a relationship of two or more individuals within a specified environment which includes both of them, not as distinct and separate entities or as individuals, but only as they are in relatedness with each other within a specific system. Neither is isolated. Each has an effect on the other which is specific to the situation in which they exist. One acts on the other, whose response, in turn, feeds back on the first. The process is reciprocal and cyclical. The setting or the system in which the transacting persons or foci exist determines and is determined by the processes going on. The system may be considered as the clinical setting with all the aura of therapeutic procedures and the therapist and patient as part of it. The specific life situation of patient and therapist in the therapeutic setting determines in the current time the nature of the transactions which are reciprocal, cyclical, and ever changing.

The physiological homeostatic regulation of the internal milieu of the body is a self-regulating, self-correcting, and continually moving transactional process. Nervous and hormonal activities maintain a relatively steady state so that internal oscillations remain within physiological limits. Similar processes go on all the time between people, in that self-corrective feedback changes are used to maintain stability in interpersonal relations. In therapy an attempt is made by the patient to perpetuate his neurotic pattern as a stable role (repetition compulsion). It is the frustration of this desire by the therapist that produces a feedback effect within the patient.

In *summary* we propose an approach that encompasses aspects of several modern major theories of human behavior. To begin with, we adopt from field theory an emphasis on the extent of influences surrounding the two-person system of worker and patient. The field may be formally termed the matrix, "surround," or the environment, but actually it is never neutral; it is constantly impinging in part or totally on the two-person group. Thus the setting of the clinic, the home environment of the patient, and changing life situations actively influence the relationship, not as a setting, but as a constantly changing and potent influence.

The two persons, therapist and patient, communicate with each other verbally and nonverbally with various forms and degrees of distortion; yet each tries to understand the other. Messages are received, acknowledged, and corrected in a cyclic transaction which changes in time and by virtue of the communication feedbacks. Hence learning occurs for both.

The communications within the transactions express forms of role performance which have explicit and implicit meanings indicating past learning and identifications, as well as current relearnings which we term therapy. Roles are expressed by forms of communication which vary with the nature of the current transaction. Thus the therapeutic field consists of mutual understanding of transactions in which role processes, their antecedents, and patterned identifications are communicated and changed.

Here we have an approach which deals with a vivid, current "here and now" relationship; understandable without such frequent recourse to intervening variables of "unconscious," "transference," "countertransference," and "resistance" as clichés. Thus, although we may profit by understanding psychodynamics, according to the psychoanalytic model, this is not adequate for understanding the immediate transactions operationally within a psychotherapeutic interview. The transactional approach can be tested operationally, as we shall do for various social work functions.

We now turn to our outline of psychiatric social work functions according to the transactional approach (Table 1). Having established a theoretical model that can be tested in the various aspects of function, we shall consider each area separately. The patient roles and the clinic roles are outlined in terms of the explicit and implicit, assigned and assumed roles of each. Interposed between them we designate a transactional system of role relationship within which information is transmitted. What information is communicated, how it is received, how the transaction is initiated, continues, or is terminated, and what is accomplished are all involved in understanding the client or patient.

The areas of functioning on which we focus are derived from our own clinic procedures. These are more or less typical of most clinic operations, although deviations may occur in some places. The axis should be viewed longitudinally from the first contact of the patient with the clinic to his separation at any point—in some cases at termination of successful therapy.

It is not possible to analyze such a longitudinal, lengthy time span without slicing it into at least five areas capable of being understood as specific transactional segments. We have chosen the structural segments of exploration, information, recommendation, supportive therapy, and insight therapy. Objections may be raised that these are overlapping areas, that they do not represent separable functions, or that all transactions are therapeutic. To this we readily agree, but for the purposes of scientific analysis each area is treated as a specific function as if it were performed to exclusion at separate times. Furthermore, we restrict the concept of treatment to an active process as opposed to a transient relationship. It has a goal oriented toward accomplishing some permanent internal and/or behavioral change, and

TABLE 1

TRANSACTIONAL AREAS OF SOCIAL SERVICE FUNCTION IN A PSYCHIATRIC CLINIC
1a

AREA	PATIENT ROLES	TRANSACTIONAL SYSTEM	CLINIC (Worker) ROLES
1 EXPLORATION (Application for clinic treatment)	a. *Explicitly Assigned Role* Statement of problems and needs. b. *Implicitly Assigned Role* Unknown. c. *Explicitly Assumed Role* Unknown. d. *Implicitly Assumed Role* Unknown.	Mutual, reciprocal exploration of range of implicit and explicit roles, undertaken by both clinic and patient. System can terminate on implicit or explicit role grounds, or move on to intake staff, diagnostic interview, and diagnostic staff. System then moves on to Area 2.	a. *Explicitly Assumed Role* Instrumental (operational) techniques for discovering patients' problems, needs, and especially motivation for help. b. *Implicitly Assumed Role* Unknown. c. *Explicitly Assigned Role* Unknown. d. *Implicitly Assigned Role* Unknown.

TRANSACTIONAL AREAS OF SOCIAL SERVICE FUNCTION IN A PSYCHIATRIC CLINIC
1b

AREA	PATIENT ROLES	TRANSACTIONAL SYSTEM	CLINIC (Worker) ROLES
2 INFORMATION	a. *Explicitly Assigned Role* Information seeker. b. *Implicitly Assigned Role* Unknown. c. *Explicitly Assumed Role* 1. Information seeker. 2. Unknown others. d. *Implicitly Assumed Role* Unknown.	Information (within mutual, explicit role system) that patient is accepted for help. System may terminate when patient agrees to acceptance with no complicating urgency, attachment to worker, or other conditions. If not acceptance or if complications, system moves to Area 3.	a. *Explicitly Assumed Role* Information giver. b. *Implicitly Assumed Role* Unknown. c. *Explicitly Assigned Role* 1. Information giver. 2. Others unknown. d. *Implicitly Assigned Role* Unknown.

TRANSACTIONAL AREAS OF SOCIAL SERVICE FUNCTION IN A PSYCHIATRIC CLINIC

1c

AREA	PATIENT ROLES	TRANSACTIONAL SYSTEM	CLINIC (*Worker*) ROLES
3 RECOMMENDATION	a. *Explicitly Assigned Role* Recommendation receiving and considering. b. *Implicitly Assigned Role* Unknown. c. *Explicitly Assumed Role* 1. Recommendation receiving and considering. 2. Unknown others. d. *Implicitly Assumed Role* Unknown.	Explicit role system: clinic gives recommendation; patient considers it. System is self-limiting if a. Patient rejects recommendation. b. Patient accepts, but implementation requires turning elsewhere. System is self-developing if recommendation accepted by patient is to Area 4. c. Patient's reactions or new information may lead to reconsideration by staff or by worker on spot.	a. *Explicitly Assumed Role* Instrumental: giving recommendation. b. *Implicitly Assumed Role* Unknown. c. *Explicitly Assigned Role* 1. Recommendation given. 2. Others unknown. d. *Implicitly Assigned Role* Unknown.

AREA	PATIENT ROLES	TRANSACTIONAL SYSTEM	CLINIC (WORKER) ROLES
4 EXPERIENCING COMPLEMENTARY RELATIONSHIPS (Supportive psychotherapy)	a. *Explicitly Assigned Role* Patient, client, mother with problem. b. *Implicitly Assigned Role* Unknown. c. *Explicitly Assumed Role* Person in trouble needing help with problem. d. *Implicitly Assumed Roles* An array of child roles such as: 1. Learner: needing help with understanding and interpretation of reality. 2. Guidance seeker: especially in standards and normative judgments. 3. Emotional communication. 4. Identity seeker.	Complementarity (and therefore equilibrium) in patient-clinic system is maintained through acceptance by clinic of implicitly assigned roles. Clinic is then instrumentally concerned with explicitly defined area of problem presented by patient. The system in this area may take three main forms: 1. Self-stabilizing transaction: where the equilibrium is so delicately balanced that system cannot change; *i.e.*, may persist for years. 2. Self-limiting transaction—through: a. Patient spontaneously finds another relationship for implicit role needs. b. Gentle verbalization of implicit role by therapist results in withdrawal of patient. 3. Self-developing transaction: Beginning definition of implicit role by patient or therapist results in patient's realization of responsibility in therapy, and system moves to Area 5.	a. *Explicitly Assigned Role* Instrumental or expressive sharing of problem. b. *Implicitly Assigned Roles* An array of parental roles such as: 1. Teacher: reality interpreter. 2. Moral authority and standard setter. 3. Emotional communicator: absorption and reflection of affect (safety valve). 4. Appreciator and identifier: primary interpersonal relationship. c. *Explicitly Assumed Role* Complementary to both explicitly and implicitly assigned roles. d. *Implicitly Assumed Role* Unknown.

TRANSACTIONAL AREAS OF SOCIAL SERVICE FUNCTION IN A PSYCHIATRIC CLINIC

1e

AREA	PATIENT ROLES	TRANSACTIONAL SYSTEM	CLINIC (*Worker*) ROLES

5
 	
MODIFYING COMPLEMENTARY RELATIONSHIPS
(Intensive or insight psychotherapy)
	a. *Explicitly Assigned Role*
	Patient able and willing to enter co-operative *working* relationship with professional helper.
	
	b. *Implicitly Assigned Role*
	Unknown—varies with problem.
	
	c. *Explicitly Assumed Roles*
	Patient, tester, expects miraculous cure.
	
	d. *Implicitly Assumed Roles*
	Varies with focus of transaction, depth of regression, and insight obtained.
		1. Explicit complementary roles develop, spiral, and close when information becomes repetitive. Patient's implicit role made explicit and new focus developed.
		2. Control of acting-out.
		3. Anxiety held to workable quantity
		   a. System may move slowly and certainly with increasing insight by patient, improved behavior in social roles, and more stable and lighter affect.
		   b. System may be disrupted by premature implicit role interpretation, etc., and patient leaves transaction.
			a. *Explicitly Assigned Roles*
			Therapist who cures by magic, words, advice, etc.
			
			b. *Implicitly Assigned Roles*
			Varies with focus of transaction, needs of patient, regression, and insight.
			
			c. *Explicitly Assumed Role*
			Complementary to explicitly assigned role until transaction becomes complete, obtains closure, then interpretation of patient's implicitly assumed roles.
			
			d. *Implicitly Assumed Role*
			Unknown depending on own unresolved problems.

the roles of therapist and patient are explicitly defined. The therapeutic *attitude* may exist in other areas, but its results, although often beneficial, are more in the nature of re-establishing equilibrium than of producing better performance or social behavior due to any internal change.

In subsequent chapters each area of functioning is discussed with case examples. From these practical examples about our theoretical concepts and technical operations we hope that the reader will gain clarity.

REFERENCES

1. Bowers, S.: The nature and definition of social case work. *J. Soc. Case Work, 130:*311, 369, 412, 1945.
2. Dunham, H. W.: *Sociological Theory and Mental Disorder.* Detroit: Wayne Univ. Press, 1959.
3. Ackerman, N. W.: "Emotional Impact of In-laws and Relatives." In Liebman, S. (Ed.), *Emotional Forces in the Family.* Philadelphia: Lippincott, 1959; *The Psychodynamics of Family Life.* New York: Basic Books, 1958.
4. Hollingshead, A. B., and Redlich, F. C.: Social stratification and psychiatric disorders. *Amer. Soc. Rev., 18:*163, 1953.
5. Spiegel, J. P.: The resolution of role conflict within the family. *Psychiatry, 20:*1, 1957.
6. Spiegel, J. P.: The social roles of doctor and patient in psychoanalysis and psychotherapy. *Psychiatry, 17:*369, 1954.
7. Pollak, O.: *Integrating Sociological and Psychoanalytical Concepts.* New York: Russell Sage Foundation, 1956.
8. Orr, D.: Transference and countertransference: a historical survey. *J. Amer. Psychoanalyt. Assoc., 2:*621, 1954.
9. Freud, S.: *An Autobiographical Study* (1925). London: Hogarth, 1948.
10. French, T. M.: "The Transference Phenomenon." In Alexander, F., and French, T. M., *Psychoanalytic Therapy.* New York: Ronald, 1946.
11. Schilder, P.: *Psychotherapy.* New York: Norton, 1951.
12. Strachey, J.: The nature of the therapeutic action of psychoanalysis. *Int. J. Psycho-Anal., 15:*130, 1934.
13. Horney, K.: *New Ways in Psychoanalysis.* New York: Norton, 1939.
14. Wolstein, B.: *Countertransference.* New York: Grune, 1959; *Transference: Its Meaning and Function in Psychoanalytic Therapy.* New York: Grune, 1954.
15. Cohen, M. B.: Countertransference and anxiety. *Psychiatry, 15:*231, 1952.
16. Fromm-Reichmann, F.: *Principles of Intensive Psychotherapy.* Chicago: Univ. Chicago Press, 1950.
17. Benedek, T.: Dynamics of the countertransference. *Bull. Menninger Clin., 17:*201, 1953.

18. Mullahy, P.: *The Contributions of Harry Stack Sullivan*. New York: Hermitage House, 1952.
19. Moreno, J. L.: "The Discovery of the Spontaneous Man." In Klapman, J. W., *Group Psychotherapy*. New York: Grune, 1955.
20. Ruesch, J., and Bateson, G.: *Communication, the Social Matrix of Psychiatry*. New York: Norton, 1951.
21. Ruesch, J.: *Disturbed Communication*. New York: Norton, 1957.
22. Ruesch, J.: "The Observer and the Observed: Human Communications Theory." In Grinker, R. R. (Ed.), *Toward a Unified Theory of Human Behavior*. New York: Basic Books, 1956.
23. Bateson, G., Jackson, D. D., Haley, J., and Weakland, J.: Toward a theory of schizophrenia. *Behavioral Sci.*, 1:251, 1956.
24. Haley, J.: An interactional description of schizophrenia. *Psychiatry, 22:* 321, 1959.
25. Whorf, B. L.: "Language, Thought, and Reality." In Carroll, J. B. (Ed.), *Selected Writings of B. L. Whorf*. New York: Wiley, 1956.
26. Bentley, A. F.: Kennetic inquiry. *Science, 112:*775, 1950.
27. Parsons, T., and Shils, E. A.: *Toward a General Theory of Action*. Cambridge: Harvard Univ. Press, 1951.
28. Alexander, F.: *Psychoanalysis and Psychotherapy*. New York: Norton, 1956.
29. Dollard, J., and Miller, N. E.: *Personality and Psychotherapy*. New York: McGraw-Hill, 1950.
30. Grinker, R. R.: On identification. *Int. J. Psycho-Anal.*, 38:1, 1957.
31. Parsons, T., and Bales, R. F.: *Family Socialization and Interaction Process*. Glencoe: Free Press, 1955.
32. Dewey, J., and Bentley, A. F.: *Knowing and the Known*. Boston: Beacon Press, 1949.

I I

The First Interviews

2

Intake Exploration

THE INTAKE INTERVIEW in most psychiatric clinics is usually conducted by the psychiatric social worker. It is essentially an exploratory interview for the purpose of obtaining significant information to be transmitted to an intake staff which decides whether the patient is suitable for further study or help within the clinic. Exploration is the first phase of an elaborate screening process, the steps of which are indicated below.

PROCEDURAL STEPS IN ADULT PSYCHIATRY SCREENING

1. Patient makes application to the admitting office, where he is financially rated and his categorical eligibility for clinic care is established.

2. Patient is given an appointment for a screening-exploratory interview with the psychiatric social worker. The primary focus of this interview is evaluative, to determine the suitability of the patient for further care in the psychiatry clinic. Although this interview is organized in sequence for recording, it does not focus on obtaining historical information. The content of the exploratory interview includes the following recorded points:

   a. Description of symptoms for which patient was referred to psychiatry and, if possible, their duration.
   b. Clear picture of circumstances precipitating the referral at the time.
   c. Description of the patient's social and economic situation.

d. Description of previous significant agency or clinic contacts.

e. Description of patient's motivation and intensity of wish for treatment.

f. Other historical material which the social worker feels is significant.

g. Orientation of the patient to the clinic and the necessary steps in the future are elucidated.

3. Case is presented at the screening staff by the intake social worker in the presence of the chief of clinic. If the patient is rejected, the social worker usually carries out the recommended disposition.

4. If the patient is accepted for a complete diagnostic study, a psychiatrist carries out the next procedure. In his diagnostic interview detailed information is obtained, sufficient at least to enable the psychiatrist to evaluate the psychiatric condition of the patient, arrive at a diagnostic and prognostic formulation, and make recommendations for disposition.

5. A diagnostic staff meeting is then held with the Chief of Psychiatry Clinic presiding. The social worker, psychiatric resident, and psychologist (if tests have been made) present their information. All this is discussed and evaluated, and a consensus as to diagnosis and disposition of the case is achieved. It is then usually the interviewing psychiatrist's or the social worker's responsibility to inform the patient of the staff's decision unless for specific reasons the staff decide otherwise.

The transactional field, in which the patient's problems and potentialities for obtaining help are explored, varies. The general policies of the clinic, the available therapists working on the clinic staff, the clinic's position in the total community (including what is expected of it by its board of governors and financial supporters), all have significance in the intake transaction.

Traditionally, social workers conduct the intake interviews in psychiatric clinics because they are better trained and more informed regarding the institutional aspects of processing patients' applications. They are aware of the general purposes and total program, the auspices (either private charitable or state supported), the changing policies and procedures that are the framework of institutional management, and the cooperative working agreements with other institutions that offer related services.

The worker assigned to the intake interview for the purpose of exploration has some idea of the cultural, personal, and scientific attitudes of the chief of the clinic and most of his psychiatric staff. He knows what types of patients are well treated and interesting to certain staff members. The size and type of the working team within the institution, the strength and limitations of the institution's program for training and supervision of developing staff members from all disciplines, the pressure of waiting lists and unmet community needs are all important in describing the field in which the worker functions.

Another aspect of the field concerns the persons who receive the elicited information. What are the relationships between the psychiatric social workers and the psychiatric staff and, in particular, the specific worker's relationships—because, as with any individual, he probably has some likes and dislikes which will affect his communication processes. In general, the information received from the patient is transmitted to a decision-making body—the intake staff. At times when there is an urgent need for decision—and this need can occasionally be forced or "made" by the worker—the chief of clinic is asked to make a decision independently of the formal staff. In certain clear-cut cases the psychiatric social worker makes his own decision to reject the patient for treatment.

An important factor affecting the transaction is the worker's position in the clinic and his habitual role with staff personnel, either those of his own or other disciplines. This necessarily involves the roles that he is most able to assume easily and those that are impossible for him to adopt. How will a particular worker relate, and how fast, to a particular patient and how much anxiety will be engendered in either or both at the first impact? In general, these are qualifications of his personality.

In summary, then, one can say that before the worker and the patient or client meet a fairly extensive field is already extant, like a ghostly shadow that surrounds the individual transaction. The setting of the institutional processes with its defined policies, the general purposes of intake exploration, the goals set by the institutional policy, the persons involved in the interview and those to whom the information is given are all elements of the field which constitute a shadowy background long before the spotlight of the exploration is focused on the patient and the worker.

When the worker approaches the patient he represents the clinic functioning as a whole and those particular disciplines that will be concerned with the patient in the future. This differs from intake in a social agency, where all functions are carried on by the social work staff. In a psychiatric clinic the social worker's intake function has a boundary, since other members of the team of social worker, psychologist, and psychiatrist will become involved with the same patient. The worker naturally develops ideas about a specific patient in relation to his colleagues.

As the worker enters the interview he already has a few ideas about the patient and his problems. Some information may have been obtained from the psychiatrist or the physicians in the referring clinic, and there may be letters from a referring agency. The worker may have investigated the patient's experiences in other clinics and agencies through written or telephonic communications. Finally, data on the face sheet from the admitting office and sometimes notations from a resident physician who may have briefly interviewed the patient are available. Thus the worker has certain explicit feelings about a particular patient whom he is to interview and has some notion concerning the roles that he will have to assume.

Another factor in the transaction is the time element, because over half of the intake explorations are completed within a single interview. This practice varies with individual workers: one of our workers has been modifying all of her exploratory interviews in order to see each patient twice; another makes it a firm rule to see each patient only once. Sometimes a second interview is necessary because the transaction is not completed in the first, or enough information is not obtained, or for some reason the interview did not go well. There are some differences in the processes of the second interview which often elicit much more information concerning the emotional readiness of the patient for help.

A good intake interview develops a description of the problems for which the patient seeks help and, if possible, the circumstances precipitating the referral at the time. Teachers and supervisors on the faculties of social service schools stress that the material of the intake exploration should be descriptive in content and that the psychiatric social worker should be concerned in writing up the results of the interview objectively; documenting, describing, and representing its true flavor as much as possible so that the intake staff can competently determine the need of the patient for treatment. The psychiatric social worker should obtain from the patient in the intake interview an adequate description of his social situation, the socioeconomic environment in which he lives and works, and his feelings about them. He should be interested in the past history of the patient's attempts to secure help from various sources, including community social agencies, his motivation for treatment, and a general picture of the family setting and its interactions. From the observations that the social worker makes and records in a descriptive manner and with careful documentation, social service schools teach that there should be enough information from which dynamic formulations can be suggested and questions raised. The data, however, should not constitute an exercise in how quickly and adequately the caseworker can make a psychodynamic formulation. In other words, the use of quick clichés and formulations is discouraged and the reading into the material of textbook dynamics is decried. Intuitive judgments not based on adequately documented material may often be correct but are difficult to evaluate by the decision-makers.

From *our* point of view, however, the intake exploration may be considered as concerned less with specific data and more with general attitudes. The specific data about the patient's life, family situation, socio-economic status, etc., described above—which are the subject matter of the usual psychiatric social worker's intake interview—should be understood only as the framework for the focus of determining the patient's needs and his capacities to accept help. What we are concerned with in our explorations are the implicit attitudes of the patient toward himself and his need for help.

The worker enters the interview with certain assigned explicit roles. However, by virtue of his own personal emotional attitudes and the information about the patient which he has already obtained, implicit aspects already modify his role at the onset. As a professional, he has ideals that initiate an attitude to be helpful. As a person, he is curious and with a degree of skepticism wants to know, "What is the score?" As he enters the interview, he makes some opening statement such as, "I know that you have come to the clinic to get help, so you and I will talk together to decide whether our clinic can be helpful to you. After that, I will consult with the chief of clinic." Or the worker may state to the patient, "You are here so that we both may understand your problems and why you need help."

This immediately stirs certain attitudes within some patients, who outwardly may be expressing eagerness to cooperate and tell everything to the worker but inwardly see him as a screen or a barrier who can block acceptance. Since the era of selective service during the last war many people have become aware of what we mean by screening and have explicitly accepted the fact that almost all applications for help and service require a screening process. This understanding, however, does not decrease the resistance to expressing feelings. Intellectuals very often state that they understand the screening devices thoroughly, yet give very little information about themselves or their problems. In fact, there are many "professional patients" who are impatient at the slowness of the intake process from the beginning. There are others who deliberately slow down the processes of communication in order to test out the clinic's tolerance to their difficulties. Many patients are anxious to talk and spill over their emotional problems, sometimes too quickly and insincerely. Still others are more curious about the worker's qualifications and view him as a person who must be scrutinized and thoroughly tested. In general, however, no matter how the interviews begin, the patient usually leaves the intake exploration with some feelings of acceptance.

This brings up a danger when intake exploration achieves a successful transaction, because it inevitably leads to anticipation for further transactions and is interpreted as the beginning of treatment rather than as an investigation. We believe this is an extremely important problem, because the patient may not be accepted for treatment in the clinic or, if accepted, another therapist may be assigned to him. Therefore, a crucial problem in the intake exploration is the setting of boundaries to the transaction in order not to disturb the patient later by a sudden interruption which may thereafter affect the development of other transactional processes.

As we enter into the transaction itself, we see how the explicit role of the worker is to find out about the patient and that of the patient is to tell about himself. In the process of this transaction the communications of each person have an impact on the other, resulting in a feedback to the other as well. This occurs not only explicitly but even more so at an implicit level where words, gestures, intonations, etc., react back and forth between the worker and the patient.

In this process a transaction is conceived of as the communications which bring worker and patient together. At the beginning both are at wide arcs of their separate life circles, and, as the to-and-fro communications occur, each one affecting the other, the arcs of their circles move closer together with gradually increasing speed until a point is reached where a sense of closure can be experienced. This end point is not quantitative—that is, it is not time- or space-limited—but it is a qualitative factor having to do with the emotional tone of the transaction. Each person gets a sense of closure and a feeling of emotional communication or what is sometimes described as the establishment of rapport (Table 1a).

We can view the transactional process in this area as having three stages. In the first, there is a phase of resistance in which the obstacles toward the assumption of ascribed roles—or, in other words, the development of defensive roles—dominate the process. Here it becomes incumbent upon the worker to understand what implicit roles the patient is expressing and to attempt either to assume complementarity or to make it known to the patient what he is doing and ascribe or assign to him a role more suitable for the expression of feelings. In the second part the transaction reaches an expression of role-complementarity indicated by a mutuality of understanding between the worker and the patient. Within this range, as defined by the needs of the setting and the limitation of time, the third phase uncovers the necessary factual information.

When there is a feeling of closure and completeness and the spiraling ceases, the transaction, for the purposes of exploration, has been achieved, and more and more information may be added. By no means is all the necessary information obtained, but a typical cross section is available. At this point there is a sense of stability in that the patient-worker's responses are circular, remaining on the same role level without much change.

Some of the overlapping indications that the end of the exploratory transaction has been reached are as follows: (1) Circular responses develop on the same transactional plane despite efforts at shifting by either the worker or the patient; in other words, there is repetitive material. (2) After mutuality of expression is achieved, the patient requests rather than gives information. (3) A sense of closure develops in the transaction. (4) The worker recognizes that further handling would be predominantly therapeutic rather than investigative.

If the worker has not learned about the patient's needs at this point, it means that there have been difficulties in communication in either one or the other of the participants. Sometimes it may be the fault of the worker whose capacities to transact with a particular patient are limited. At the point when the worker feels, however, that he can make a decision regarding the treatability of the patient, the point of termination is reached.

This point is often arbitrarily conceived, in a time sense; an hour and a half for an interview or even less if the patient is late or things are not going well. But it can frequently be determined that the decision to close the interview is really made on the basis of implicit factors which are only discernible on retrospection. The interruption of the interview may be difficult if the patient has exposed too much of his inner life and needs immediate supportive help. In general, the patient is told about the next procedure—that is, the report to the chief of clinic or intake staff—which helps to drain off expectations of further immediate therapy. The patient may be told, in order to indicate the need for a time lapse, that the decision must be made not only whether to accept him for treatment but also who his therapist should be.

A word might be said about the data presented to the intake conference. What is reported, although documented by written example, is not the complete reality of the intake transaction, but the interpretation of the transaction by a participant who at the same time attempts to act as an observer. His internal organization and perceptual systems affect the actual processes of the transaction.

Sometimes a report that is made to the staff contains the statement that the patient is not motivated enough for treatment. This is an unfair assumption unless adequately documented. It often occurs blatantly in people who are forced into the clinic through the needs of others. However, most individuals who voluntarily undertake the responsibility of going to a clinic for an intake exploration have some nucleus of motivation which could be worked on and amplified or expanded if sufficient time could be allocated to the task.

In summary, intake exploration is aimed at securing a knowledge of the patient's problem or problems, its historical and precipitating factors, his current functioning, and, most significant of all, an estimate of the patient's motivation and suitability for psychiatric treatment. It is an area of investigation. Although the worker's attitude is that of helpfulness, he does not enter into actual treatment at this time. Screening processes for eligibility, agency contacts, categorical eligibility for the clinic, etc., have already been completed. Exploration of conflict such as we do in diagnostic uncovering of psychodynamics is not yet to be done. The intake exploration lies between these two processes.

With this general introduction, we now present a series of patients who were explored prior to admission to our particular clinic. In giving an abstract of the interviews we shall try to clarify the concepts which have been stated in this introductory portion of this chapter.

CASE 1

Exploration into the Problem of a Ten-Year-Old Negro Boy Whose Foster Mother Considered Him a Potential Murderer

THE PATIENT was referred to Psychiatry from the Pediatric Clinic with the symptom of enuresis, often occurring two or three times each night. He had been living in the present foster home for approximately three years. The worker was called upon to interview the foster mother for an intake exploration. Before the worker saw the foster mother, she sent a letter to the supervising foster home agency requesting early family history which the foster mother would probably not know. The answer indicated that the patient had been in three foster homes prior to the present one. The patient was the oldest of three siblings, with a sister one year his junior and a brother two years younger. He lived with his biological mother until the age of two and a half, when she died during the birth of the third child from a chronic rheumatic heart condition. Until the mother's death, the child was cared for by a housekeeper supplied by a social agency. At the age of four the patient was placed in the first foster home because the father was unable to stabilize the family and because the home had burned down. The father's whereabouts were unknown following his remarriage.

There was a note in the agency report that the boy had been observed engaging in minor stealing and was generally difficult to handle, although quite intelligent.

The worker met the foster mother in the waiting room and found that she was a middle-aged, somewhat perky and articulate individual who had no trouble in communication. She talked directly and frankly. Her energetic willingness made the interview pleasant, stimulating, and enjoyable. She was dressed in black, with a rather simple, somewhat severe sailor hat perched on her head. She had a married daughter and two grandchildren. In addition, she had two other children who were not in the home. This foster mother also had taken in the patient's siblings, so that all three children of the family lived together.

The foster mother presented the patient's problems in a sermonlike presentation as she elaborated on his lying, stealing, and wetting and told about her approach to these problems and the success that she had. She knew that she had taken in a sick boy but nevertheless wanted to turn him out eventually as a decent citizen.

The enuresis had completely cleared up during the past two months by using the technique of buying the patient a dog that was not house-broken and forcing the patient to clean up after him. In general, the patient was somewhat lazy, and she had to go after him continually to see that he discharged his responsibilities. She elaborated how frankly she disapproved of his stealing as being unacceptable to her. The way you should behave is to "save a penny and spend a penny."

The worker agreed with the mother that the patient had probably made considerable strides in improving, but apparently the mother was not totally happy about him because she was here at the clinic for additional help. The worker asked her to tell something about herself. She was evasive about her own life, saying that she loved children and flowers. She then brought out that she had never met a child like this who had no fear of punishment. When the teacher told him to stay after school for misdemeanors he asked the teacher to continue the punishment. If the mother told him he couldn't go to a movie, he said it was all right with him. Although at first the child seemed to be afraid of adults, he later had no fear whatsoever. Punishment was so gratifying to him that he apparently devised methods for receiving it.

The mother said that this was how criminals acted, and she wondered whether she was raising a potential murderer. In asking this question her affect was that of being genuinely concerned. The worker asked the mother whether she was not expecting more serious results than seemed warranted and tried to get her to understand her attitudes of apprehension, but she continued to be evasive about her personal feelings.

The worker was impressed that this was a basically solid type of person who had made a real investment in the foster children's lives. As she described her relationship to the patient, she indicated that she was quite observant of his needs. She did not understand the reason for his search for punishment but observed the pattern and, therefore, abstained from using the approach of punishing. Apparently she got a great deal of pleasure from the children but, on the other hand, there was an element of rigidity as she outlined certain duties that she assigned to them, such as one night one does the dishes and the next night one washes the kitchen floor, etc. She was able to give the patient rewards for his taking up responsibilities with his puppy and she was planning to get him a bicycle.

The worker's impression in general was that this was a sound and truthful mother who needed reassurance in relation to the way that the patient handled his aggression, since this frightened her, and her fantasy that his aggression was predictive for future murder would have to be dealt with. The worker felt that during the interview the foster mother had discussed what was really bothering her and realized that she was continually preoccupied with this child as a potential murderer.

Following the interview, the foster mother did not keep two diagnostic appointments. The first was canceled when she called to say the child was sick. The second appointment was not kept without communication of any excuse. The mother did not notify the referring agency that she had not completed the diagnostic study.

COMMENT: The worker entered the interview with curiosity concerning several unanswered questions. In the face of previous foster home failures, why was this particular placement sustained? There was no indication as to the pressures involved in the referral to the psychiatric clinic. As the mother went on to tell about her experiences with the child, the worker maintained a complementary role in acknowledging and accepting the fact that she was not happy with the total situation. At the same time, the worker indicated that she would like to know something about the mother herself. At this point, it was obvious that the exploration was going in two different directions at the same time.

It became apparent that the worker implicitly felt that the mother's concern regarding the potential criminality of the child was a defense against her own expectation of him. In other words, the worker assumed that the child's search for punishment was a defense against his anxiety about being a criminal that the mother wanted him to be. The worker thus implicitly assumed that the mother herself was the unconscious criminal. The worker apparently was shocked and angry at the mother and seized upon the fact that the child had improved in every area except his aggressions. She implicitly fell in with the role expectations set up by the foster mother and agreed that she was raising a murderer who wanted to be punished, as many criminals do. At this point the worker focused on what she thought was the basic source of the child's criminality; namely, the mother's unconscious wish for him to be a murderer, and shifted the exploration to the mother and her anxieties.[1] She implicitly presented to the mother the thought that the patient did not require as much attention as the mother did. As a result of this focus on the mother as the patient and an implicit disbelief in her anxieties, due to the worker's own anxiety, there was apparently a shift in the mother's role. She could not accept any exposure of her own problems and became extremely evasive about her personal life. As a result, the mother's implicit role was that of defensive rejection of further transactions with the worker or the clinic.

We see here that, correct or incorrect, the worker did not respond to explicit roles and statements of the mother after a certain point in the interview. Rather, she seemed to discern an implicit aggression in the mother, which was being expressed by the child, and communicated her anxiety over this situation. As a result, the mother retreated from the transaction and all further contact with the clinic. This represents, then, a failure in exploration based on a transaction which evoked anxiety in the explorer.

CASE 2

Exploration into the History of a Pretentious Young Woman Who Attempts to Conceal the Essential Problems of Her Life

A THIRTY-YEAR-OLD, white, single, English-speaking European woman, a musician, was referred to our psychiatric clinic by a male friend who knew of our services. The admitting room medical examiner obtained from the patient the presenting complaint that she had "misgivings about certain personality traits." She has repeatedly sought out as lovers men who are emotionally unable to marry her. Because of this, she felt that she needed psychiatric treatment. The medical examiner, on the basis of these statements, agreed with her request and referred her to the psychiatric clinic.

The worker learned from the form filled out by the patient that she was living alone, rent-free, in a friend's apartment located in an attractive, expensive neighborhood. She earned a modest income. Also, the patient had been in the United States about five years and her parents, though separated, were both still living abroad.

The worker's interest in this case was stimulated because of the request by a young, foreign woman for psychiatric services for the particular problem specified. The worker did not know whether the patient was here on a visa or on a permanent basis and wondered about the rent-free, semiluxury apartment. In the waiting room she met the patient, who was the picture of harmonized attractiveness. She looked like a professional model on a magazine page, dressed in smart, well-tailored clothing, complimenting her excellent figure. In acknowledging introductions, she was charming, poised, and soft-spoken, with an aristocratic and sophisticated air about her. She had an accented speech and seemed both controlled and, in the worker's opinion, almost too ladylike.

The patient launched immediately into an intellectual discussion of her problems, elaborating her statements that she had given to the admitting physician. The patient had never been in love with men who have loved her. Instead, she has repeatedly become involved emotionally with men who were unable to make decisions about marriage. She wondered why this always happened to her and if it had something to do with her personality. She did not wait for, or seem to expect, an answer from the worker. Instead, she talked further of her problems.

At that time, she was in love with a thirty-year-old single man, a "complete introvert but wonderful." He started psychiatric treatment recently, and the patient stated that she would not be here now if this man would marry her or even ask her to wait for him. Since realizing that this relationship could probably not end in marriage she has had fits of depression and crying spells. She did not know how she should behave with him to make their relationship happy now. She still hoped that she could marry him, yet even in this relationship she has never had an orgasm. She has told her lover otherwise, however, feeling that truthfulness would hurt him deeply.

The patient has never had complete orgasm with any man, but denied that this was a problem that concerned her. She saw this fact as a curious phenomenon which she thinks would be cured in the security of marriage. A gynecologist whom she consulted several years ago told her that she was too sensitive to have an orgasm before marriage, so that this "really did not bother [her] too much."

The worker suggested that, before they continued discussion of the patient's problems about marriage and men, the patient should speak more about herself and other aspects of her life. She compliantly went on to tell that she lived in a lovely apartment that she could never afford if she had to pay for it herself. She was living there rent-free with no obligations or "strings" while the owner, a wealthy single man, was in military service. It was his suggestion that she stay in his apartment rent-free, since he would have to pay rent anyway, in his absence, in order to keep the apartment.

The patient has a permanent visa to remain in the United States and hoped to consider this country as her home. She planned, however, to return to the Continent in the near future for a visit of several months. She wished to see her mother briefly, to find her estranged father in order to talk with him "out of curiosity," and to visit friends.

In the meantime, she hoped that her friend would decide to marry her after working out his problems. Should her life hopes and plans not work out, however, and in view of choosing this type of man several times only to be disappointed, the patient would like to be placed on our waiting list. Part of her waiting at least would be occupied by her trip abroad. She did not seem to be concerned about financing her travel because she was going at postseason rates, using her savings and counting on the hospitality of friends. She has supported herself since coming to this country and has already financed one other lengthy trip home.

The worker asked her to tell more about her parents whom she had mentioned. The patient then spoke of her mother first, stating that she was all that the mother has now, although "I've grown away from her, too, since school." Since she first left home in her late teens, the patient never stayed in her mother's apartment when she visited. Instead, she lived in a private home or hotel and saw her mother only on day visits. The mother earned a meager livelihood but received some periodic help from the father and an occasional small contribution from the patient. The mother has been sickly with allergies. Patient felt that she hurt and disappointed her mother by leaving her but there was nothing else she could do because there was little in common between them. The patient stated that the mother was "really a sweet person" whom she had periodically despised because she let "this thing"—the separation from the father—ruin her life.

The worker questioned the patient about the father. The response was that he was a self-sufficient businessman but that, since he has been out of her life since childhood, she had no feelings about him and could not see how or why he should be involved in her problems here and now. When the worker questioned why she thought this, the patient became indignant and affronted, angry enough to say that she couldn't understand why Americans were always asking about one's family. "It's like asking how much money you have in the bank—it is so personal." Then the worker pointed out that the patient had apparently not felt this way when she discussed her mother or her sexual relationships which, indeed, were highly personal and spontaneous discussions on the patient's part. The patient fell silent, shifted in her chair, and seemed deep in thought. She then said she would prefer not to bring her father into this at all unless the worker insisted, as she had never discussed him with anyone before, because she was too ashamed.

The worker suggested that this was good enough reason for talking about him here and now although, of course, she would not insist on it. It was really up to the patient. The worker felt, however, that the patient had many feelings about her father, or she would not react in such a disconcerted manner to the simple questions about her father's business. The patient expressed concern over her own reaction. Worker commented that patient would meet the problem of expressing her real feelings during the course of psychiatric treatment and not just present a glossed-over picture. She would talk about painful feelings or events sometimes as well as ones that she could deal with more comfortably. The patient laughed in a shaken way and said that she had never told anybody that her father really held a menial job. She divulged this information in tones as though he were at least a murderer. When the worker asked what was so disgraceful and painful about this, stating that she was obviously not so shocked as the patient expected her to be, the patient scornfully answered that such men were all alike, making vague references to their loose living and the fact that her father had had multiple extramarital affairs. The worker suggested that she relate this more specifically to herself, which she then did.

There then developed an account of her life which was given with relaxed ease, real interest, and some bright-eyed warmth and tearfulness, including many details about her childhood and her father.

From the point of moving into discussion of the father until the end of the hour the patient seemed more real, less intellectualized and bitter, and at times even like a somewhat helpless, naive, plaintive, and wondering but likable child. Her air of sophistication and seductiveness was never totally dropped, but she left the interview on a quiet, thoughtful, and controlled note, stating how differently the interview had finally gone, as contrasted with her expectations. She mentioned this specifically and seemed somewhat subdued and confused that she had been asked to think and talk about matters which she had not planned to divulge. Her final comment was an expectant question: "When will I hear from you?"

COMMENT: The worker was obviously curious in beginning her interview with the patient. This curiosity concerned the cause of referral and its source, the peculiar circumstances around the economic status, and the uncertainty of citizenship. However, explicit in the worker's role was a strong degree of skepticism mixed with curiosity. The first contact with the patient evoked in the worker, as evidenced by her descriptions, a natural, critical attitude. The patient seemed to her to be artificially poised and superficially untroubled. Explicit surprise was stirred up by the first contact by the patient.

In contrast, the patient's explicit role was that of an intelligent young woman who came for a solution to a problem that concerned marriage, about which she talked as if she were discussing a third party. Her intellectual attitudes seemed to be related to the possibility that she had received some intellectual interpretations before from her boy friend. It was clear, however, that the explicit role was that of a person who knew her problems well, wanted a specific form of therapy, and had the whole situation well in hand. As she went on talking it became apparent that this was an illusion of great strength, but that the patient seemed to know how to behave under the circumstances.

Responding to this attitude in the patient, the worker listened for a time and then apparently became impatient with the unproductive conversation about marriage and men and, as if she had had enough of the whole thing, interrupted the patient's stream of conversation and asked specifically about other aspects of her life. As the patient went on to discuss her financial arrangements, etc., the worker's skepticism increased and her reactions to the patient's lack of concern about finances indicated that here might be a cadging person who had no guilt about her behavior.

As the patient went on and revealed that she had reserved little time for treatment in view of her plans to travel to Europe, she accidentally brought out that one of her goals in going to Europe was a visit to the father, "only out of curiosity." At this point the worker became curious because she felt that in a person whose problem with men was so outstanding there probably was some difficulty that related primarily to the father.

In talking about the possibility of treatment and being placed on a waiting list, however, the patient was intellectual and realistic. There was no chewing of the fingernails with impatience for treatment. She could wait, and she could come back at just the right time. Again the worker obtained a negative impression, as if this woman were representing herself as a member of the upper class with lots of friends with whom she had a casual, detached, and uninvolved relationship. There was an implicit comparison with the mother, as if to say, "Mother is a failure, but I am not," without understanding that she too was a failure with men.

When the worker brought up the problem of the father, there was at first a denial, followed by a still more angry repudiation of any concern about him and, finally, a blocking of associations. The worker, however, continued the pressure on the patient by pointing out that the information which concerned the father was no more personal than that regarding the mother.

The worker, although pressing, explicitly stated that she was not insistent on hearing about the father and that it was really up to the patient. Here we see that the worker apparently had now controlled the skepticism and impatience that had dominated her early roles. Instead, there was an increasing state of noncomplementarity in the role relationships. The worker would not accept the role that the patient had assigned to her and, instead, conveyed the impression that the patient had problems which she could not handle and that the worker could help her to handle.

It was then the worker who actively structured the roles of the transaction when she said to the patient explicitly, "These are the things that are expected of you in psychiatric treatment." By doing so she denied that she was at all upset about the patient's life story and that she was determined to rise to the challenge and crack the external façade of the patient, who was continually expressing concern over her role in the transaction. In addition, the worker clearly implied to the patient that "I know—I can see your pretentiousness," following which a change in the transaction took place.

The patient then made a confession of her pretentiousness and indicated that she has never before told the true story about her father. At first she had generalized and simply included her father as one of the many men toward whom she had bitterness, but, as she moved into further details about her father's abandonment, she became more real and specific about her own feelings. It became apparent that her own life was a compulsive repetition of rejection which possibly was initiated in her father's early abandonment of her. The effect on the worker was to make her less tough and more understanding, and it is indicated in the report that she even began to like the patient. It was as if she had conquered the patient's resistance by forcing her into the patient role and could, therefore, be more benevolent and achieve complementarity.

The patient lost control of the interview, her façade decreased in effectiveness, she became more confused, and the role of a person who needed help became more explicit. The patient left the interview behaving as if she had obtained a sense of therapeutic experience, and on her return from Europe she was taken into treatment.

After this interview (which was concerned with exploration of an applicant for treatment) the worker made a recommendation to the intake staff that she be accepted. We can see, however, that a different recommendation might have been made if the interview had terminated at another point, for the staff decision is based entirely on a report of the transaction between the person obtaining information and the pa-

tient giving it in the exploratory interview. The initial transaction between the worker and the patient was explicitly hostile, defensive, and
nonunderstanding. It was only later in the interview that the implicit
roles changed or at least became more explicit. The patient's implicit
roles were uncovered; the worker's role changed as the transaction
spiraled to completion and the patient divulged the essential and basic
problems of her life.

One might ask whether this technique is to be recommended and, if
so, under what circumstances. Techniques depend upon multiple variables in the total field, which include the setting of the clinic, the personalities of the workers, and the types of patients and the processes
of the transaction. In retrospect, however, the attitude of the worker
might be criticized under ordinary circumstances, but it did result in
the breakdown of the patient's defensive façade and the uncovering of
an implicit role which made her acceptable for therapy.

CASE 3

Exploration into the History of an Initially
Overtly Aggressive Female

THE PATIENT was a thirty-nine-year-old white woman who
worked as a telephone operator in an educational agency. She was
referred to the psychiatric clinic about one month prior to her initial
application for services. A private doctor's referral was brought to our
admitting department by the patient herself, who stated that she
needed psychiatric treatment for which she could not afford to pay.

Information from the application revealed that she was separated
from her husband and lived with her aged, part-time employed father.
She shared expenses with him for a small apartment. She had debts to
doctors, friends, and loan companies totaling over $1,000. This informa-
tion was all that the psychiatric social worker possessed prior to her
first screening interview. The patient was imagined by the worker as
a woman approaching middle age, who was obviously having difficulty
in dealing with life's problems, especially financial and emotional ones.

As the worker approached the patient in the waiting room, patient
appeared to be angry and agitated, pacing the floor with hands on hips
flaring her smartly fashioned topcoat. She was a tall, fairly attractive,

large-boned woman with dyed hair, startlingly white skin emphasized by bright lipstick. She looked tense and exasperated. The worker's introduction was acknowledged with a loud and annoyed comment that she had already waited fifteen minutes past her appointment hour and did not appreciate it. In the worker's office, she sat tensely on the edge of her chair, frowning and grimacing, obviously still angry. In response to the initial question as to why she had come to the clinic (worker was unclear from patient's record as to whether or not patient had seen a doctor in our house physician's office or instead had been interviewed only regarding her finances), patient blurted out in angry, jerky tones that she had seen no one yet except a girl in the admitting office. Speaking in acid tones, patient angrily bombarded the worker with cynical questions about "this business," and finally asked whether anybody really knew what was going on here. She did not wait for answers, assuming that the worker would not discuss the clinic routines with her either, and finally shouted defiantly that she "might as well give it all up as a bad idea."

The worker said that patient sounded very angry over waiting and certainly this waiting and the confusion of the intake process was understandably irritating to her. Patient calmed down momentarily and began to talk about her problems. Her first statement about herself, however, was a defiant and somewhat hopelessly disparaging comment: "I drink, and I gamble, and these are male characteristics." The worker explained to patient quietly that she was not sure what patient meant. Could patient try to help worker understand the problems better by elaborating? Patient went on to say, more slowly then, that she was not concerned about being a homosexual or a masculine person but, rather, that her behavior was unwomanly. Therefore, there was something wrong with her. "Isn't there?" she demanded in an angry voice. Worker told patient that she sounded unhappy and that was all that concerned her. Patient was told to go on, and she did, stating that her behavior was disturbing to her because drinking and gambling kept her in debt and offered no lasting satisfactions. She added cynically that these would not be serious problems if she were rich because she enjoyed them so much.

The patient went on to say that she was not an alcoholic, although she occasionally got drunk enough to be sick and to lay off from work for a day, but her drinking did not cause her to lose her jobs. She admitted, however, that she has used up more than her share of sick leave and is concerned that her boss won't stand for this indefinitely. Patient drank almost nightly, in a neighborhood bar predominantly, where she went alone and knew most of the people. In this bar there were few transient customers, but she almost always paid for her own drinks. The patient stated that she was rarely picked up by a man, although she admitted that this had happened on occasion.

Patient stated that she was liked by most of the bar customers, "who are nice people," and she had played the role of a good person who was interested in other people's problems. She found herself watching and listening to the people, finding out a great deal about them but revealing little about herself. She added, "This is because the people don't ask me." Patient said, half humorously, that she was nosy about other people but did not actively seek out this information, merely acquiring what was volunteered.

Patient also felt that her real problem was her loneliness, her guilt over not being nicer to and neglecting her old father, and the fact of her never having found happiness with any man. She talked about her sense of loss and personal selfishness. She recounted that she had many frightening dreams. A typical recurrent dream had the content of the patient's being caught in a net and frantically trying to push her way out without success. She stated, "This is my life. Lots of things in my mind have to be untangled." She believed that she has always been the misfit of her family—the ugly duckling, the mess.

After describing her symptoms and problems in more detail, the patient, at the worker's request, gave a family and personal history in logical time sequence, with little need for questioning. She came from a rather large family, but was on poor terms with her only male sibling, who lived in this city. With great warmth, she tearfully described her brother's two children as wonderful persons whom she sees and to whom she devotes considerable time on their vacations. She showed worker their pictures and shyly but proudly stated that they made her feel that she belonged to somebody. This burst of warmth was followed by a harsh statement that she was only fooling herself because she belonged to no one.

As the patient continued her personal history, her mood and attitude swayed often through the hour. She vacillated between harshness and rising anger and silent preoccupation followed by depressed affect or calm, wistful thoughtfulness, frequently expressing a longing to be helped, understood, and accepted. At the end of the hour, which was terminated by the worker, patient suddenly looked up and said, "I liked the way you talked to me and looked at me, even when I shouted." The patient then broke down and cried and said it was very hard for her to talk about herself "because I feel so ashamed." The worker's conclusion was that the patient appeared to be of average intelligence, superficially sardonic, biting, and hard, but capable of warmth underneath. She seemed to be frightened about her life, her dependent longings, and the future.

COMMENT: Prior to the first interview, the worker had practically no information about the patient except that she was probably another example of a middle-aged woman with problems derived from a limited economic and emotional life. We cannot tell at the beginning of the interview what the worker's implicit role was, although it develops as she went along.

On the other hand, the patient entered the interview set for battle, with very slight realistic basis for the extensive anger that she demonstrated. The worker was fifteen minutes late, and there was some annoyance in the admitting room. Nevertheless, the patient attacked the worker and expressed herself clearly as being overtly angry at the person of the worker and at the institution that she represented. At the same time, from both of these she was seeking help. Up to this point it was not clear what the patient's implicit role might be because the angry attack covered it almost completely.

The worker responded with understanding and acceptance of the realistic basis for the patient's anger. At the same time, she avoided quarreling and did not enter into a complementary role which the patient had assigned her and, so, neither answered the attack nor rejected the patient for attacking her as it seemed was expected. The worker recognized that the patient was defending herself against her great needs, that she had been in jams most of her life but had overcompensated against her feeling of helplessness by assuming the role of a tough and hard person. As a result of the worker's response, this external façade rather quickly folded, and it became obvious that the patient's needs for help in the clinic were very great.

In beginning to talk about herself, however, she made another but somewhat different attack on the worker by a rapid and extensive confession of drinking, gambling, masculinity, or homosexuality. She confessed to unwomanly behavior and practically demanded to be told that there was something wrong with her, or, more implicitly, the demand was for a statement that she was no damned good. The worker did not assume this role, but responded by pointing out that the patient was unhappy and that is what concerned her. She did not accept the complementary role by wishing to discuss or evincing an interest in her homosexuality. Thus the first attack with anger and the second attack by shocking confession did not evoke a rejection, a corresponding anger, or a punishment from the worker.

With the worker not responding, the patient continued a frank and open discussion of her life story and indicated an underlying warmth, tearfulness, and great need for affection and love. In discussing her role in the bar of listening to and watching other people, she stated that nobody asked about her feelings or listened to her. The worker's implicit role was an understanding, listening one and evoked from the patient a role of asking for help in an extremely needful manner.

At the termination of the interview, initiated by the worker, the patient finally broke through with her basic problem concerning her life difficulties. She cried and said, "I am so ashamed." We can see that the patient explicitly and continually asked for rejection and punishment in response to her angry attacks as a wish to substitute guilt feelings, which were more readily acceptable, for a deeper, more fundamental, implicit shame over her past life. At that point, the patient had given sufficient information to indicate to the worker that, as a result of her exploration, she was a person whose implicit needs for therapy were great and she could accept them under the proper circumstances. It became quite clear that her anxiety, her dependent longings, and her concern for the future made her a suitable patient for acceptance in clinic therapy.

This case demonstrates how both therapist and patient entered the interview, which was for the purpose of exploring the possibilities of the patient's entering therapy, without implicit roles being obvious. Actually, through the transaction the implicit role was developed in that the worker refused to accept the attacking, provocative behavior of the patient, but simply wished to understand her. The patient, seeing that she could not evoke a complementary role in the worker, expressed her underlying implicit needs and exposed enough of her personality so that it became clear that she was acceptable to the clinic for treatment. At the same time, the end phenomenon consisted in an explosion which revealed the basic problem and the meaning of the defensive explicit roles which the patient habitually used in interpersonal relationships.

CASE 4

Exploration in the Case of a Paranoid Schizophrenic Boy Closely Attached to his Mother

THE PATIENT was an eighteen-year-old, white, unmarried male who came to the clinic with a brief letter of referral from a member of the psychiatric attending staff. This private psychiatrist's referral letter informed us that the patient had been in a private psychiatric sanitarium for about a month because of a fairly severe emotional illness. He had been at home for several weeks and needed outpatient treatment. The referring doctor had been a consultant on this case and not the patient's therapist, and he indicated that the patient could not afford further private treatment.

When the worker called the patient's name in the waiting room, he sauntered over rather casually. He was well groomed, nattily dressed; a short, well-built young man. He had a suspicious, provocative air and seemed to be on guard and wary in the waiting room. At once he began a rapid series of comments about what he saw and suspected in "this place." There was an air of bravado; yet penetrating through was apparently a good deal of tension and fear. When he was asked to come into the worker's office, he first said that his mother would come with him and then asked, "Don't you want to see her, too?" The worker replied no, that she wanted to see him alone, after which we could decide whether the mother should come in, too. The patient was obviously surprised but commented only that that was swell. On the way to the worker's office, he made many remarks about the layout of the floor, finally stating at the door to the worker's office that she must be a big-shot executive to have an office like that. As he entered, he asked where he should sit, saying, "I don't want to take your chair." Once seated, he plumped into the chair, locking his arms around its back, and started firing more questions, such as, "What's this psychiatry all about? What are you going to do to me here? How come you didn't see my mother?" The worker explained that in adult psychiatry we saw the person who was interested in getting psychiatric treatment himself and that, for our purposes, he was an adult since he was over eighteen. The patient immediately responded that he was no adult until he was twenty-one, interjecting that girls were adults at eighteen, but not boys. However, he thought that was O.K. and the worker should go on, and he followed with a question, "So what are you going to do?"

The worker suggested that he tell about how he got to the clinic, for she knew only what the doctor had written. The patient then said immediately that the worker should tell him what the doctor had written, and so she briefly paraphrased the original referral letter and then suggested that the patient tell more about it. He stated briefly and vaguely that he was hospitalized in a sanitarium several months ago because he "went nuts for a short time" following a group date. One of the girls invited the boys to their room after the date, and, although the patient wanted to go, his boy friend, who was the driver of the car, refused. This forced the patient to go home with his friend, since he needed the ride. The third young man went upstairs with the girls. The patient stated that he worried about this experience and wondered what they did or didn't do up there. He was furious with himself for not going and got all mixed up about it because he had to go to the hospital a day or two later to calm down. He added that he had never had any sexual experiences, that he was kind of scared of them, and he admitted that he needed to go to the sanitarium—although he hated it and wouldn't go back for a million dollars.

The patient then said, "You've asked all the questions up to now, now I'll ask you. How come you have no wedding ring and you're a Mrs., and how come you're working?" He barely hesitated between questions, as though he expected no answers. Then he asked the worker what she knew about schizophrenia. The worker wanted to know if he didn't have some particular reason for asking—perhaps he'd recently read about this somewhere or heard about this trouble while he was in the hospital. The patient relaxed somewhat and agreed that he had wondered about schizophrenia because that was his diagnosis at the sanitarium. Again he wanted to know from the worker what she thought it was. The worker gave a brief general explanation and told him that she thought what was more important was that he worried about this diagnosis. The patient admitted that he was worried and said applaudingly, "Good—you know something." He added that he had been frightened at the sanitarium because he had shock treatment and had recalled little of what went on.

Because the patient had so much amnesia and could tell little more about the treatment at the sanitarium, the worker told him that she would like to get a report from the sanitarium and his consulting doctor. The patient immediately became very suspicious, telling her over and over again that he would sign nothing. The last time he signed papers at the hospital, he got into trouble. It was explained to him, however, that we needed these reports for our information and we would like to know what went on at the sanitarium as part of his diagnostic work-up. The patient said he was confused and couldn't make up his mind about going back to school or working or what to do. Then he added that he had to admit that the sanitarium had helped him some, but he refused to sign anything. "Maybe psychiatry can help me, but I won't put my name down on any paper."

The worker then suggested they call in his mother to explain to her all the procedures and to tell her about the need for reports in his presence so that she, too, would know what we do here. Then he could talk over signing permission with her. He agreed to this but stated that he was staying right where he was, and the worker told him, "Of course you will; I want you to."

The mother, who was a short, pale, tense woman, appeared very apprehensive, and, as she entered the room, the patient said to her, "See, she saw me first," as though this was a new triumph and a source of some satisfaction. The worker explained the procedure to the mother and noted that whenever she tried to ask a question the patient would interrupt her and say, "Now that's up to me, see? Quit shoving me into

this place like you did into the sanitarium." He made many side remarks to the interviewer that the mother wanted to get rid of him.
The mother protested and attempted to hush the patient as though
embarrassed at their relationship. The worker suggested that the patient think over the procedure of getting reports and call the doctor
to discuss it with him since he seemed to feel some confidence in him.
The worker felt that the patient should talk to his doctor before signing the application blanks for information, and called the doctor's office
in the patient's presence—and at his request—to explain that he would
call and talk to the doctor later in the day.

The patient took the permission slips with him as he left quietly with
his mother, saying that he would make up his mind on the following
day. As he left, he indicated his wish to be considered for treatment.
The next day, to the worker's surprise, she received the permission
statements in the mail, duly signed by the patient. Before the mother
left, she had stated to the worker that there would be a great deal of
dejection by the patient if there was any possibility of a wait for treatment. Actually, the patient was placed on the waiting list as an accepted candidate for treatment, but, when his name came up for assignment to a doctor and the beginning of active treatment, neither the
patient nor his mother responded to telephone calls or repeated letters.

COMMENT: This interview, as an exploration, uncovered
little factual material about the patient and his disturbance, but it is
an example of a transactional process between worker and patient
under rather unusual and adverse circumstances. The worker explicitly
anticipated a boy with severe emotional disturbance but, having confidence in the referring doctor, felt that this was a valid referral and
that the patient could endure outpatient treatment. From the patient's
manner and behavior in his progress from the waiting room to the
interviewer's office, it was apparent that he was there under pressure.
The worker, therefore, felt that she had to test the patient in order to
see whether he voluntarily felt any need for help and could give any
adequate information.

The patient's first responses were described as suspicious, provocative, and wary. To the worker this indicated an explicit paranoid role in
an individual who suspected everything. She knew, therefore, that she
had better be completely honest with him, for he would interpret any
hesitancy or subterfuge in his typical paranoid manner.

The patient had a defensive air of bravado which, however, did not
hide his underlying tension and fear. He both tested the worker and, at
the same time, wanted a protection against his fear by suggesting that
his mother come in with him. To his surprise, the worker asked to see
him alone. This indicated an open and honest evaluation of him as an

adult, but at the same time stirred up his implicit fears of being separated from his mother. Thus, to some extent, the worker did not assume a complementary role in bringing the mother into the interviewing room.

The bravado that the patient showed on being greeted at first continued in his elevation of the worker to the role of an executive and, at the same time, elevated himself who was, by implication, important enough to be interviewed by this big shot. Immediately after entering the worker's room, however, his suspiciousness broke through again and he seemed to expect the worst.

Immediately, in answer to his question as to why the mother was not present at the interview, the worker assigned to the patient the role of an adult. She weakened it somewhat by stating that he was an adult only because he was over eighteen years old, implying that at least temporarily she would consider him as an adult. The patient immediately declined that role, stating that he would not be an adult until he was twenty-one years of age.

Again, in discussing the psychiatrist's letter, the suspiciousness of the patient demanded that the worker first tell him about the letter. He seemed to be satisfied and then discussed the precipitating factor of his confusional state as an overwhelming sexual curiosity. It became clear, however, that he implicitly recognized the resultant confusion as an illness and that he needed help. His curiosity was further expressed by his questioning the worker regarding her marital status and absence of a wedding ring.

In discussing schizophrenia, the patient tested the worker, who apparently passed successfully, not only in describing schizophrenia but also in adding a bit of knowledge that she understood his implicit worrisome role. She could obtain little factual material, however, because the patient was so amnesic following the shock; she therefore reacted to the sparse information. She asked for reports from the sanitarium and the doctor in order to help fill out the memory blanks. She did not handle the emotional reaction that the patient experienced when he said, "I was frightened at the sanitarium." She did not go into this specific anxiety, but immediately jumped for help from sources which could give her more information. At the same time, she was testing the boy's voluntary cooperation.

The worker met with resistance immediately, since the boy suspiciously stated that he would not sign any paper. It was as if he had said over and over again, "I need help, but you must tell me openly and honestly what you plan to do."

Again the worker seemed to need help and called in the mother to explain the procedure to her, but with this suspicious patient she felt that nothing should be said behind his back, and so she kept him in the room. The patient's first response to the mother was triumphant, which indicated implicitly that the mother was probably the source of his suspiciousness, and his later words corroborated this when he told her to "quit shoving me into this place." At this point the patient felt that the worker was his ally, who would give him enough strength to combat the mother.

The scene in the interviewing room between patient and mother probably indicated that, although the worker had shown a great reservoir of strength at first, she recognized an attachment of the patient to the mother and the patient's great need for her, which weakened the worker's position considerably. She gave up—that is, relinquished—the business of obtaining more information and, instead of asking for a second interview, depended then upon reports from the sanitarium and the referring doctor. It was as if she implicitly wished to close the transaction without giving the patient a real test of his desire for treatment. This resignation became obvious when the worker was extremely surprised at receiving the signed permission slips, as if she had not expected them. All through the interview information was being given that the patient really felt in great need of continuous contact with the mother. He stated in his first response that the worker had better see the mother first, although he was troubled by this possibility. He needed the mother; without her the treatment would be sabotaged. The mother made a correct prophecy when she left, saying that the patient could not wait for treatment, which was actually her feeling rather than that of the patient.

The patient was lost to the clinic, which seemed to indicate that this mother was threatened by the possibility of treatment for her son—which would detach him from her and permit him to be in a relationship with another woman. The transaction spiraled outside the interviewing room after the patient was informed of his acceptance on the waiting list. Apparently the mother's attachment won over the worker's honest and open acceptance. We cannot conjecture what happened to him. He probably made a regressive adjustment in the community at a lower functional level.

Although the interview had the results stated above, nevertheless, without any explicit or implicit knowledge of what would happen, this sort of interview proved to be an adequate test of the patient's motivation and his capacity as well as that of his mother to loosen their attachment and enter into therapy. It was not by intention that this testing situation occurred. The patient's amnesia required outside sources of information. If the worker had felt equal to the task of competing with the mother, then she would not have asked for outside help but would have continued to interview the patient to obtain more information or to begin an actual therapeutic relationship.

CASE 5

Intake Exploration in the Case of a Frightened
Schizophrenic Young Man

THE INFORMATION SHEET indicated that the patient was a thirty-two-year-old, single, white, unemployed man, born in the Middle West but now living with and supported by his mother. He came to the clinic on his own initiative, seeking psychiatric care. He had first sought help several years ago from a small private medical clinic in another state, where he was diagnosed as "a neurotic with some gland trouble." There he received no treatment. Later he came to Chicago, where he had some initial interviews at another psychiatric clinic. Psychiatric therapy was recommended but for some unknown reason was not given. A year after first seeking help, the patient had a course of electric shock treatments which he himself interrupted because he was so frightened of them. In the admitting room interview the patient told the doctor that he came to the clinic now because he had a watery, smelly feeling in his head and he felt weak and unable to work or to be with people. He stated that he had no emotions; yet he strongly desired affection and some day hoped to get married.

Prior to her interview with the patient, the worker reviewed the above-mentioned material and suspected that she would be dealing with an ambulatory schizophrenic. His self-description seemed bizarre and hopeless. She wondered about his past abortive but continued efforts to get help, and she felt that he must have possessed some awareness and sensibility to have escaped from further electric shock treatments, which frightened him, and yet still be capable of seeking help again.

The worker met the patient in the waiting room and saw that he was a rather good-looking young man. In spite of his tall, well-built frame, he seemed more like a young adolescent because his face was chubby and touched by pink in the cheeks. He was well-dressed but appeared scared and self-conscious, with a masklike unchanging facial expression.

The patient was quiet-voiced, despondent, and tense in the interviewing room. He sat on the edge of his chair and his eyes were averted. He obviously was in contact and knew everything that went on around him, but he seemed very self-preoccupied, especially about his own body reactions. He was isolated, withdrawn, and terribly fearful. The patient stated that he was scared about being in the clinic, for he was fearful that someone in his family, other than his mother, would find it out and think that he was crazy. He thought maybe this was true because he didn't feel as if he were right in his head. He stated that he felt bad physically and couldn't think. Nothing came into his head, and all the information he ever had was gone. This he remarked many times during the interview.

He had to say about himself that he felt empty, useless, and generally no good. He was unable to hold any job, although in the last four years he had not searched for any occupation. His mind, he stated, was a blank as if it were empty and dark. There was a terrible smell in his head, like a decaying odor, although at some times his head also felt watery. He stated that his mind had weakened early in adolescence, shortly after he had "done something," but he could not tell the interviewer for some time, in spite of many allusions to this guilt-producing act, what it actually was.

The patient described his nervousness alternately as if he had no nerves whatsoever and then at times his nerves felt like taut electric wires. He stated that his face was nerveless, and it felt as if it were frozen. The patient asked the worker several times to watch his face to see its lack of expression. He stated also that he had a terrible feeling in the pit of his stomach which he could not describe.

He expressed considerable fear of people. If someone said a cross word to him, he slunk away like an animal. He was constantly deathly afraid of almost anything and could not concentrate. In fact, he stated that he couldn't even find his way around, being brought to the clinic today. He remarked that all people look alike to him, for he can see no distinguishing features about them. Although he knew where he was as to location and he knew the time of the day, he was quite certain that he would have been too frightened about getting lost or mixed up to try to come to the clinic on his own.

The patient stated that he did nothing all day long except sit in the one-room apartment he shared with his mother. He used to attend movies, which he reached by walking down side streets, but did not even do this any more. He slept on a couch in the same room with his mother, and existed on her meager factory labor earnings.

In recounting the interview, the worker stated that she could not recall the content of words and the interplay in the process of exploration. However, by the worker's quiet, simple encouragement that he actually was remembering and by stating that she understood what he was talking about and that she appreciated that he was making a great effort toward helping himself and obtaining help from the clinic by his talking, the patient seemed to have kept moving toward telling about himself. It was in this context, after many indirect allusions to the bad thing that he did in his adolescence, which the worker told him was all right to tell, that he felt able to confess. He seemed to understand that the worker would appreciate his feelings of shame and was helping to make him feel more comfortable. He then told of an experience of sodomy with resultant fantasies, fears, and guilt concerning it.

At this confession, the interview was ended with the patient's hopefully stating that he would come back to see the doctor and enter treatment. As a result of this exploration, the intake staff accepted him for therapy, which he began and continued for a period of several years. At the end of two years it was reported that the patient was able to come to the clinic alone, that he walked down the streets and was able to look at people who passed him by, and had actually gone out with others without the crippling anxiety that he complained of in the intake interview.

COMMENT: The worker's explicit attitude toward this patient was based on the story of his four years of experience with therapy that was ineffective. Yet there was indicated a hope for affection and a desire to marry, which made the worker feel hopeful in spite of the apparent severity of the illness. In her mind, the patient was not completely withdrawn and there were positive assets in his favor. The first appearance of the patient indicated that he was very frightened and self-conscious and was protecting himself from an expression of these fears by his masklike facies and unchanging expression, but the very fact that he reacted in this way indicated to the worker that underneath was a person who still was capable of having deep feelings and of being quite sensitive to the attitudes of others. Furthermore, she recognized in his first expressions that he had insight into the fact that probably he was psychotic, and his unwillingness to have others know of his attendance in the clinic revealed his shame over his illness.

He immediately ascribed to the worker a pessimistic role of hopelessness which he explicitly felt. The worker, however, refused to accept this pessimistic role and constantly reassured him that there was hopefulness in his case. As a result, the patient continued to talk about himself and revealed not only his internal communications within himself but also the guilt and shame over some precipitating factor at the age of twelve. Throughout the interview the patient vacillated between condemning himself as a nothing and indicating his hypersensitivity. As he stated, he felt that his nerves were either completely absent or sensitive and vibrant like electric wires. He also revealed his implicit attitudes toward himself as being like an animal who had to slink away from people along the back alleys. He also indicated that he was constantly on the verge of giving up in the hopelessness that seemed to be the result of his previous bad experiences with doctors.

The worker indicated that her transactions with this patient were largely intuitive. She did not accept him at his presenting values but indicated a quiet confidence and reassurance. She refused to accept a complementary role that was ascribed to her by his self-depreciation. By not accepting his overt role and not conducting the interview with a series of questions and answers, she indicated to him her implicit confidence that something could be done for him and that she did not accept his lack of feelings, for he could discuss them and talk about them. What the worker stated was an intuitive notion and really a response to his nonverbal communications. She accepted his implicit role of hopefulness and sensitivity by reacting to it in a manner of a person who recognized suffering and encouraged the hope that it could be alleviated. In response to her gentle pushing, prodding technique and encouragement, the patient step by step divulged more about himself. Because she did not react to his sense of shame and indicated that she had heard stories such as his before, the patient was finally able to confess his experience of sodomy.

On the basis of this transaction which spiraled to the final confession, the worker experienced a complementarity to the hopefulness of the patient's implicit role and, therefore, recommended his admission to therapy to the intake staff. If she had dealt with the patient intellectually and reported only the diagnostic rubric into which he fitted as a stereotype called ambulatory schizophrenia, then the possibilities of his acceptance would have been markedly reduced. Her reactions, to the contrary, were directed by a complementarity to the patient's crying out for help which indicated to her a hopefulness that he could establish in relationship with a therapist and in some way thereby profit. As it turned out, the patient was helped a great deal, within the limits of his capacities. Nevertheless, he still, as a schizophrenic, was only able through years of therapy to avoid hospitalization in a mental institution and to feel more comfortable in a still withdrawn role in society.

We have given several examples of intake interviews completed in a single session. Usually all that is necessary for the purposes of determining motivation may be obtained in such an initial interview. However, it is usually somewhat longer than the ordinary forty-five- or fifty-minute session. Most intake interviewers require between an hour and an hour and a quarter for their purposes.

Sometimes the necessary factual information cannot be obtained in a single session. Although the transaction between the worker and the patient has been established in the first interview, there is sometimes not enough of the essential life story transmitted and the worker requires more time. For that purpose, he makes an appointment for a second interview.

Usually the need for a second interview concerns the clarification of the patient's motivation and capacity to endure anxiety. At times the worker will test the patient's ability to endure the necessary waiting period while the entire diagnostic work-up and staffing is accomplished. We know that, aside from the intake interview, there is an intake staff, a diagnostic interview by the resident, psychological testing, and staff consideration of the material before the patient can be informed of the recommendation of the clinic. If a period of a week or more is set aside between two intake interviews, the patient's tolerance to wait during the diagnostic procedures may be ascertained. If he cannot tolerate this period, it may become necessary to initiate further work-up on an emergency basis.

A case in point is that of a young professional student who came into the intake interview with a statement that he really had no problems except that in high school he was considered to be the most reserved boy in his class. He watched the worker carefully and adopted a very guarded attitude. He seemed very suspicious lest he be misinterpreted and was always careful not to be misquoted. He insisted on quizzing the worker a great deal and seemed to intellectualize about his life background. The worker knew that he gave false names and other false information. He asked for another interview and made an appointment. The patient, however, came to the clinic twice and insisted upon seeing the chief of clinic. The psychiatrist insisted that the patient return to the psychiatric social worker. When he did so at the second interview, he was confronted with the fact that he had given not only his wrong name but also his wrong telephone number and other misinformation. At that point he gave a correct history, and, after a short wait of about two months, he entered treatment, in which he has been quite faithful in his attendance and cooperation.

Some applicants for treatment, especially those who are bizarre in their appearance and presentations, tend after a time to change their manner of presentation and the material which they divulge in the second interview. Frequently they bring in a list of their symptoms; with this in hand they seem to be able to talk more freely. They often apologize for their bizarre behavior, saying that they were really not as sick as that, they were not themselves, and they feel that they have been misunderstood. After the second interview, during which the dramatic change to the better has been communicated, these people often can tolerate considerable waiting before being taken into treatment.

To the contrary, there are some individuals who take a flight into health after the first interview, saying that they have obtained enough information so that they do not need to enter into treatment. Other individuals seem to be well held together and controlled in the first interview, but fly apart and seem to disintegrate at the second interview, at which time confidence in the worker enables them to present their real underlying confusion and conflicts.

In the first interview some individuals are bland and silent and seem poorly motivated. Although they may cling to the worker in an effort to get him to give them all the information possible while they reveal nothing about themselves, some nonverbal clues indicate that they have something to say. A second appointment often reveals that their diffidence has been related to serious real-life situations going on at the time. At the second interview they may reveal that they lost their nerve and had been holding out information, but they then divulge the real problems and indicate a serious motivation for therapy.

At times the worker needs to check another source of information—from another agency, a private doctor, an employer, or someone who has not yet communicated to the clinic. In fact, the waiting for a second appointment for further information to be received in the intake interview may reveal that the patient is in treatment elsewhere. Often a worker cannot make up his mind about the qualities revealed by the patient in the first transaction, requires an interval to think about it, and, hence, uses the technique of making a second appointment for that purpose.

When the patient is obviously to be rejected for external reasons, a second interview is sometimes necessary to help terminate the relationship. This is done often with, and sometimes without, a recommendation, or a suggestion that the patient should call the clinic again in the future when he feels that he really needs help.

Our psychiatric social workers are free to make more than one and even more than two intake appointments with their patients when they feel the need. As they gain more experience, they restrict the second interviews to those who absolutely need them. The one-interview technique is most advantageous because it prevents a therapeutic relationship from being established with the worker and with the clinic. The clinic may not accept them after the consideration by the intake staff, nor may the patient be assigned to this particular worker for therapy.

The decision regarding a second interview involves not only the experience of the worker, his own individual personality, but also the behavior in the intake transaction of the specific patient. Decision-making becomes more certain for each worker as he becomes more experienced and knows the signals indicating that there is a sense of closure in the transaction.

SUMMARY

The case examples reveal the operations involved in several specific intake transactions and their results. Within the setting of the clinic the explicit role of the patient is to tell about himself with particular reference to his motivation for treatment. The explicit role of the worker is to find out as much as possible about the patient's motivation and treatability so that he can intelligently present the various nuances of the patient's problems to the intake staff. In the transactional process the patient and the worker have an impact upon each other which is reflected by a feedback of information on an explicit semantic verbal level and on an implicit level of gestures, intonations, and hidden attitudes. Through these modes of communications the unknowns are ascertained.

The transaction is the process through which worker and patient move toward each other, seeking for a level of communication understandable by each. At first they begin at the separate arcs of their own circles, but, as the interview proceeds, each moves spirally closer and faster toward the other until they are in phase and close communication is felt as achieved. The end point is not quantitative, that is, space- or time-limited, but is experienced subjectively in the "more than space or time aspect of mentation." [2] This point is not correlated with reducing all tension or learning all about the patient, for such complete closure defeats the purpose of subsequent phases of our procedures. Tension should be maintained for subsequent diagnostic investigations to maintain motivation and a push to talk and reveal the self at greater depth.

The rapport within the transaction is an emotional experience which develops within three stages:

1. *Resistance* due to preliminary discord in role performance. The worker refuses to accept role ascribed by patient, or patient's implicit role is obstructive toward information-giving.

2. *Transactional movement* in which the worker, recognizing the patient's anxiety, sets or defines roles for the interview in which complementarity is comfortable for both.

3. *Information* within the complementary role transaction flows freely and reveals feeling and content of patient's troubles.

We have not gained all the available information by any means when the transaction is completed, but feel that we have a typical segment or cross section. If we have not learned enough about the patient's needs, it means that there have been difficulties in communication, arising within either the patient or the worker. As always in interpersonal transactions, there are certain aspects of the worker's capacity which limit the procedure. At the point when the worker feels he can make a decision, the point of termination is reached, usually realized implicitly and becoming explicit only on retrospection. The information presented to the screening conference is not reality as such but reality influenced by the organization of a worker's perceptual system, a report of a transaction which may be close to or far from reality. An important check is the weighting of the chief of clinic's opinion, based on his knowledge of the worker's specific personality.

Some of the signposts that we have reached the end of the exploratory transaction are:

1. Circular response on the same plane to efforts or questions by the worker—repetitive material.

2. Patient requesting rather than giving information.

3. Sense of closure in the transaction.

4. Recognition that further handling would be therapeutic rather than investigative.

The point at which this spiral is reached may vary with the following:

1. Knowledge and subjective state of worker.

2. Patient's degree of communication with himself and awareness of problems.

3. Kind of information needed.

REFERENCES

1. Johnson, A. M.: A contribution to treatment of super-ego defect. *J. Soc. Casework,* 31:135, 1950.
2. Herrick, C. J.: *George E. Coghill, Naturalist and Philosopher.* Chicago: Univ. Chicago Press, 1949.

3

Information and Recommendation

Ⅰ<small>N ALL TRANSACTIONS</small> between the social worker and his client or
patient, information is communicated. In the context of this chapter
we use the term "information" as the communication of specific "recommendations" to the patient.

The function of "information," as we use it here, is to inform the
patient of his acceptance or rejection by the clinic for help with his
presenting problems. The clinic's recommendations are based on exploratory transactions which have been discussed in the previous chapter. Thus, in time sequence, the transmission of our recommendations
follows the intake interview, the decision of the intake staff, further
diagnostic studies, and the diagnostic staff conference. After all these
processes have been completed, a decision is reached, which is conveyed to the patient. At this time, the transactional roles are structured
or focused, insofar as possible, so that the worker has the explicit task
of transmitting the recommendations of the clinic to the patient, who
is assigned the explicit role of a person receiving recommendations
and considering, accepting, or rejecting them.

The person transmitting information concerning the recommendations of the clinic is usually the psychiatric social worker who has conducted the intake interview. There are times when the nature of the
psychiatric illness specifically requires the utilization of the authority
of a psychiatrist to make the recommendation. This may be the resident psychiatrist who has been involved in the diagnostic study. At
any rate the choice between the social worker and the psychiatrist is
determined by who has the best relationship with the patient and who

is needed to express certain recommendations authoritatively. When there is sufficient evidence of the patient's implicit reactions from anecdotes of past transactions and from the diagnostic study, it is often possible to plan how to present the recommendation.

It might be expected that the recommendation transmitted to the patient is a final and definite statement regarding the future functions of the clinic in relation to a specific patient. If this were the case, then the information could be given by letter or telephone. As we shall see later, however, the final decision transmitted to the patient is subject to considerable modification. It also is extremely rare and unusual for the interview to consist entirely of transmission of information, because many questions and reactions arise from the patient, all of which need adequate professional responses.

Recommendations are essentially of two types: acceptance for therapy in the clinic, or advice and aid in setting up other plans for help. When the recommendation includes the information that the clinic accepts the patient's initial request for treatment and the patient agrees, both the social worker and the patient are often involved in a short-lived uncomplicated transaction involving the giving of the recommendation and its acceptance. Very frequently, however, the patient asks numerous questions, such as, "How soon will my treatment begin?" "Who will treat me?" "What is this treatment that I am going to get?" "Is it medicine or something else?" "How can just talking to someone help me?" Other individualized questions, too numerous to mention, are frequently asked and call for responses sufficiently informative to allay the patient's anticipatory anxiety.

Sometimes, because of mounting anxiety or depression, the need of the patient may, at the moment, be greater than the simple notification of acceptance. In fact, the patient may urgently require more immediate therapy and yet, in the opinion of the clinic staff, had not been an emergency case at the time of its considerations. The worker's task is then directed toward helping the patient await his turn or, if necessary, seeing him several times for temporary supportive therapy, or bringing back to the staff a recommendation for more immediate assignment.

Some of the implicit roles which the patient assigns to the worker as he listens to the recommendation are expressed as follows: "Tell me what I want to hear." Some people ask the clinic or the worker to take responsibility for them: "Tell me what to do." Others adopt another attitude which is expressed as: "Tell me how I should go about helping myself. I need help in starting off so that I can carry out those procedures most likely to benefit me." Still others reject any direct help by asking the worker only to "help me help myself" with the attitude of "I alone can help myself—I need nobody and can accept nothing from anyone else." There are many variations and quantitative degrees of these attitudes, which are based largely on old patterned processes firmly entrenched in behavior.

The defining of the roles and the limits of the transaction are important if slipping into therapy is to be avoided. Thus, information-giving and recommendation is seen as a sharply focused transaction, insofar as it can be identified as a transaction. When the person transmitting the recommendation plans to continue in a new role as a therapist, which sometimes happens in collaborative treatment, the transaction becomes more complicated at once. In all other cases, however, the slipping into a therapeutic transaction should be strictly avoided in order to prevent future disturbances of the patient and difficulties of transferring him to his own therapist who will be assigned later. Consulting psychiatrists in private practice have exactly the same problem even though the evaluative or diagnostic nature of their interviews is explicitly defined.

The patient's desire to continue a relationship with the social worker with whom he has had initial contact may be reciprocated by a positive feeling in the social worker himself, in which case a therapeutic transaction may implicitly develop in spite of the forewarned need for specificity of purpose. In some instances this reaches such a degree of strength that it may become desirable or necessary for the chief of clinic to assign the worker as the patient's therapist.

Many patients, when told that they have been accepted for clinic therapy, immediately set up certain conditions which are impossible to meet. They wish to prescribe the frequency of interviews and the time at which the therapy should be conducted. Such hedging frequently gives the worker an impression that the patient is not as well motivated as it seemed in the exploratory interview. It may then be suggested to the patient that he delay treatment and perhaps return later when he is more interested in coming to the clinic at the times that are open. In such cases when the patient returns anew, it is on the basis of his own decision.

Often when a patient rejects the acceptance of the clinic, the worker may make no effort to retain him or to give him further understanding of his needs. This frequently happens when it is recognized that he may be a very difficult case who would be a great problem to the clinic anyway. With the recognition that many other people are applying who need treatment and can profit by it more, the worker may be agreeable to the patient's rejection.

Some patients, when informed that they have been accepted for treatment to begin soon or after a short period of waiting, reject the decision because they have been pushed into applying for treatment by relatives or friends and sometimes by therapists of their children. When a patient is forced into collaborative treatment, the motivation does not come from him and therefore the outlook for effectiveness of therapy is much less optimistic. In these days, when there are too few therapists to meet patients' demands, resulting in overcrowding of our clinics, there is usually very little effort made, as in the past, to woo the patient into therapy.

Although the patient approaches the clinic asking for treatment, he may reject acceptance by the clinic at the same time that the interviewer transmits the staff decision. Sometimes this is a blow to the self-esteem of the interviewer who may react with annoyance, in a reciprocal manner (implicitly angry at the waste of time), telling the patient that maybe he is right after all. Sometimes these patients require an interval of time before they can accept the recommendation and begin therapy. When they return after a lapse of some months, they sometimes say, "Now I know that you were right. I really do need help." Other patients may return with resentment toward the interviewer who did not force them to accept the recommendation.

When the recommendation is a refusal, the transaction becomes much more complicated than simply transmitting this information. It is the task of the recommender to clarify the reasons for rejection whenever this is feasible or advisable and when the content is not destructive. In instances where this is not advisable, the worker is faced with the task of leaving unverbalized and dealing obliquely with reasons for refusal, as in rejection for further treatment of a very infantile, anxious, or chronic, hopeless patient.

When the recommendation from the clinic indicates that the patient is not acceptable for therapy and his application for treatment is rejected, the patient may respond by asking for a further hearing and may make an attempt to convince the worker that the decision is erroneous. Sometimes the patient may desperately try to influence the worker by producing cogent arguments and offer histrionic demonstrations regarding his need for therapy. In other cases, the patient may be so disturbed by the rejection that a flow of genuine feeling may indicate for the first time a stronger motivation for therapy than had been uncovered during the previous exploration. The patient may respond to his rejection by giving additional clues which clarify his position and cause the worker to re-open the possibility of the patient's acceptance for therapy. Thus, a new transaction, similar to what has been described in the area of exploration, may take place. Through new attitudes or influences which are catalyzed by the anxieties of either the social worker or the patient, or both, a new decision may be reached. Thus, information-giving may evolve into a transaction involving further exploration.

In certain instances the worker who gives the information may be implicitly anxious or disturbed over his task of rejecting the patient from therapy. He may be in disagreement with the staff's decision not to treat this particular patient, or he may identify with the patient and react as he does to the rejection.

In the case of some inexperienced workers, the transmitted recommendation may not sound convincing, and many unverbalized or unconscious undertones may be present in the interview. Usually the doubts and arguments of more experienced workers have been discussed openly at staff meeting, and they strongly identify with the clinic so that their anxieties do not confuse the issue.

We have spoken of the social worker's attitude in terms of his intellectual disagreement with the clinic staff and identification with a specific patient. There is also, however, the universal attitude of workers who find difficulty in rejecting or refusing people who request help. This intense, almost missionary, dedication often decreases as the worker becomes more experienced and he becomes less angry at the psychiatrist who has to make the decision for rejection. Generally after a time less guilt develops when he is involved in rejecting people who ask for help. There are, however, certain built-in specific guilt reactions among the therapists when rejecting certain personality types because of their own personal problems. These add complications to the transaction but are mitigated through intellectual control and experience, and often decrease through self-analysis of the worker or through a personal psychoanalysis. In such cases there is a subtle slipping of information-giving into a pseudotherapeutic situation. Often it becomes a vacillating and indecisive process which ends in the worker's presenting so-called "new information" to the diagnostic staff for the purpose of having the patient accepted into treatment.

To be effective in this area of information-giving, the worker's explicit roles must be fairly well maintained and emptied of those implicit roles that disturb the process and threaten to extend the relationship into a continuous supplication. Since therapeutic processes are not included in this transaction, a distant rather than a close relationship must be the correct attitude, so that implicit role systems do not become unduly activated or elaborated through feedback mechanisms.

In some instances the patient who has applied for treatment may react to his rejection with relief because he has not really been motivated for therapy. Actually in many situations a rejection of the patient may have a positive value for him, since he then interprets that he is not sick enough for clinic treatment.

At times the patient's great need may so dominate the transaction that he may unconsciously reject the refusal for clinic care and may not be able to hear or understand the information that is being given to him. He thus may misinterpret not only the decision but also the basis on which it is reached and not be receptive to further recommendation. Even though the worker's approach may be direct and his communications verbally specific and semantically correct, misunderstanding occurs quite frequently when the information is not what the patient wishes to receive.

The transactional process involves more than the explicit roles of information-giving and receiving, but includes implicit nuances elicited by the methods of communication. The information-giving should take into consideration the implicit aspects of the patient's needs and demands; for, even though the patient may be rejected from therapy, this can be accomplished without hurting him and often at the same time with a positive, beneficial effect. Many patients after a single diagnostic interview and subsequent recommendations of whatever kind have felt so much better that they have felt no need for help for many years or a subsequent lifetime. When the clinic does not accept the patient for treatment, it becomes the task of the social worker to develop further plans for the patient when possible. If these are clear and explicit, they do not complicate the transaction, since the explicit recommending role remains clear and uncontaminated.

Certain implicit doubts having to do with the soundness of the recommendation may creep into the transaction. During the transmission of the recommendation, the plan developed may be perceived as unsound because of new information revealed by the patient and new insights gained by the social worker or, for that matter, new developments in the transaction between the social worker and the patient and new information received regarding the intervening life situation. The course of action is then to defer decision and re-evaluate the situation with the diagnostic staff, which may result in reformulation of the plan. In some instances emergency psychiatric intervention may be indicated when the patient who is about to be refused treatment reveals the possibility of an acute panic reaction, depression, or suicide.

The plan arrived at by the diagnostic staff may have been a compromise after disagreements and much arguing among the members of the staff. There may have been contradictory information about which clear-cut decisions could not be made. In some cases the final decision is then left up to the worker to be based on new information that may be revealed in the second interview. The transaction may bring out such information, or define circumstances for treatment that enable the worker, as the representative of the clinic, if he is experienced and competent, to make a clear-cut decision which previously had been impossible. In such cases it is more likely that a tentative refusal from the diagnostic staff is turned into an acceptance.

The role systems contained in the giving of information and recommendations involve reciprocal feedback mechanisms so that the worker is able to determine the proper mode of making the recommendation and its timing. If the clinic is sufficiently flexible and the worker is invested with sufficient authority, further transactions may lead to changes in the recommendation or plans for the patient which had not been decided by the staff. It must be re-emphasized that the transaction itself will reveal new responses to the form or content of the recommendation which will expose aspects of personality requiring a change in plans. The worker needs to deal flexibly with the problems of the actual transaction at the moment.

A series of case examples indicating various transactions occurring in the process of giving information and recommendations follow (see Table 1b and 1c, pp. 22–23).

CASE 6

Erroneous Recommendation Not Accepted by the Patient

THE PATIENT was a twenty-one-year-old, white, single, Protestant man who was referred to the psychiatric clinic by his mother, an employee at the hospital. In view of her special connections, the mother was given the unusual privilege of applying for treatment for her son. She came to the clinic alone and gave the admitting clerk the data required for the face sheet, and furnished the necessary financial information. Following this, an intake exploratory appointment was mailed to the patient.

It was known in advance from the mother's information that the patient shared an apartment with his parents and that the patient had previously received private psychiatric treatment from a male doctor who recently left the city to practice elsewhere. The patient was known to be a college student, who also worked part time. The father, living at home, was unemployed following a serious illness, and he was not expected to be able to return to work. Although the patient worked part time, he contributed nothing to the family, the members of which were oppressed by numerous bills.

The patient failed to keep his first appointment, without notifying the clinic. Following this, the mother telephoned, crying hysterically and begging that something be done. She described the patient as outrageous in his belligerent, inconsiderate behavior with his parents, whom he was "killing," and she stated that she suspected her son was acting out his homosexuality. Apparently he stayed out until all hours of the morning, slept all day, and refused to give any information as to his whereabouts. The mother had tried to talk the patient into getting more psychiatric treatment, but he resented such discussions. She wanted to come and talk over the situation, but the worker refused to see her, telling her instead that the most helpful thing she might do was to have the patient make an appointment himself if he wanted help. The mother reluctantly agreed to this, although she expressed her feelings as being hurt at the worker's rejection of her request for an interview.

Several days later the patient called for an appointment, which he kept. He was a handsome, bright young man with a quiet, likable but remote and diffident manner. He stated quickly and unabashedly that, although he was a homosexual, he was trying to control this behavior and his real problems were the continuous arguments that occurred with his parents over a variety of issues. He admitted to some feeling of desertion by his previous therapist, who left the city abruptly, but he had never called the therapist who had been recommended to him as a substitute because he thought he could work out his problems on his own.

The mother had paid for all of the therapist's fees, and the patient had not contributed anything toward his treatment. He admitted that he could probably use some psychiatric help—as things were pretty bad at home—but he seemed little concerned, stating that he was thinking of leaving the city anyway for a job elsewhere. He would be able to find work in the West with an older woman friend. He finally stated that he would consider seeking help with the doctor that his former therapist had recommended, and he promised to return to the clinic after his case was staffed even though he did not expect to be accepted or obtain any help here.

The decision of the staff conference was to recommend that the patient seek private treatment for which he should pay himself. This was considered as a test of his real motivation for help. Furthermore, it did not seem that his problem could be treated by the resident psychiatrist on our clinic staff, for he seemed to need several years of treatment with an experienced therapist. The staff recommended that the patient get in touch with the person recommended by his former therapist or, if he desired, the worker should recommend other experienced therapists.

The patient canceled his first appointment for the reason that he had overslept and asked as a special favor that a second appointment be given at which time the staff's recommendation would be transmitted to him. In this interview the patient was less bland and aloof, apologized for his former behavior, and demonstrated some real anxiety regarding his parents' interference. He knew that his mother had called three or four times before he was seen, and for that he was very sorry.

During the interview, at which the staff's recommendation was transmitted to the patient, he seemed more concerned regarding his homosexuality than he expressed verbally. He wondered if there was any hope for him. He seemingly accepted the recommendation and even asked for the telephone number of the male therapist who had been recommended to him so that he could call for an appointment on leaving the interview. He asked for no other names, but he was told that if he ran into problems in getting into therapy he should let the worker know so that she could find other sources for help.

Several days later the mother telephoned and informed the worker that she thought the patient did call the therapist and possibly saw him once. However, she wanted the worker to know that, in the meantime, the patient had been in jail overnight on a homosexual charge but was released and promptly left for California. The mother was distraught, asking for help for herself. She came in for one interview, but no further contact was had with her or with any other member of the family.

COMMENT: An exceptional procedure was permitted in this case in that the mother was given the privilege of applying for her son's treatment. The clinic rarely permits one adult to make an appointment for another, but because of her connection with the hospital this special privilege was granted. From this and other information it seems as if the worker had fallen into the mother's role and considered the patient a boy rather than an adult. Apparently his first broken appointment was somewhat of a defiance of his mother's taking the role of clearing the way for him into the clinic. When the mother called again, the worker had apparently realized the mistake that had been made and indicated, even though the mother might be hurt at this information, that the patient would have to make his own appointment.

Pessimism about the situation pervaded the staff conference, and it was decided that the patient needed an experienced therapist. For some reason the staff conference did not take cognizance of his intended flight to an older woman friend in another city. If they had recognized the implicit meaning of this flight, they would not have recommended that the patient seek out another male therapist. All through the material of the interview the implicit request for help from the female worker or someone like her was evidenced—in retrospect.

The patient was forced into the role of a good son of a dominating, directive mother. He implicitly requested help from an older, more understanding woman, but this need was not met; as a result, the patient ran away. In so doing, he acted out his need to cling to a woman and at the same time thwarted both his mother and the worker. When the worker gave the patient the recommendation of the staff, she did not receive the implicit message from the patient; her mind was not open regarding the treatability of homosexuality or the patient's need for a female therapist. The worker recognized only her assigned role— to be used as an instrument of obedience to the dominating mother. The patient was acting out the role of a little child doing what mother says but, behind it all, planning to defy her.

Because the worker did not recognize the implicit needs of the patient and therefore could neither communicate them to the staff nor pick up the feedback from the patient at the second appointment, the patient could not accept the recommendation. This is a case for which recommendation of any kind was an error. Rather, it was necessary, by immediately initiating a therapeutic relationship with a different kind of woman, literally to compete with the powerful dominating mother against whom no verbal recommendation could be effective. Treatment should have begun through a continuation of the interview, without specific labeling, before any staff recommendation was made. The explicit lack of motivation of the patient disguised from the worker his implicit cry for help from her as a good and understanding mother. The result of this series of errors in understanding the transaction contributed to the patient's getting into considerable trouble and having to run to a mother-figure in another city.

CASE 7

Recommendation for Treatment Rejected Because Patient Needed a Special Type of Supportive Relationship

THE PATIENT was a thirty-two-year-old, white, Protestant woman, mother of five children, who had been separated from her husband for about three months. She was a small, attractive person who spoke in a low voice but related superficially to others easily. She was emotionally labile, and, because she felt unable to carry on, she was seen as an emergency two days before Christmas. She complained of being near a nervous breakdown; crying, depressed, lonely, and anxious.

During the screening and diagnostic appointments the patient described the current situation with her husband as being mutually provocative and confused. He apparently had a girl friend and had openly defied his wife's threats of divorce. The patient had had a previous disruptive marriage and a nervous breakdown thereafter some seven years before, resulting in two hospitalizations and treatment by electric shock.

She was markedly self-depreciatory and anxious, but seemed to function well although erratically. A diagnosis of a depressive reaction was made, and, because the family finances were fairly good, it was decided to recommend that the patient be treated by a psychiatrist privately if her husband would agree to pay the bills. The patient was advised to see a psychiatrist for treatment to avoid a serious breakdown and to tide her over the current crisis. The patient accepted the recommendation overtly but dubiously because she felt that her husband would not pay the bills. She was informed that if this plan did not work out she might return to the clinic for treatment.

The husband was interviewed and agreed to pay for her treatment, but did not carry out his promise. The patient returned to the clinic and was placed on the waiting-list in the belief that this would test her motivation to get help and would help stabilize the confused life situation in the meantime.

For the next three weeks the patient called the worker 12 or 15 times day and night, crying, begging for answers as to how to handle herself, her husband, her children, her husband's girl friend, her own sleeplessness, divorce, lawyers, etc. The patient was told repeatedly that the worker could not answer these questions because they were part of a larger problem and needed regular contacts for their solution. However, the patient called again and again, clinging to the phone, even though the worker repeated her statements many times.

The patient was placed on the waiting list for about a year, although she did not really accept the recommendation for treatment. A year later, at Christmas time, she returned to the clinic and again started calling the worker in the same fashion as before. She was removed from the waiting list because it was not possible to treat her while her confused life situation continued. She took no steps to alter these external situations. However, the patient called several times day and night. Finally, she was removed from the waiting list and was advised to consult a family agency for total social planning, which, however, she did not follow through.

COMMENT: It was discovered later that for several years the patient regularly suffered from a similar "near" nervous breakdown close to the Christmas holidays. Her mother had died during her childhood just before Christmas, and each year at that time she has gone through a mourning process, which has been described by Josephine Hilgard as the anniversary syndrome.[1]

The worker's recommendation that the patient receive treatment was not accepted by the patient because she wanted immediate treatment from the intake worker. Actually it was an erroneous recommendation. The patient, whose sado-masochistic marriage was the only defense that she had against a possible breakdown, attempted to force the clinic to give her what she wanted. At the period of recurrence of mourning she needed much continuous attention like a confused and bewildered abandoned child. Her repeated questions and excitable talk were efforts in an emergency to receive the substance of maternal attention without which a breakdown was threatened. The failure of the worker to meet this implicit need of the patient resulted in a repetition of the same demands a year later. The patient wisely rejected the recommendation for continuing therapy.

Here again we see a transaction in which the patient's implicit needs could not be met by the worker within the clinic's formalized structure. Instead, the reaction to an exploratory technique was accepted as evidence that the patient needed to be tested further as to her capacity to undergo the kind of therapy that this woman could not have endured. For her, the exploratory process was inappropriate for her needs.

CASE 8

Recommendation for Treatment to a Woman Who Explicitly Denied Her Wish for Help

A THIRTY-SEVEN-YEAR-OLD white Jewish woman called the worker to inquire for help for her son. She disclosed that a psychiatrist had referred her to the clinic because the family could not afford private psychiatric treatment. She stated that she had been a social worker and knew many of the professionals at our clinic and wondered whether that would not interfere with her obtaining help. At the same time she asked for an emergency appointment because she felt that she could no longer cope with her unhappy and hostile son. The worker offered the mother an early appointment after an agreement was reached that they would discuss her feelings regarding getting help from our clinic. It was agreed that her social work background and associations might complicate matters.

Although the mother had asked for an emergency appointment, she came forty minutes late, leaving time enough only to meet the worker and receive another appointment for the following week. For this she again demanded an emergency appointment, and was given the earliest possible time available. For the second appointment she was on time. The worker met the mother in the waiting room and observed that she was extremely tense, holding several long lists describing her son's behavior and the ways in which she and her husband had tried to convince him that they loved him. She appeared under intense pressure and talked incessantly as if she were close to panic and forcibly had to control all her words and actions.

She stated almost at once that she needed no help for herself but only wanted the clinic to make her son accept her as his mother. She felt that an unhappy adolescence and manhood could result from his present behavior, indicating the possibility of delinquency. The mother was uncomfortable and tense, hence the worker did not discuss the primary question—whether she herself could accept help. Instead, she was asked to tell the worker in what ways her son was upset. The mother used many technical terms and gave several examples which illustrated her inability to discipline the boy and her desperate fear that they had a poor relationship. The boy did not listen to anything she told him. He would not wash his face. He rode his bike recklessly on ice, and he would not go to sleep. The parents did not know whether to let him have his way or insist on his following their instructions. The mother wanted the clinic to give her specific techniques for handling the boy, and, on this basis, she would accept help for herself. In fact, her husband too would come in for helpful advice. The mother stated that the teachers at school told her that the son had superior intelligence but would not work to the full extent of his potential. They reported that he was running around with wild Gentile boys who had a bad influence on him. The worker reviewed the mother's present economic life and plans. Her husband had recently changed his job as an engineer, earning relatively little. She herself wanted to return to work and believed that she could get a job as a teacher. The mother asked if her records would be given out to anyone, or information divulged that she was registered at the clinic. She was informed that her presence would be treated confidentially. We would, however, want the summary of her diagnostic contact with the private psychiatrist who first saw her and referred her to the clinic. She agreed to give her signature for release of information.

The worker then explained the administrative planning of the diagnostic study that would have to be gone through and outlined the history-taking, psychological tests, and other procedures. The mother agreed to accept the recommendations of the diagnostic study and treatment planning at the clinic. After these were completed and she was told that she herself needed treatment, she accepted without any objection.

COMMENT: Although the mother had indicated explicitly she did not want any therapy, the worker sensed throughout her interview the pressing need and almost panic state of anxiety for personal help. It seemed likely that her first appointment, to which she came late, was only to survey the clinic setting and meet the worker for the purpose of testing her. Her pressure to get another early and emergency appointment indicated the urgency which was evident in her implicit motivations for personal help.

Automatically the worker made arrangements for the diagnostic study of the mother, which was an implicit statement, never made explicit, that the mother needed treatment and that the clinic was interested in giving it to her. Here we see a recommendation for therapy which was made prior to the diagnostic studies, entirely implicit in both aspects of the transaction. In other words, the mother was telling the worker, "I desperately need help," and the worker was communicating, "I know that you desperately need help, and we will give it to you." This transaction was never made explicit until after the diagnostic studies were completed and the mother was told, "You do need help, and we will try to give it to you." On this basis she entered treatment.

CASE 9

Information Given to a Woman Demanding Admission to the Hospital

THE PATIENT was a single Protestant woman in her early forties, referred by the Admitting Department for a screening interview after she made application for outpatient treatment. For some reason the Admitting Department had called for an emergency appointment.

The patient's face sheet indicated that she had been in our psychiatric hospital the previous week. She was a college graduate in chemistry, but on the record was a notation that she had been a drug addict and had had a previous hospitalization for alcoholism at a state mental institution. Since the patient's previous hospitalization had involved care by a private psychiatrist, the worker contacted him and he revealed that the patient was unable to pay for further private therapy.

The worker met the patient in the waiting room and obtained the impression of a somewhat masculine person. After introductions were made, the worker asked the patient to tell about her present situation and selected the work area as a good place to begin. The patient was living with friends who had paid for her previous hospitalization, and they and everyone else told her to talk to a social worker at the clinic, who could get a free bed for her. The worker responded by telling her that this was not true, because the doctors at the hospital make these decisions; whereupon the patient got up from the chair, paced the room with intense anger, and reiterated that she knew that Social Service could get her a bed. The worker repeated that she had no control of hospital beds but she might be of help to the patient if she were informed of her current problems and what plans she had about them.

The patient walked to the door and stated that if she can't get what she wants from the worker there is no use staying. However, as she was walking away, the worker called her back and asked her to sit down. Then, with the information she had obtained from the various sources available, the worker reviewed the patient's life. She had not worked for six months. She did not have a home. Her problem of alcoholism had been chronic for several years. Obviously she needed long-term therapy which she could not afford. In Illinois, the worker continued, there were good state hospitals to which she could go for an indefinite period without financial worries. With a good deal of authority the worker stated this is a much wiser plan than attempting to get back into a private hospital where even a stay in a free bed is limited to a relatively short time.

The following day the worker received a call from the Psychopathic Hospital stating that the patient had entered of her own free will and had used the worker's name to help facilitate hospitalization.

COMMENT: The worker had no knowledge of what her role in the transaction was to be. She had anticipated that there was a real emergency and that the patient was to be screened for acceptance in the clinic. The worker was curious regarding the disparity between the patient's delinquent life and her college education but otherwise was not prepared for the fact that the patient explicitly wanted to pressure herself back into a private hospital on a free basis through the social worker's interference. It soon became obvious that, when the worker did not accept a complementary role, the transaction, as far as the patient was concerned, could be considered ended. The worker, however, then assumed the role of a person giving information and called the patient back to review her past difficulties and her present isolation. Following this she very authoritatively gave the patient an explicit statement which was highly informative—that what she needed and what was hopeful for her was a long stay in a hospital without financial worries. Apparently after some hours of germination the seed sprouted, and the patient followed the worker's advice and entered the Psychopathic Hospital. Here we see that information given was appropriate to the situation and was accepted by the patient even though explicitly she was angry and disappointed.

CASE 10

Information Given to the Mother of a Disturbed Child that She Also Needs Treatment

T HE PATIENT was a thirty-nine-year-old woman referred for the purpose of giving her the information that she, in addition to her child, needed treatment. Her six-year-old adopted daughter had been hospitalized in the children's unit at our hospital for five months and had just returned home. The psychiatrist felt that the mother needed some help for herself as well as information as to how to handle the child. The mother had unfortunately not received any direct help for her problems during the period of her child's hospitalization.

The child's therapist described both the mother and the father as being confused and felt that it was difficult to obtain a clear picture about them or their home. Nevertheless, as she presented herself to the worker in the first interview, she was neat in appearance and looked well groomed, which did not coincide with the psychiatrist's description of the mother as severely disorganized.

As soon as the mother settled herself down in the interviewing room, she started with a barrage of statements regarding the child's peculiar behavior. Each statement ended with a question to ascertain whether she, as the mother, was doing right or wrong. The worker attempted to interrupt this stream of talk by indicating to the patient that no one could determine what was right or wrong and that until the worker got to know her better it was best to go ahead and use her own common sense. The patient continued to pour forth examples of the child's disturbed behavior with a great deal of anxiety and inappropriate laughter. When the worker commented that the mother seemed to be caught in an impossible struggle, she became silent, seemed to be depressed, and asked what made her child so disturbed. The worker responded that perhaps it was due to some disturbances existing in the relationships between the mother and other family members. The mother's comment was that she had known that she was the one who made the child disturbed. The mother was then informed that more would have to be understood before we knew what had contributed to the child's disturbance. Another appointment was made to see the mother the following week, but in the meantime the mother called the worker several times on the telephone, asking for help in coping with her child's compulsive behavior.

When the mother was seen for a second interview, she began by denying all her troubles, stating that the child had shown wonderful improvement and that the child's therapist thinks that everything is all right except that the mother should control her anger more. At the same time, the mother brought out her distrust of the clinic, based on the fact that she felt she was not being informed as to what we were thinking and what our future plans would be regarding the child.

The worker told the mother that there were two aspects in planning therapy. The first was a treatment relationship between the worker and the mother in an effort to relieve stresses which, in turn, could react deleteriously on the child. The other aspect was to treat the child directly to attempt to decrease her inappropriate behavior. The worker added, however, that if these methods did not succeed the child might have to be placed in a foster home. Following this explanation, the mother began to talk about herself and her difficulties in the years back. We need not go into the details of the mother's statements about her strange and difficult life, which prepared her for failure in the current maternal role, except to state that following this interview the patient was seen regularly by the worker in a therapeutic relationship, having accepted the information that she needed treatment for herself.

COMMENT: The worker expected to see a very disturbed woman with whom she would have difficulty, and perceived her role to be that of explaining her need for treatment. The mother, on the other hand, explicitly came for information as to what was going on in the child and what she should do. The first information given by the worker indicated the need to know her better, the knowledge that there was a struggle going on in her, that she did play an important part in the child's difficulty, and that she probably needed treatment. Although the mother implicitly was asking for help and reassurance and pleading with the worker to tell her that all this was not her fault, the worker's natural tendency in the transaction was to point a finger at the mother as the sickest member of the family and attribute to her the major cause in the child's disturbance. Thus, the worker implicitly accepted the mother's image of herself as a bad woman and a bad mother and agreed that she was responsible. Therefore, between interviews, we can see the reason for the frantic and anxious telephone calls from the mother, who was quite upset by the first interview.

In the second interview the mother explicitly stated that nobody told her anything and that she was not accepted as an important person in her child's life. The worker went over the ground and gave her information about the child's treatment and the need for the mother's help in obtaining a therapeutic result. She thereby established a transaction which enabled her to convince the mother that one aspect of the total planning would be the mother's therapy. The indications that this transaction was completed developed out of the feedback from the mother when she stopped talking about the child and began to reveal considerable information about her own disturbed past.

CASE 11

Information Given to the Wife of a Psychotic Patient
that She Was Not Responsible for Her Husband's Illness

THE PATIENT was a forty-year-old Jewish woman, wife of a physician who was hospitalized in the psychiatric unit. The referral was based on the recommendation of the psychiatrist treating the husband, who felt that the wife needed guidance and advice as to how to deal with the patient. He believed that she was overanxious about her husband's illness and depreciated him somewhat. The husband was a manic-depressive who had been hospitalized several times. His present hospitalization followed a physical attack on the wife which resulted in her legally committing him.

The worker entered the interview wondering whether the wife had done something to provoke the husband's attack, and the worker also felt that if the wife had an etiological role in her husband's illness she would probably not accept information regarding her relationship to him.

The wife was a large, heavy-set woman with a rather pretty face, who came to her appointment ahead of time. She was anxious because she felt that her husband might blame her for committing him and that he would fool the doctors into discharging him too soon and then come home and attack her. She described her husband's history of taking drugs, of his hyperirritability, and of his physical abuse of her and her children which finally led to his commitment. She described his manic spending of money, his calling the hospital where he worked at all hours of the day and night, thus endangering his career. She seemed to be appropriately anxious in the current situation. On the other hand, when she described his depressed states, she seemed sympathetic and concerned.

The worker informed the wife that the clinic would like to know how her husband was doing when he was at home and that, therefore, the worker would continue to see her while the husband was seeing his doctor and that the doctor and she would communicate with each other so that the husband would not be sent home if there was any danger to her. The worker continued to see the wife weekly for a time and then less frequently after the husband was discharged, and finally interrupted the relationship when they moved out of the city. The wife's anxiety diminished considerably when she learned that she could turn to someone who did not hold her responsible for her husband's illness. The worker, armed with the doctor's information, was able to point out that her husband wanted professional success, but was also afraid of it and he reacted to his fears by an exaggerated bravado and extravagance. The wife was encouraged to praise him whenever she could legitimately, but in no way to consider herself responsible for his illness. Most of the interviews were taken up with the wife's asking questions and seeking guidance and advice about specific issues.

COMMENT: Here is a transaction which was established for the purpose of giving the wife reassuring information and negating her guilt feelings. This was accomplished not in one interview but over a period of time. During these information-giving sessions it was also possible to indicate a mode of behavior through which the wife would contribute to the husband's stability or at least not be contributory to any future attack. It was learned that the woman was quite dependent and turned to the clinic for support when she could not get it from her husband. In giving her this support, the worker was able indirectly to facilitate the treatment and readjustment of the husband. It became quite clear that the worker's notion that the wife might want the husband to be ill was erroneous. Both the worker and the client explicitly assumed complementary roles of information-giver and information-receiver, and this transaction was quickly and easily established and durable over a considerable period of time.

CASE 12

Attempt to Give a Mother Information Regarding Her Involvement in Her Daughter's Illness

THIS MOTHER and her twenty-five-year-old daughter were referred to the worker because they were interfering with the treatment of a twenty-year-old daughter, who was at that time hospitalized in the psychiatric unit, and also for the purpose of securing needed social information. This mother and sister had been seeking out the patient's therapist for the purpose of getting information about the patient but implicitly were competing with the patient for his attention. It was decided that the worker should give the mother and daughter the necessary information.

The worker called the mother for an appointment, but she was not home and the older daughter answered the telephone in an attitude that suggested that she had assumed the role of the mother. The worker's first contact was with the mother alone. She was an attractive fifty-year-old Russian Jewish woman, well dressed, outgoing, and rather dramatic. She spoke very quickly and intently, and with an accent. The mother stated that she did not know why she was referred to the worker. The mother was told that the doctor needed additional information about the sick daughter and, in our experience, the doctors had so much to do just to treat their patients that social workers spent more time with relatives and this usually worked out better for everybody.

The mother then launched into a series of complaints about her sick daughter. As she went on, she constantly held up her older daughter as an example of everything good and the patient as everything bad. The worker finally asked whether there had been any time when the patient had been different. The mother responded that the patient had always been troublesome from the time she was born, she was a bad eater, etc.

It became clear that the mother's own artistic ambitions to become a singer had been frustrated very early and that the older daughter was fulfilling the mother's ambitions for herself. The patient's efforts to be accepted and to compete with her older sister were discouraged, which was exactly what the mother had done to her own younger sister, to whom she had always been hostile and depreciating.

The mother saw herself as a wonderful parent, unappreciated by her selfish child. As she went on, the mother indicated clearly that the first response to the patient's request for anything would be negative. Then when the patient would continue her request, she would capitulate but tie all sorts of conditions to what she gave and constantly complain that they were not met. A specific problem arose in relation to the monetary allowance given to the patient. The worker asked the mother what she could afford and suggested that she stick to this and not interfere with whatever way the patient wanted to spend this allowance. The mother agreed to this verbally, but the worker suspected that she would not follow through on it. It seemed to her that the mother got satisfaction from the situation of conflict with the younger daughter and had little wish to change. At the same time she wanted approval from the hospital authorities, so that for a time she might comply.

It turned out that this is what happened. Contact was irregular but rather frequent. She would complain about her child. The worker would sympathize with the difficulties, commend her when she was able to be consistent and fair with her, and point out her deficiencies when she was unfair. The mother complied for a time, but then the entire process would be repeated. Finally the patient was discharged from the hospital considerably improved, but there was no change observed in the mother.

COMMENT: In this transaction of information-giving in an attempt to control the behavior of the mother by virtue of the authority of the hospital, the clinic, and the doctors, it was soon seen that the mother was sick herself and needed treatment. It was this that prevented her from receiving the information that concerned her external behavior in relation to the patient. The transaction was significant for other reasons. The mother, in her relationship to the social worker, was constantly giving information about herself which could be fed back to her daughter's therapist. On the basis of this information the therapist was better able to handle the general and specific problems of the child's future planning. The worker attempted to transmit in as neutral a way as possible the information from the therapist to the mother without exciting her and without taking the role of the therapist. However, by virtue of the mother's own illness, in which the worker did not become involved, the information was not accepted and the authoritative transaction was a failure. The go-between authoritative role of the social worker was only temporarily effective. In any further transactions there would have been involved the development of a therapeutic relationship with the mother which would be doomed to failure because mother was poorly motivated and was using patient primarily for her own gratification. For the most part we attempt to avoid becoming involved in therapy if we wish to continue to focus on information-giving. This is often difficult, especially when we are dealing with mothers who are involved in the causative processes that contribute to a child's illness.

The next three cases were evaluated diagnostically by a psychiatrist and recommendations were transmitted to the patients without filtering through a staff conference. The recommendations in two of these cases were made during the first interview. The third patient was given recommendations after psychological tests were performed.

CASE 13

Recommendation for Treatment to a Young Woman Who Explicitly Came for an Authoritative Statement that She Could Help Herself

A TWENTY-FIVE-YEAR-OLD, white, married, Jewish woman came to the therapist stating that she had been ill for about ten months following the death of her father several months after the birth of her second child. Her illness manifested itself in nausea, vomiting, loss of appetite, crying spells, and depression. She had been to a number of medical people for studies of her physical condition. She had been examined thoroughly by several internists and had been told that she was physically healthy.

Nevertheless she kept going to doctors at the urging of her family, who considered that she must have a physical disturbance. She was hospitalized twice for thorough studies and medication including tranquilizing drugs, which did not agree with her. During the second admission her doctor had called in someone who was supposed to be a psychiatrist although his name was not familiar. This physician gave her electric shock treatments which frightened her and produced a decrease in memory for a time, but there was no permanent beneficial effect.

Apparently the family was convinced that there was no physical basis for her difficulties and adopted a regimen suggested by a number of her doctors that she could control her illness and that all she needed to do was to "pull yourself together." The patient made desperate efforts to control herself, to divert her attention, and to ignore her very disturbing emotional states. This was not at all effective, and she steadily became worse. She had thought of going to a psychiatrist, but her family vigorously objected, stating that psychiatrists make people worse, they keep them under treatment for long periods of time, and charge exorbitant fees.

The patient had accepted the statements of those around her that she herself was responsible for the disturbance in her body and in her emotions. Since she could not control these, her guilt feelings mounted. She felt, however, that help was needed and sought an interview with the therapist on her own. The interview began with her statement that she was responsible for her illness and that she should be able to have the strength to control herself. In telling her story it seemed quite clear that this was an immature person whose dependent satisfactions had been minimal during her early life and whose efforts at maturation had been superficial and unsuccessful. Any stressful situation involved in the marriage or in relation to the birth or care of the children threw her back to a caricature of early dependency in which she enacted the role of a sick, vomiting child who needed more intensive maternal care.

In this respect it seemed apparent that her regressive position was truly a communication for help. It in itself created guilt feelings as if to say, "I should be grown up at my age and with my responsibilities as a wife and mother. I feel guilty for having regressed to this childlike position, and those who tell me that I am responsible are correct." Thus we see a nucleus of truth in the accusations of people around her and those of her conscience.

With this communication of both explicit and implicit factors involved in her illness, the therapist authoritatively told her exactly the opposite of what she explicitly came to hear. She was told that without question her illness was not her responsibility or her decision. She had not decided to be sick and, therefore, could not decide to be well. For her illness she needed help, in respect not to the physical symptoms—which were only the communications of inner turmoil—but to the nuclear problems that her physical symptoms represented. She was given information to indicate that the recent stress situation of her father's death and the birth of her second child was in itself only precipitating to a disturbance of a personality that had not yet been able to assume a mature, adult role in interpersonal relations.

The patient resisted and demanded over and over again statements that she herself could do the job and attempted to make the therapist assume the same position as her conscience; namely, that she was to blame and, therefore, through some terrific struggle and expiation could overcome the illness which she assumed was evidence of her guilt. The therapist refused to accept this assigned role and continued to indicate that it was quite apparent that the patient implicitly knew otherwise, for she had come of her own volition to the therapist for help and that was enough to indicate that she recognized its need.

As the interview progressed, the therapist assumed the role of a helpful maternal parent, promising succorance and help for the end goal of cooperation in attempting to mature. This the patient recognized as she fed back an increasingly supplicating attitude and request for firm promises that she could be helped. What she meant was that she wished the therapist would be able to give her the kind of gratification that her illness indicated she needed. The transaction was completed when the patient experienced an implicit recognition that this was a possibility even though the end goal was something more mature and toward which she must struggle with the therapist's help. As a result of this transactional process the patient convinced her family of her need for treatment, obtained their support, and started treatment the next week.

CASE 14

Information Given to a Wife as to How to Handle
Her Sick and Paranoid Husband

A MIDDLE-AGED FEMALE requested help because of a problem concerning her husband who had recently entered the hospital with a mild stroke. The attending physician felt that this patient's stroke would clear up and that he would be reasonably well again and able to return to his work. In the weeks immediately following the shock of the stroke, however, the husband's latent paranoia broke out to the point where he accused his wife of being responsible for the stroke because she worried and bothered him so much. With this accusatory attitude he also brought out a reservoir of latent hostility toward her, in that he indicated at every visit how worthless and disturbing she was to him, even accusing her of having affairs with other men. His conclusion was that he would never return to her.

The exploratory interview with the wife revealed that she and her husband had enjoyed a sado-masochistic marriage for approximately ten years. The husband was the more passive of the two, denying his passive wishes to be cared for by an overcompensatory aggressiveness and by projecting the aggressiveness that he wishes his wife to have. The situation in the hospital became desperate in that the wife could not control herself and, in the transactions occurring during the visiting hours, became aggressive and retaliatory to the husband, resulting in some violent scenes which did his physical condition a great deal of harm.

The information given to the wife, without touching any of the crucial personality problems of the husband or of her own, had to do with the restructuring of their relationship at the present time. The wife was informed that people who are shocked by strokes very frequently attempt to explain the catastrophe by some outside agent. Demons and other gremlins were now out of fashion. He had only one target to use, and that was his wife. One could expect a man in the prime of his life to react as if something awful had happened to him for which someone was to blame.

The wife was also taught the structure of the role of solicitous spouse who responded to questions and refused to counterattack against the unfair accusations of a sick man. She was also advised that her visits be structuralized in time by the attending doctor who should tell the patient and his wife, through orders written on the chart, the exact time of day and length of time for each visit. It was also suggested that the husband be told that the wife was seeing a therapist so that he would know that a third person was hearing about the transactions that would go on between them in the sickroom.

COMMENT: In this transaction information was not given as to the basic character of the husband or of the aggressive, masculine nature of the wife's personality, both of which seem to make a good fit in a sado-masochistic marriage. Instead, information was given that the situation was temporary and induced only by the illness. The therapist was certain that this marriage would not break up. It had endured for long on the basis of two personalities' satisfying each other. Information was given to structure the transactions between them to the point where both the patient and his wife knew exactly what could be expected of them. At the same time it was felt that the sick man in the hospital could not be stopped from expressing his aggressions toward the wife. In fact, the ventilation of these feelings might even be therapeutic and helpful in a later marital adjustment. That he should know there was a therapist involved, listening to his wife, would lessen the burden on her tolerance; for through this means the husband would be less likely to make such seriously unrealistic accusations.

As a result of this information, which was reinforced through several visits, the wife became less agitated, was no longer depressed, and felt more confident in the future. At the same time, as it became clear to the patient that the wife was seeking therapeutic help for her problem with him, he spoke to his attending doctor about his feelings toward his wife. After ventilating this emotional outburst to the medical man, he felt so much better that he realized he should have some psychotherapy himself and asked that a psychiatrist visit him at the hospital.

CASE 15

Information: Rejecting Patient for Treatment

THE PATIENT and her husband had originally sought help from a family agency for their marital problems, precipitated by the fact that the husband had found another woman for whom he had left his wife. Although this had occurred often during the last years of the marriage, this present affair seemed the most serious. The husband took the other woman out with family friends, who reported the information back to the wife. He even took the other woman on a boat he owned jointly with his wife, and left his wife at home with their three children.

The husband had a great deal of confusion and uncertainty as to what to do, although to the wife he presented a firm stand that she did not satisfy him and he wanted to leave her. His anxiety and depression as part of his uncertainty resulted in his entering treatment with an analyst. The patient saw a social worker at a family agency several times and presented herself as so upset that the worker advised her to seek treatment from a psychiatrist. In addition, the husband's analyst had considered that she needed therapy.

The patient and her husband met in an Eastern city while he was still in college. They lived together prior to marriage for about a year and seemed to be happy and mutually satisfactory in their sexual relationships. During the first years of the married life the patient rapidly had one child after another, totaling three, and took seriously her responsibilities as a mother and housekeeper, letting herself go to the point where sometimes she even appeared slovenly. She was less concerned with her husband and his needs and apparently was far less satisfactory to him sexually than she was at first. As he complained to her, she attempted to resume the attitudes that were present in their "green years." Nothing she did, however, seemed to satisfy him, and she felt that she was a depreciated and unworthy person who could not compete with the other woman. The husband publicly repudiated her and made her feel that the break in the marriage was entirely her fault.

In the exploratory interview she did not look at the therapist and had quite unrealistic attitudes about herself, about money and numerous minor matters of ordinary living. She was primarily concerned with her sexual techniques and often laughed with shallow affect at matters that were quite serious. As a result of this initial transaction the therapist felt that she was quite a brittle schizoid personality and asked for psychological tests.

The psychological tests were administered by a female who seemed to have upset the patient. Prior to the reporting of the tests, the patient wrote a long letter indicating her annoyance with the psychologist for not really being a woman. When finished, the psychological report revealed an ambulatory schizophrenic with very little ego strength and a specific recommendation was made against intensive treatment.

The patient returned to the therapist for information following the diagnosis and psychological testing, and the question arose: What should she be told? The interview was opened with a statement that she would not be accepted for regular treatment. At this point the patient started to cry and stated: What can she do? She had been counting so much on being treated and being made into a wife that her husband would want.

The therapist took a realistic approach and stated that the patient was not entirely a healthy person but she seemed to be doing and planning things on her own and she was apparently not a helpless and hopeless person. Sick she was, but not sick enough to have the kind of treatment that would make her into a different person. The therapist informed her that she apparently felt that the disturbance in the marriage was all her own fault, but that obviously she had satisfied her husband in most respects until very recently. Perhaps it would be a good thing to wait and see whether the husband's therapy would not reverse his flight from the marriage. After all, she was not much different from when he married her, and, therefore, if his treatment was successful, he could or could not return to the kind of person with whom he had originally fallen in love. The therapist then intimated that change was not necessary in the patient herself, but she could wait out the results of her husband's treatment. In the meantime, if any crisis developed in her life, she was free to consult the therapist.

The patient seemed to brighten up a good deal and smiled and said she felt much better and thought this was a good idea, but suddenly she said that the therapist should tell her husband what he had told her because he wouldn't believe it—he thinks she is so terribly ill. The therapist responded by stating that he would not tell the husband but would tell his therapist. On this note the interview was terminated.

COMMENT: Here we have a transaction in which information must be given to a woman with a precarious balance that therapy would not be undertaken. Certainly any kind of uncovering therapy would have been dangerous for this person. The possibility of seeing her regularly for supportive treatment was not entertained because this patient had enough information from her husband and from others in her family to know the kind of therapy that attempts at rehabilitating or altering personality, and she would have recognized that no serious efforts were being made to change her. It was felt wiser to give her a notion of competence and adjustment better than she had, in order to keep her on an even keel for some time. It was hoped to prevent her from seeking continuous professional help. The therapist wanted to prevent her from going elsewhere for treatment to avoid the danger of her falling into the hands of someone who would injudiciously uncover her latent psychosis.

The reaction to the first information by the patient as if it were a catastrophe was followed by an explanation from the therapist to indicate that her present status was no different from before and it was good enough for her husband if he could get rid of his own problems. This not only reassured her but also made her feel that her own role in the marital disturbance was not so great as she had been accused of. The therapist, however, left the door open for her to return if any crisis arose and promised to tell her husband's therapist of the reasons why she was not taken into therapy.

In summary, then, we may view this transaction as one in which rejection is mitigated by the re-establishment of a role in which the wife would perform with lessened hurt to her pride and self-esteem.

In this chapter we have illustrated a variety of communications between worker and patient as recommendations are given and received. There is an endless variety to the contents of such transactions and many individual resolutions. Giving recommendations is not a routine, highly structured telling of decisions, but a dynamic interplay of role relations for which the worker needs to be acutely alert and adaptable to receiving information through new roles of the patient and many nuances of information. Skills necessary for the successful outcome of this transaction are slowly acquired by learning from experience and restrospective study of each transaction.

REFERENCE

1. Hilgard, J. R., and Newman, M. F.: Anniversaries in mental illness. *Psychiatry,* 22:113, 1959.

4

Experiencing Complementary

Relationships

COMPLEMENTARY RELATIONSHIP IMPLIES a form of psychotherapy that is usually depreciatingly termed superficial because no "deep" psychodynamics are uncovered and personality reconstruction is not its aim. Rather, through a complementary relationship some of the patient's current needs are satisfied. The patient and the therapist begin their communications with clearly defined explicit roles. The patient is in trouble and needs help with a problem; the therapist assumes the role of a helper.

The patient, however, implicitly assumes one or several of the roles of a child, depending on and requiring counsel. A partial array of the most frequent childish roles are: (1) a learner needing help in understanding and interpreting reality; (2) a guidance-seeker searching for knowledge of standards, values, and judgments; (3) a seeker for a sympathetic person to whom he can express pent-up feelings without shame or fear of retaliation; (4) an identity-seeker asking for knowledge and appreciation of his status in relation to others (Table 1d, p. 24).

As the therapist accepts the explicit role of one who shares the patient's problems and feelings, he ascertains the patient's implicit needs and accepts the necessary role assignments. Therefore, he assumes complementarity for both the explicit and implicit roles of his patient. Thus for the learner, he becomes a teacher; for the guidance-seeker, he authoritatively sets standards, demands adherence to values, and pronounces judgments; for the emotionally burdened, he listens, absorbs, and reflects; for the identity-seeker, he appreciates and identifies the patient's self and essential attributes.

The therapist's skill consists first in establishing a good relationship in which the explicit life problem is exposed. However, he cannot deal with this problem adequately until he knows and assumes the implicit role-complementarity necessary for the patient at the time. This process requires much training, skill, and experience; it is certainly not a simple task. If the proper role needs are accurately ascertained, the real-life problem may be resolved automatically and indirectly.

The transaction may take several forms: (1) an equilibrium is established and persists unaltered for considerable time; (2) the equilibrium is sufficiently satisfying for the length of time the real problem requires for solution; (3) the patient finds another person with whom complementarity may be achieved naturally in a real-life situation; (4) when the patient becomes aware of the nature of his implicit role, he takes flight from the transaction; (5) definition of the patient's implicit role results in his realization of the need for his own responsibility and efforts in therapy, and he moves into an area of intensive psychotherapy.

We shall now exemplify the four essential child-parent role relationships mentioned above.

CASE 16

Reality Interpretation

THE PATIENT was a forty-seven-year-old, white, Jewish woman who requested psychiatric treatment for her only child, a nine-and-a-half-year-old adopted boy, described as rebelliously acting out by lying, stealing, tampering with matches, and failing in school. The staff decided to focus treatment on the mother rather than to treat the child directly. In a telephone conversation, prior to exploratory interviews, the patient expressed the feeling that she had to "get into the clinic by fair means or foul." Although this was said with reference to her son, it seemed a reflection of her own desperate need for help.

The initial impression was that of an attractive, well-groomed, intelligent woman, with extremely anxious, somewhat flighty behavior. She covered up her concerns by suppression, denial, and facetiousness. In talking she used many epithets, including colorful and descriptive slang phrases. At times she expressed herself somewhat provocatively, obviously testing the worker's reaction. She had capacity for insight, for when reality interpretations were given, she responded with obvious relief that worker could put this "on the line."

Although the patient sometimes reacted with initial tendency to deny or minimize, her defensiveness was readily given up. In the first exploratory interview, the patient talked about her son's behaving in a "vicious circle again," his "goading" the parents, getting them "wound up to a climax" so that one or the other parent would slap him. When the patient described the family, worker pointed out that it seemed that everybody was on a merry-go-round, getting dizzier and more mixed up as time went on. The patient agreed to this description.

The worker then concentrated on the patient's own feelings of being threatened by her son's behavior, which included attempts to wrestle with her. The patient gradually began to focus on her own feelings and concerns. She implied concern about surgery and X-ray treatments which she had undergone several years ago for what was later learned to be cancer of the uterus and cervix. Worker expressed the feeling that patient was very concerned about her health. The patient denied this, saying that she never thought about it. Worker considered that the patient did not dare to allow herself to think about it, but that she probably had had a great deal of underlying worry for a number of years. Eventually the patient was able to express her feelings, stating that at times she did worry about her health, knew that she should have had a medical check-up a long time ago, but that she was too scared.

In subsequent interviews over a period of five weeks, the worker was very firm with the patient, interpreting reality factors in respect to her problems, her anxieties, and responsibilities within the mother-son relationship which she has projected to others. She responded positively to such interpretations and evidenced awareness and acceptance of the clinic's change in focus from the child to herself: "Golly, the tables have really been turned about." On a few occasions patient reported some acting-out behavior by the son and asked to have him seen at the clinic, but this seemed to test out the worker's actual acceptance of her and her own problems. Patient appeared relieved at worker's explanation that it seemed advisable to explore the situation further with her, and at the worker's more concise statement that she did not believe it advisable to have the child come to clinic at this time. When worker eventually explained the staff decision regarding treatment interviews with the patient and the necessity for her to be seen in a diagnostic interview with a psychiatrist as part of our routine, the patient felt quite threatened. It was explained that the patient might continue with worker, or that the clinic staff might assign her to another therapist. Patient said that if she could state her preference she would like to continue with worker, saying sarcastically, "You have not exactly been a crutch to me, and at times you've needled the pants off me, but we do have *some* rapport."

After several sessions in which worker verbalized patient's concerns about the previous medical problem, patient herself was able to focus on this area. At first she said that she never had known the details of the surgery, that she hadn't bothered to ask the doctor. Worker commented that the patient was probably too scared to inquire. She eventually verbalized that she had ignored the medical situation because of her own fears of actually finding out what the operation was about. After some discussion regarding her need for a check-up, with encouragement by worker on the basis of a routine plan, the patient expressed her intention of making an appointment with her gynecologist. She went on to say that ever since she was a child she has kept herself busy, not allowing herself to think of any of her fears, or to express them. When she was told that she could talk about her fears here, patient registered surprise, heaved a deep sigh, and then with much affect exclaimed, "Oh, you're a darling."

In subsequent interviews the patient was able to deal with her "fears" and her behavior more realistically. Her initial responses to some of the worker's interpretations were defensive; *i.e.*, when she talked about her son's lying or inability to think things through, worker reminded patient that this is what she has said about herself. The patient then said that she only tells "little lies—white lies." When worker explored the circumstances, the patient recognized that she "lied to get out of a situation," just as her son does, or that she can never think anything through, can never make a decision, and that she's had these patterns all her life. When patient complained that son feels she doesn't trust him, and she doesn't know why, worker stated, "But you don't trust him." After some thought patient agreed this was true, but added defensively, "But I don't see how I can."

There was movement in the patient's capacity to know herself and to admit she felt desperately in need of help. In spite of trying hard to control her feelings, she sometimes just "exploded." Patient's son has evidenced improvement as a result of her lessened anxiety since coming to clinic. Worker once asked why she had need to have her son "stupid." This she denied, but patient dealt with the problem effectively after worker suggested that if she did want him to pass his school work she would get this idea across to him. She now says she really did know that she had a cancer, has faced her fears regarding this, and has completed a medical check-up with negative findings. She expressed surprise that she has continued with psychiatric interviews, but she's determined to keep on.

COMMENT: This woman had been accustomed to dealing with painful reality by denial and distortion, intimidating and provoking people to agree with her. Her adopted boy seemed to have assumed a similar role pattern and accomplished his goals also by "fair means or foul." The worker was not intimidated and avoided complying with the mother's desire for someone to manipulate. She slowly, firmly, and with emotional support held up a mirror to her patient in which she had to see her behavior as it really was. The result was a lessening of anxiety and an increasing capacity to behave appropriately which reacted beneficially on her son.

Slight though the internal changes might have been, this was a form of psychotherapy which facilitated leverage for further work with the mother and hopefulness for the child. It consisted of a special form of relationship in which the worker gave emotional strength to her anxious patient. The worker demanded the price of endurance from the patient for the understanding of her behavior in the light of clarification. Here was no deep emotional insight, no character or personality reorganization, but rather a clearer view of the patient's own reality.

CASE 17

Authoritative Interpretation

THE PATIENT was a forty-eight-year-old, white, Jewish housewife who had been treated by a psychiatric social worker who was leaving the staff. She felt that the patient should continue treatment. Information from the first therapist described the patient as a "nice but somewhat pitiful old lady who shuffles along." Her nineteen-year-old son had been a chronic schizophrenic since childhood. He never had a friend and was always an odd, sick, inept person. The precipitating event which originally brought the patient and her son to our clinic was a sudden personality alteration in adolescence, changing him from a withdrawn character to an overwhelming, provocative, and physically abusive person.

The worker first met the patient without a prearranged appointment as she dropped into the psychiatric clinic following an appointment in a dermatology clinic where she was having a skin infection treated. She immediately started to pour out her feelings that she couldn't go on with her son since he was getting worse and was threatening her with a knife. She continued on in this vein as if she had known the worker for a long time. From this beginning contact, the patient structured her role as that of a helpless, abused woman who had sacrificed her life for this son and the therapist's role as that of being her "last port of call," the only person in the world on whom she could depend. The worker's initial reaction to her was one of pity. The patient looked older than her stated age, and there was no doubt that she had lived a self-suffering life. During this first contact with patient, worker offered her regular weekly interviews at a scheduled time. She objected to this, stating she would like just to drop in. During the first few interviews she came earlier or later than the stated time, but she eventually settled down to accepting the time schedule.

For five months worker listened to the patient describe an intense, provocative relationship existing between herself and her son. An example of the conversation and interpersonal family behavior taking place in the home was her son screaming, "I need a little sexual love," as he grabbed at the patient's body while the father condoned his son's demandingness, stating that he sees nothing wrong with his playfulness. The content of the patient's interviews was consistently her preoccupation with her dermatitis, various other diseases, and suffering. Although her explicit role was one of being helpless and abused, her implicit role was the opposite. She tried to use the worker for the purpose of finding out what her son told the doctor and to get her to influence the doctor in his treatment to include electric shock or tranquilizing drugs.

From the very first the worker's therapeutic role was that of an authoritative and directive figure. The patient was given direct recommendations that certain types of acting out, such as her son's fondling her body, should not be allowed. Her anxiety would then increase, and it became apparent that the equilibrium in the family could not be shifted. Only two possibilities existed: that the patient and her son would remain in equilibrium within this old type of relationship, or the son would have to be sent to the state hospital. Hospitalization was achieved only because there was a twenty-year-old daughter in the home who was bitterly ashamed when she was attacked by the son. Even then hospitalization was accomplished only on threat of withdrawal of the clinic from the case.

COMMENT: After hospitalization was effected, the patient did not return to her therapist. When the worker did not continue to accept her assigned role, that of identifying with the patient's suffering or controlling or manipulating her son's life, no other type of communication was acceptable to her.

CASE 18

Emotional Unburdening

THE PATIENT was a thirty-eight-year-old mother of an ambulatory psychotic boy of fifteen who had been seen weekly in collaborative treatment over a five-year period. The boy responded with slow sporadic improvement which invariably precipitated a frantic desperate plea from the mother not to encourage him to go too far, ending up with: "Every time Joe gets better, I get worse." Slowly an intensely seductive relationship between the mother and boy was being broken up so that the mother no longer hovered over the boy physically, kissing and stroking him even publicly.

When the mother was first seen, she appeared to be breezy, seductive, and provocative, boasting about what a tomboy she had been as a child, and how feminine things and tender feelings meant little to her "except for Joe," for whom she wanted to do anything. She depreciated her husband for his falsetto tenor voice which made her shudder, and for his unproductive work record. Her husband's drinking reminded her of father's, although father was a cold autocrat unlike her passive husband in other ways.

When her smiling breezy defense was interpreted as hiding her worries and fears, she abruptly gave up and became intensely depressed, producing dreams and fantasies which showed clearly her psychotic character structure. She had nightmares of Joe being brutally killed; she revealed her belief that she was directly responsible for her mother's death when she was sixteen. She also revealed that intercourse was impossible because of vaginal strictures for which she flatly and desperately refused treatment. After this actual and threatened disintegration, a hurried attempt was made, which proved reasonably successful, to reinstitute her defenses.

The patient then became very attached to the therapist and stated that she would try to help her husband and Joe if she could "just be let alone." She became more positive toward her husband to the extent that he kept his job and gave up much of his drinking. But she wanted to go "no further" (sex), and a kind of brother-sister relationship became the bargain between them. She gave up some of her hold on her son and stated openly at times to the worker, "I'll let it out on you."

COMMENT: The interviews were characterized by the patient's starting with intense pressure and need to talk, rattling off in rapid succession almost any kind of association, whether relevant or important, accompanied by decreasing sighs as the interview progressed, and she usually left each interview "calmed down until next week." It was as if steam were permitted to escape from a valve until the level of pressure was safe again for another week. Tentative attempts from time to time to get at underlying meanings were not successful. The interviews had to be abreactions for the patient, in order to maintain her precarious equilibrium.

CASE 19

Example of Attempt to Provide a Primary Interpersonal Relationship with an Otherwise Isolated Individual

PATIENT was a twenty-three-year-old, single, Jewish man who lived with his parents. He had three older married sisters whom he occasionally visited. One of the sisters and his mother pressured him to seek psychiatric help. He was accompanied by his sister to the diagnostic interview where he described his inability to get along with anybody, "inferiority complex," fear of girls, fear of the dark, fear of remaining dependent upon his parents, fear of being noticed and stared at by people in the streets, excessive sleeping, chronic tiredness, difficulty in getting and keeping jobs, expecting to be attacked or injured. These symptoms had been present for four years. The examining psychiatrist described patient as being a "withdrawn, isolated schizoid boy with both adolescent difficulties and a more severe, underlying, schizophrenic problem, having phobic, obsessive, and depressive symptoms." "A supportive, nonprobing relationship with a male therapist upon whom he could depend without feeling depreciated or too weak and with whom he can later identify" was recommended.

Patient was assigned to a male social service student who could be available for nine months. The student was a strong, pleasant-looking man in his forties, who had had some psychotherapy himself, and was eager "to help" people. The patient did not respond to the student's appointment letters, but his sister and mother indicated that they were pressuring patient and that he was becoming more negativistic. They and the student were advised to let the patient know that he could call for an appointment when he felt ready, and to take the pressure off him. About a month and a half later the patient initiated contact, and weekly interviews were arranged. He kept all his appointments except one at the end of the student's stay.

Patient was of medium height; he was strong, dark-complexioned, bushy-haired, with a sallow and slightly pockmarked face, and generally presented a sad, depressed expression. He never looked at the therapist except on the few occasions when he smiled. (When he smiled, his appearance changed dramatically.) He came to the interviews consistently dressed in gray work pants, sport shirt, and usually unshaven. He related in a compliant self-depreciating fashion. He verbalized very well with a tendency to exaggerate his problems.

Patient implicitly made a bid for the student to see him as a weak, helpless, deprived, and exploited boy; at the same time he explicitly stated his wish to be treated as an adult, voicing his anger at his parents and sisters for telling him what he should do. The history and the initial behavior of the patient brought out clearly one factor in the patient's problems; namely, that patient's parents and sisters both "pushed" and infantilized him. They pressured him to compete in work, social, and sexual situations while at the same time treating him as a child, telling him what to wear, giving him spending money, and generally depreciating him and his abilities. Since neither position was tenable for him, the patient had reacted for the most part by isolating himself.

With the awareness that patient would become tremendously anxious and run from treatment if either an authoritative or submissive attitude were taken by the therapist, and also that patient was too weak to support an "uncovering" or "analytical" approach, the student comfortably and rather easily accepted the role which the patient wanted him to assume—that of a benevolent, nonaggressive but protective parental figure who would permit him to go at his own pace. In social work terminology this is understood as aligning oneself with the client's strengths; in psychological terms, this is "strengthening the ego." The actual interaction between patient and therapist during the interviews can be briefly summarized from the point of view of explicit content.

During all nineteen interviews the patient subtly attempted to force the student into a position of either depreciating him or expecting too much of him. Patient gave the impression of more adequate social functioning than the earlier history and diagnostic interview noted. Although he depreciated the type of job he held, he had held it for a year; he had never really been fired from a job but rather had been laid off, or left before he could be fired and had been reinstated on his job after being advised to take time off for his health. Although he spoke, at the time his history was obtained, about his fears of social contacts of any kind, and his flight from them, he spent one or two nights a week playing basketball with a group at the Y.M.C.A. He did not speak of excessive sleeping, and because he was working in the day and going out in the evening it seemed that he did not sleep excessively. In almost every interview he brought up memories of past gratifying experiences, but would follow this with much self-depreciation in his present situation. He felt that he was different from other people in that he lacked something others had, that he was "stupid" and a "phony" and that others readily saw these qualities in him whether they knew him or not. He felt that he could not ask for a date with a girl he liked at the store for fear she would see that there was something wrong with him and would reject him. This type of rejection, he stated, would cause a relapse for him. In response to these self-depreciating statements he was told that they were either unrealistic or inconsistent with his past satisfactory relationships.

The patient attributed the cause of his current difficulties to never having opportunities in his home environment to mature. He felt that his parents made all decisions for him and now he must suddenly make them for himself. He believed that others were expecting this maturity all at once and were impatient with him. When it was pointed out that some of the activities he felt others were pushing him into were things he wanted for himself, such as getting a better job or moving out from home and parents, and that the worker was not pushing him into these activities, he felt that the whole situation was too confusing. He began to withdraw by saying that he was as well as he could ever get. At the same time he expressed fears that his anger would get out of hand. Patient, however, was able to use the help offered him as demonstrated in the following example: On his job he was delegated the task of assisting a particularly difficult salesman who did not get along with people. When the salesman made an insulting remark to him, he reacted by walking away from the job in a rage. Upon questioning he revealed that he had been chosen for this job because of the ability to control himself. The kind of confidence his superior had in him was pointed out. When he returned the next week he reported a similar episode, but added that this time he was angry but was able to control it and remain with the task until it was finished.

There was also a good deal of discussion about relationships with girls. In the beginning he was afraid to approach girls for dates because of a fear they would reject him. As he felt better, he said he did not need to have dates. Later, although he expressed a desire for dates again, he was afraid the girls would "like me too much." These fears were discussed while trying to focus on the realities of the problem, his feelings of inadequacy, what he felt he really wanted, and why he felt he could not get involved with girls. When he talked about a date a year ago in which he could easily have had sexual relations, he explained his refusal on the grounds that "it was too easy." The worker's reaction was to accept this as a normal adolescent difficulty because this was the way he presented it.

As can be seen from the foregoing data, the patient's communications became more and more revealing as the therapist was perceived as a nonthreatening person. Patient's job performance improved, and his sister reported that he was doing better at home—not so provoking to parents, etc. The worker, in the few attempts to get patient to look at his own contributions to his problems (his wish to be dependent on mother or his hostility which was so frightening to him), was immediately sensitive and aware of patient's tendency to take flight in confusion or paranoid projection, and, therefore, returned to the pattern of aiding the healthier defenses. The patient's discussion of his anger toward his fellow employee, and his fear of expressing it, was directly related to the transaction with the therapist, following the attempt to point out to the patient that he was being self-depreciating for a purpose. The worker wisely did not attempt to consider the anger part of the therapeutic relationship but dealt with it only in the area of the job. When the worker announced his impending departure, the patient was able to talk about its meaning for him. He acknowledged his need for help and his intention to continue at the clinic. He saw a new relationship as having to start all over again, and demonstrated this fact by missing the next to last appointment, and in the last interview by returning to the testing situation of extreme self-depreciation as he had in the very early interviews. Patient was given the name of his new therapist, but missed the first several appointments with him. He later re-established contact, and "supportive therapy" continued.

COMMENT: This is the kind of patient who without supportive therapy would probably deteriorate and wind up in a state hospital, but with support is able to handle anxiety, and function at a constructive marginal level. This type of patient is well known to social workers in all kinds of agencies. The "supportive therapy" is general and inclusive. In transactional terms, therapy consisted in accepting the role the patient implicitly desired the therapist to take—the role of a nondemanding parental figure, rejecting the omnipotent, demanding parental role when it was attributed to him. The feedback in the transaction did not result in the type of spiraling that occurs when the assigned role is rejected *in toto,* but rather it seems to result in the expanding of the circular transaction at the same level, strengthening the patient as long as the therapist remains in the reciprocal relationship.

In this chapter we have exemplified four dependent patient roles in which supportive therapy is indicated. The therapists recognized the implicitly assigned roles which they adopted and in which they were effective in helping the patients solve their problems. These therapeutic problems become very difficult when the therapist becomes too ambitious and attempts to move the patient into an area of intensive psychotherapy or insight therapy too soon or when he is unable to undergo its strain.

Because the role relationships require so little effort after becoming stabilized, there is danger that the supportive, re-educational, counseling, and directive aspects will be continued interminably. When are the patient's real problems solved? When does he find an analogous relationship in reality? When is he ready to go it on his own? There are few reliable criteria for the answers to these questions. The therapist should help the patient test his strength by gradually becoming less active and asking the patient to make more of his own decisions, to endure less frequent interviews, and to experience interruptions in therapy for weeks or months at a time. Sometimes a termination date may be set well in advance or a crucial decision may be demanded of the patient by the therapist.

At any rate, this form of therapy—involving a long period of complementary relationship—should be considered temporary and not as an end in itself; otherwise the patient's ego will be weakened instead of strengthened.

III

Psychotherapy

5

Critique of Psychotherapy and
the Social Worker's Participation

W̲E HAVE TERMED THE NEXT AREA of social work functioning the
process of *modifying complementary relationship* (Table 1e, p. 25).
This, in essence, is what usually has been termed psychotherapy oriented toward effecting considerable internal change in the patient and
modification of his behavior. Others have spoken of it as intensive,
deep, uncovering, insight, dynamic, and modified psychoanalytic therapy. How intensive or deep the therapy goes, or how much it results in
personality reorganization, or where its boundaries with respect to
psychoanalysis are, constitute questions as yet not answered adequately.
Before elucidating our concepts of the transactional systems involved,
and demonstrating one case in detail, we shall first present an overview of the field of psychotherapy with special reference to the social
worker's participation.

DEFINITION OF PSYCHOTHERAPY

In our day, when anyone patient enough to listen sympathetically to
another's troubles and to give evidence of empathic understanding considers that he is a therapist, an adequate definition of psychotherapy
should aim toward establishing limits. Despite the beneficial effects
from pouring out emotional reactions or troubled thoughts to a listener,
psychotherapy is a purposeful strategy learned and modified by a pro-

fessional person (therapist) whose training, experience, and skills are oriented to helping a sick person (patient). Thus, psychotherapy is defined by the special transactions occurring between two persons who assume specific explicit complementary social roles.

In his comprehensive textbook Wolberg [1] quotes 13 definitions of psychotherapy propounded by leaders in the field of psychiatry. Their differences are not very great, probably because all of the concepts are vaguely formulated. Wolberg himself has presented a general definition which, although also vague, includes the essential variables.

> Psychotherapy is a form of treatment for problems of an emotional nature in which a trained person deliberately establishes a professional relationship with a patient with the object of removing, modifying, or retarding existing symptoms, of mediating disturbed patterns of behavior, and promoting positive personality growth and development. [1]

Perhaps a few other professional opinions will convey both the vagueness and the slight differences of definition maintained by various leaders in the field. For example, Alexander [2] contends that psychotherapy is a corrective emotional experience leading to a discriminatory learning process. Dollard [3] and his co-workers state that psychotherapy is based on the assumption that neuroses constitute an undesirable and symptomatic failure in learning due to early fears which have reduced the capacity of the subject to think, work, and love. Therefore, psychotherapy is a learning process. Frieda Fromm-Reichmann [4] maintains that psychotherapy is a clarification of the patient's difficulties with his fellow men. In contrast, Rogers [5] contends that psychotherapy is a means of changing the person's perception and concept of self. Nolan Lewis [6] considers that psychotherapy produces psychological integration or reintegration of the personality and integration of the patient within his family, society, and culture.

In a report by the Committee on the Role of the Psychiatric Social Worker, psychotherapy is defined as follows:

> Psychotherapy is a systematic process in which the relationship between the worker and the client is used for the purpose of resolving a problem arising from inner conflict, manifested in some disturbance of personality functioning. It requires the conscious participation of the client and the mutual understanding between client and worker that they are engaged in this endeavor. . . . [7]

Wolberg points out the common factors in psychotherapy of all types. They are goal directed; they are organized around the patient-therapist relationship with varying degrees of activity; they require interviews; the subject matter on which a focus is made depends upon the theoretical bias of the therapist; they all evoke emotional responses. Their goals, although overlapping, are supportive, re-educational, and reconstructive, and, to quote Knight's [8] clichés, they deal with support, rapport, and import. Supportive therapy consists in establishing a working relationship dealing with environmental factors, planning for ways of coping with the external difficulties, and lasting for a limited period of time. Re-educational psychotherapy deals with conscious irrational attitudes and, through understanding of the positive assets and liabilities of the subject, attempts to reintegrate them. Reconstructive psychotherapy deals with unconscious processes, attempts to develop insight into them, and translates insight and understanding into action.

Austin [9] makes the point that three subgroupings of aims together constitute psychotherapy: (1) A supportive therapy with techniques of manipulation, environmental and psychological support, suggestion, and emotional relief where the goal appears to be an immediate diminishing of anxiety in order to preserve ego strength. (2) An intermediary therapy—also called experimental therapy, clarification, counseling, or insight therapy of a qualified kind. Techniques used include manipulation, suggestion, emotional relief, clarification, interpretation of certain kinds of content, and use of the transference for a corrective emotional experience. (3) A therapy aimed at partial or more complete reorganization of personality structure, clearly not belonging in the province of social casework.

It is our opinion, however, that Austin is involved in the current confusion that we discussed in previous chapters when she attempts to differentiate methods of psychotherapy on the basis of qualities and quantities of transference and at the same time points out that transference is an important factor in any method of casework and is the medium in which treatment takes place. According to Austin, all caseworkers must understand unconscious forces and when necessary deal with them, *but* only in prescribed and limited ways. Such a statement as "The transference development is manipulated rather than interpreted and diluted rather than stimulated" indicates the futile hope that differing techniques of dealing with transference can resolve the confusions among psychotherapeutic methods and differentiate casework.

Gordon Hamilton defines psychotherapy:

. . . as rooted in a two-person relationship in which one is therapist, or helper, and one the "patient" or client. It is assumed that the patient consciously involves himself to some degree in a therapeutic process and that the transference is used as the chief medium of treatment. The psychodynamics of personality must be understood, and the treatment is based on diagnosis.

The psychotherapies that derive from psychoanalytic hypotheses include a wide variety and many contributions of therapeutic techniques. The characteristic casework method is interpersonal and combines *both psychological and social therapies.* One rarely sees a case carried in "pure" psychotherapy, although phases of interviewing may not be easily distinguishable from psychotherapy conducted by psychiatrists. We remind ourselves, however, that psychotherapy, no matter how sound, is not *psychoanalysis,* although psychoanalysis lies within psychotherapy.

The striking fact is that Freudian concepts were worked into casework practice *so fully as to make casework a therapeutic process* long before there were acrid debates as to the nature of psychotherapy and who should, or should not, be allowed to practice it. For more than twenty-five years casework has practiced its distinctive forms of psychotherapy, and, at its best, it has continued to make use of all the familiar social services as social therapies.[10]

From these several definitions, and many more that could be mentioned, it becomes clear that psychotherapy has to be viewed—as Wolberg has done—from several frames of reference. These include the subjects who do the psychotherapy, the persons toward whom psychotherapy is directed, the methods employed, the process of change, and the anticipated results. Finally, most psychotherapies are also defined on the basis of psychodynamic theories concerning causes of illness, from first to final causes, and theories of reversibility or change. It should now be apparent that a simple definition of psychotherapy is impossible. In order to determine the range and specificity of the many extant psychotherapies, we shall consider each of the above items separately.

Who does psychotherapy?

Perhaps this question should be stated in another form, such as: Who doesn't do psychotherapy? Galdston [11] has enumerated the persons who have been engaged in this form of treatment, including parents, ministers and priests, teachers, faculty advisers, counselors, social workers, nurses, doctors, psychologists, and psychiatrists. He indicates that psychotherapy is universally performed in almost any two-person relationship. This broadens the definition to indicate that all emotional experiences and all learning achieved through relationships between people, are psychotherapeutic.

In contrast, others consider psychotherapy a separate scientific discipline, and Alexander specifies that the therapist is a scientist engaged in research in each case that he accepts for therapy. In a study of psychotherapists in contrast to organically oriented and directive psychiatrists, Redlich [12] found significant cultural differences between the two groups. Hence psychotherapy or not may be determined by the type of psychiatrist that the patient chooses.

Such a statement unduly simplifies an extremely complicated issue that has fomented considerable controversy in and among the disciplines of psychiatry, psychology, and social work (Szasz,[13] Handler,[14] etc.). Between psychiatry and psychology the arguments have been noisy, reaching to the top echelons of national societies and threatening to involve legal battles. The psychiatric social workers and psychiatrists, on the other hand, have attempted to resolve the issue through careful investigations, sensible and well-considered speeches and articles, and experimentation in the field. Through all this a definite and irreversible trend has slowly emerged, placing the psychiatric social worker among the professional psychotherapists. Let us now review the opinions of some authorities in the field.

Greta Bibring [15] indicates that the social worker functions by suggestion, permission of abreaction, manipulation of the external environment, and intellectual clarification through interpretations. She states that considerations of personality and environment are interwoven by the social work therapist who modifies the environment, supports psychologically, clarifies, and develops insight.

Coleman [16] states that the psychiatrist and the caseworker utilize transference; both attempt to reduce anxiety and maintain a situational focus. There is a differentiation, however, in that the caseworker strengthens defenses and supports the neurotic equilibrium. She helps to solve practical problems and shares in decision-making processes. But the social worker does not fractionate the patient from his social environment, and insight always refers to the conscious ego. Psychotherapy and casework, according to Coleman, are separate techniques. But Coleman's differentiation of psychotherapies creates an artificial dichotomy of inner and outer which cannot be substantiated by what the relationship between therapist of any type and patient accomplishes.

Perlman [17] attempts to define social casework as a problem-solving process which involves ego functions. The therapeutic goal is to help persons cope more effectively with their problems in social functioning. She implies that transference impedes and interferes with this rational process and thereby emphasizes only one segment of a very complicated transactional system.

Such limitations are quite appropriate when the problem is concrete, but in the therapeutic process repetition compulsions, phobias, projection, etc., interfere with realistic solutions of life situations. This intellectual approach is the antithesis of the attempt of one human being to understand communication from another in a therapeutic relationship where both are trying to illuminate and make explicit the inner problems that are impeding the client's own understanding of his destiny and his ability to take decisive action.

Towle,[18] in a recent speech at the University of Chicago, states that the early fusion of casework and psychiatry still left social work as a separate profession. She recognizes, however, that since World War II social workers have become or are becoming "pseudo-psychiatrists." She contends that the social worker solves problems with the emphasis on personal real-life problems rather than on the internal psychology of the patient. The social worker functions in ego building or sustaining, so that the patient can cope better with his problems in current life. Social work, according to Towle, is "psychotherapeutic without being psychotherapy, and its goal is only to improve social functioning." By her frank admission, however, psychiatric social workers are doing psychotherapy.

Gordon Hamilton comments as follows:

> Still there is the insistent question: Why does the caseworker assume the role of therapist, rather than the psychiatrist himself? This challenge is not simply met with the negative argument that there is a current scarcity of trained psychiatrists. There is a positive rationale for such a plan. From the social worker's point of view it is difficult to separate sharply social problems from psychological ones. The social worker is primarily concerned with the interaction of individual persons with social realities. Properly to understand this he must have precise knowledge of ego-adaptive functions and their relations, both to external social realities and to unconscious conflicts. Psychotherapy is a function derived from the dynamic nature of the patient's problem, not a technique arbitrarily patterned to suit the conventional training of any single profession. Good psychotherapy must be essentially the same process whether executed by one profession or another.[10]

Garrett[19] indicates that there is no sense in differentiating psychotherapy from casework. If the treatment takes into account the patient's feelings and emotions, then the caseworker is a psychotherapist.

The preceding quotations are typical of a vast literature in which authors attempt to discriminate between the functions of psychiatrists and psychiatric social workers. Such terms as manipulation, clarification, insight, problem-solving, social action, etc., cannot be well defined theoretically. They can be properly understood only in the context of the actual operations employed. Why is there such interest in differentiation of functions instead of concern with the therapeutic process itself and how can it be furthered no matter what the label placed on the therapist? Perhaps, as Zander[20] has indicated, this stems from the unique professional cultures of psychiatric clinics and hospitals, where role relations among the various disciplines are complicated transactions involving considerations of status and prestige.

The question of the psychiatric social workers doing intensive therapy is by no means a closed issue, and controversy still exists, some taking a strong stand against this position and others supporting it. Many who support the practice of psychotherapy by social workers are not willing to commit themselves to this position in print. Many permit the social worker to do intensive therapy only on a highly individual basis, making the permission specific to a worker in a specific case. In some specialized clinics the psychiatric social worker is expected to do only intensive psychiatric therapy. Our position has been that the social worker should perform all psychiatric social work functions including psychotherapy.

When we come to grips with the problem of role differentiation from a practical standpoint, the answer is simple. Clinical psychologists and psychiatric caseworkers are doing psychotherapy. Without the former, the public mental hospitals could furnish virtually no psychotherapy; without social workers doing psychotherapy, community clinics would be seriously handicapped. At the present time, however, there is much confusion stemming from the many divergent theoretical and operational concepts of psychotherapy and from writers and teachers who think that a difference in name indicates a difference in function.

Economics (private practice) and professional dignity and jealousies are behind some of the quarrels. Even though we consider psychotherapy a medical (psychiatric) treatment, and the medical practice acts of many states would seem to so imply, psychological intervention is a form of drugless therapy and not subject to restrictions of licensure. For our purposes we consider that psychotherapies are conducted in clinics *under psychiatric administration* so that we can transcend the problems of training, supervision, and responsibility. Let us be clear that we are discussing psychotherapy no matter who the therapist may be. Let us not try to use the escape hatch of calling it by other names. Leaders in the psychological and social service profession may state that their professions only counsel or do casework, but they do not abide by such artificial limitations. They all do psychotherapy. Who does psychotherapy depends only on the individual's qualifications. In this context Kubie [21] has recently advocated a separate professional discipline with its own specified training program leading to a special degree.

Grinker,[22] in 1953, made the following comments on training in psychiatry, which can be paraphrased for psychotherapy as practiced by all disciplines:

It has been said repeatedly that, in addition to his medical education, the potential therapist should be a warm, sensitive person with intuitive grasp of hidden feelings and a sincere liking for people. In fact, candidates who strive to be selected for training all tell us that they have these characteristics in correct proportions. Our acceptance of such characteristics as criteria would be just as bad as the rejection of candidates on the basis of some nosological diagnostic classification of their particular neuroses. What living being isn't to some degree and at some times warm, sensitive, intuitive to other humans? Contrariwise, what living person is not to some degree paranoid, phobic, compulsive, homosexual, depressed, or what not? A therapist cannot be defined by his temperature, rate of oxygenation, sensory thresholds, or by his neurosis. The problem concerns the processes of communication of information and involves the times, situations, and degrees for which special forms of communication are utilizable when one person attempts to help another. The patient communicates to the therapist. The therapist undergoes a process of internal communication or association and communicates through a feedback mechanism to the patient. Patient and therapist exist in a two-way circular transactional process within a special environment, each assuming a role pertinent and specific to his position in this process.

To perform the functions assumed in the role of therapist, a person should first have the capacity to communicate with others. He must know the implicit and explicit social roles which his patient enacts and those that are expected of him in transaction with his patient. Therefore, he must be able to understand and accept the cues of others and be able to express himself to and be understood by the other human beings with whom he is in transaction. The therapist's skill in adapting to the rapidly shifting social roles which are cued by the patient's needs is most significant. This, of course, involves the necessary function which the potential therapist should possess, and that is the capacity to endure the processes of communication within himself. Furthermore, the therapist must have the ability to maintain his intra-psychic transactions and his relationships with the patient without disintegration under conditions of stress severe enough to strain his dynamic equilibrium.[22]

How to select or determine what individuals have these qualities as therapists or can develop them with proper training remains one of the unresolved problems of our professional world.

Who receives psychotherapy?

Many psychotherapists neither discriminate the nature of the complaint nor establish a diagnosis for people who seek help. Thus, in their view it is unimportant whom they treat. Frieda Fromm-Reichmann points out that persons who benefit from psychotherapy are suffering from difficulties in relating to their fellow men. Lewis indicates that it is necessary to know the nature of the problem with which the patient comes for treatment in order to determine the therapeutic approach best suited for him. Although this might be theoretically correct, it is not clear how the matching of the problem with the method utilized is achieved. Writers such as Ackerman,[23] Coleman, Austin, and others have attempted to select groups of patients on the basis of sociological (mostly the upper classes according to Hollingshead and Redlich[24]), biological, and psychological diagnosis, and to determine which patients should be treated by various disciplines and under what conditions.

In the traditional medical sense a patient who goes to a physician for treatment is a person who is sick. With his sickness he has specific complaints and, because of them, is usually highly motivated for treatment. Immediately we become involved in definitions of mental illness. Is it a special quality developed in certain unfortunate persons, or is it the same process found in everyone but of such intensity that it creates suffering for the subject and difficulties in his interpersonal behavior?

Whether we consider man's internal sufferings or problems of his adjustment to group living, the definition of sickness depends ultimately on judgment of the cultural setting. The expectation of how one should feel—depressed, anxious, guilty, etc.—is derived from the compulsions of the subject's social group. Adjustment to society is dependent on what society expects and on its threshold of intolerance. Secondary adjustments through escape hatches facilitating movement in space, change of spouse, job, class, or isolation are possible to some degree in each society. Failures in these escapes or defenses push the overly deviant over the line of eccentricity into the area socially defined as sick.

In the heterogeneous cultures of Western civilization and especially in the ethnically mixed culture of the United States each subculture has its own threshold. These are dependent on socioeconomic levels, education, other specific ethnic derivatives, and value systems. These determine not only when illness is recognized but also how long spontaneous recovery is awaited, what home or folk remedies are first utilized, and what type of therapist is ultimately sought. As Szasz [25] has indicated, the psychotherapist requires patients who can participate in the process of treatment and do not demand that the therapist does something (gives medicine) or tells him something (guides and directs). Hollingshead and Redlich have demonstrated that not only type and severity of illness but also type of therapy accepted and the prognosis for relief are based on cultural factors indicated by social class.

When then can we conclude about the people who can be helped through psychotherapy? Do we need to have specific labels of various psychoses or neuroses derived from a diagnostic evaluation before we treat them? True, many patients whom we see in most clinic settings and who constitute the large majority of office practices of psychiatrists have well-defined clinical entities according to our official classifications. Countless others come to us with vague statements of interpersonal difficulties, failures and lack of expected successes in a variety of activities, and others with more circumscribed feelings of internal distress. For these we have had to find a label seemingly to justify their being treated as sick; we call them "character disorders." In sum, these humans with varying degrees of dis-ease *demand* more time than all the existing therapists from all disciplines are now able to offer. Yet they are only the sophisticated vanguard comprising less than one per cent of the population. The *needs* of the remainder have not yet become articulate.

THE GOALS OF PSYCHOTHERAPY

It becomes exceedingly difficult to define goals without taking into consideration the criteria of illness. If a person is ill as defined by his culture, then the goal of psychotherapy is to bring him back to health. This is not possible in terms of a rigid standard of health or a strict discrimination between health and illness, although Jahoda [26] believes that there are criteria for positive mental health. Whitehorn formulates the goal of psychotherapy as oriented to "health." By this he means to convert disability into working well, distress to feeling well, and dread to expecting well (cf. ref. 47).

Goals are dependent on the patient's motivation, the therapist's capacity, skill, experience, and the tools he has available, and the desires or values of the social group to which the patient belongs. Unfortunately, too many psychotherapists set goals of an absolute nature, based on their own value systems, and often are discontent with betterment and speak hopefully in nineteenth-century terms of "cure." Goals cannot be predetermined, even after careful screening and diagnostic studies, as many social work and psychiatric writers have attempted to do in describing specific techniques.

Even the setting of limited goals implies a prejudgment on the part of the therapist. It seems more natural that goals be developed out of the transactional experiences between the therapist and his patient rather than set before therapy begins. Slowly the motivation, the degree of illness, the capacity to endure the suffering of therapy, the ability to learn, as well as the special efficacy of the therapist in any particular case become clear. Thus, goals can be predetermined only in the general sense that both the therapist and the patient will begin and continue treatment as long as the transaction moves satisfactorily for both of them.

THE METHODS OF PSYCHOTHERAPY

Reviewing the literature pertaining to methods of treatment is a relatively unproductive task. Writers tend to use clichés labeling and by inference describing therapy, such as persuasion, suggestion, hypnosis, conversation, psychological analysis and synthesis. Others write about support, clarification, ego-strengthening, re-education, and corrective emotional experience. Levine [27] lists 25 methods of psychotherapy for general practitioners, five advanced methods for them, and ten methods

for the specialist! Few authors state their specific operations in sufficient detail to enable the reader to grasp what is done. Very few
case presentations are published in full; either they are summarized or
the patient's verbalizations alone are reported, without those of the
therapist; the elements from which the nature of the transaction may
be understood are rarely presented. Often the contents of the case presentation are in contradiction to the theoretical framework within which
the therapist says he operates. The puzzled reader rightfully concludes
that he can learn only through experience and supervision during
which he suffers with depression and anxiety from frustration, until by
trial and error and adequate instruction he develops his own therapeutic style. We shall give a few examples of methods culled from the
overabundant literature of psychotherapy.

Whitehorn,[28] in attempting to understand psychotherapy and psychotherapists, contrasts two methodological patterns. The first is an attempt
to learn about the "causes" of the patient's difficulty and undo them by
insightful disclosure. This pattern is very popular at the present time,
based on the influence of psychoanalysis in developing concepts and
methods of "uncovering" psychotherapy. The second pattern is an
effort not only to ascertain the patient's "bad patterns" of reactions but
also to evaluate his assets and potentialities. The therapist then evokes
constructive utilization of the patient's potentialities by helping him
better to handle his unresolved problems which are significantly representative of his morbid reaction patterns. This method of psychotherapy
has been depreciated as lazy and superficial, but it is associated with
an attitude of optimism in the therapist. In the hands of persons whose
personalities enable them to operate within this pattern, the results
with many patients seem to be quite beneficial.

Ingham and Love [29] consider that the culture of the place and time
influences the development and use of different kinds of psychotherapy.
Nevertheless, despite divergent theories, the practices of psychotherapy
are more alike than would seem apparent. The process of change or
learning in therapy is usually associated with anxiety, which can be
dealt with provided the therapist respects his patient, is honest toward
him, and assumes a role somewhere between the authoritative and permissive. These authors utilize transference as a means of effecting insight, but they are also supportive, and intellectually discuss both
insight and resistance and attempt to instill value judgments. It is difficult to follow their case reports, since the therapist's role and communications are not clearly stated.

Diethelm [30] explains distributive analysis and synthesis according to
the school of Adolf Meyer, of which he is one of the most prominent
representatives. The therapist investigates thoroughly, through an
anamnesis, the patient's present and the past and then focuses actively

on a significant problem and guides the patient toward a solution in a constructive and positive manner. The therapist maintains considerable activity as he questions the patient, suggests to him problem areas to think about, and critically reviews his statements in light of reality. Frequently during the course of therapy psychological tests are carried out in order to choose from their responses specific topics on which to concentrate.

Carl Rogers,[31] a psychologist, is an exponent of nondirective therapy, utilized by a large following of students who function as counselors (the euphemism for psychotherapy by psychologists). The technique is claimed to be suitable for all emotionally or mentally ill persons, and preliminary diagnostic evaluation is not considered necessary. The patient is considered to have latent capacities in the self which are released by the psychological climate created by the therapist. There is acceptance, sensitive attempt at understanding, with no effort to diagnose or alter feelings. There is a continuing attempt at giving of empathetic understanding and acceptance of the client as he is. In this emotional climate it is claimed that the patient changes his emphasis from reality, to internal problems, to experiencing his own feelings in the immediate present without inhibition. It is not the content but the recognizing of experience for what it is that becomes important. As a result the patient alters his perception and concept of the self. His experiences felt in the therapy become generalized, especially when he finds that the core of his personality is nondestructive. Thus, he becomes more confident and comfortable in himself, cares for others more, and takes an increased amount of self-responsibility. Scrutinizing descriptions of Rogers' operational procedures, we find a great deal of difficulty in determining the actual techniques. As Mowrer [32] points out, the essence seems to be the echoing or reflection of the feelings of the patient by the therapist repeating kindly in other words what the patient already has said. In addition, such phrases as, "I see," "I understand," "So you thought this, etc., etc.," are echoes of what the patient said but with the added warm caring attitude of the interested therapist-participant.

Dollard [3] states that psychotherapy deals with the immediate problems of the patient. Therapy is a learning experience, facilitated by the prestige of the therapist, the warm permissive atmosphere which he creates within which the patient has free expression. The therapist does not judge; therefore, he helps to extinguish the patient's fears. Finally, the transference relationships, if properly managed, also facilitate therapy. This brief psychotherapy deals with real everyday life, exposing conflicts in the present situation, although knowledge of past events is necessary. The therapist focuses on a single conflict and indicates when the patient should change the substance of his communication. If the therapist is puzzled and requests clarification, his doubts lead to more data from the patient and to the patient's re-evaluation of his conclusions. Dollard points out that the movement of the focus of therapy is from the outside to the inside, from the environment to the psychological structure, and from projection to self-blame.

Dollard tried to devise a therapy combining psychoanalytic and learning theory. Under new and favorable conditions the therapist helps the patient to discriminate reality cues, which have been generalized from a traumatic experience. Anxiety is dosed as the conflict situation is decoded, and verbal rewards are plentiful when the patient thinks rather than acts and speaks out even if anxious. Yet his techniques as demonstrated in a case report are essentially a kind of active psychoanalysis which is only interpreted to fit learning theory.

Deutsch and Murphy [33] in the second volume of their series devoted to therapy state that all therapies other than psychoanalysis are limited in contrast to their so-called sector-psychotherapy which is a goal-limited treatment based on psychoanalytic principles. In this the patient is given to understand the present in relation to the past; patients' thoughts are continually guided into past relationships from which they are reintegrated with the present. These authors not only encourage a positive transference but they also deliberately play roles even to a point of speaking like the patient. In this sense, they are contradictory, for at the same time they contend that role-taking is artificial, inadvisable, and unsuccessful. They talk about treatment weaving past and present together, especially in the latter part of the therapy. They indicate that confrontation of the patient with his behavior is associated with encouragement for growth.

Goldman [34] utilizes the adaptational or reparative psychotherapy of Rado [35] in which "repair" is considered in the sense of building up weakened ego defenses. There are four goals in this form of therapy: (1) the alleviation or elimination of symptoms; (2) the improved level of adaptive functions; (3) the stabilization of improvement; and (4) further growth and development. The conditions suitable for reparative therapy are mild neuroses, neuroses too serious for psychoanalysis, or when psychoanalysis is unavailable, and for preliminary exploration with the possibility of later psychoanalysis. The therapist first attempts to manage the patient's dependent needs as emotional reactions are evaluated with a positive frame of mind. He attempts to review objectively the stress situations that precipitated the current difficulties and to help the patient establish an appropriate emotional decompression, or what is called abreaction. Ego defenses are reinforced by educational processes. The therapist helps the patient make an effective change in his life situations and modify them whenever possible, and at the same time he strives to modify the patient's goals and demands of life and to decrease the patient's need for omnipotence and magic. During all this, the dosing and management of transference are carefully carried out.

Gill, Newman, and Redlich [36] report verbatim initial interviews in psychiatric practice. They state that traditional medical procedures are divided into an initial diagnostic period, including systematic eliciting of facts separated from treatment. In modern psychiatry, history-taking, examination, and treatment constitute a combined operation. They contend that, although psychoanalysts do not utilize separate steps in preparing treatment, many psychiatrists obtain a prior history before they start psychotherapy in order to allay anxiety. In combining the operations, more freedom and flexibility develop. They enumerate four determinants from the structure of the psychotherapeutic process. The first has to do with the personality attributes of the two participants— the patient and the psychiatrist. The second is the way in which they view their own and each other's roles. The third includes the conscious and unconscious purposes each is pursuing, and the fourth concerns the special techniques used by the therapist.

Alexander,[37] and Ross and Johnson [38] believe that psychotherapy should be a corrective emotional experience conducive to a discriminatory learning process. Their preliminary psychodynamic formulations are the basis of planning for therapeutic roles which help to develop a favorable emotional climate. Thus, if the patient's spontaneous emotional responses are based on past experiences with a harsh father, the therapist plays the role of a kind father. If the patient can learn from this one experience that such persons exist, his neurotic expectations are replaced by more realistic ones and characteristically result in more realistic and less stereotyped behavior. The therapist maintains the intensity of the patient's emotional participation at an optimum level, preventing excessive dependency by decreasing the frequency of sessions and temporarily interrupting at the necessary times. The patient is permitted extratherapeutic experiences and experimentation. Although fixation on a particular infantile mode of behavior may be based on excessive gratification during that period of development, it is more likely to represent a regressive flight from a painful present reality. Therefore, the therapist works on the problems of the present derivative conflict, hopefully removing the necessity for regression. In this procedure, however, the revival of infantile memories often results from successful understanding of the current situation.

At our clinic psychiatrists' seminar some significant principles for treatment of clinic patients were presented. Against the background of a warm permissive attitude for free expression without judging and with an optimistic belief in the patient as well as recognition of his limitations, the therapy may take one or more of several forms: (1) suppressive or authoritative for patients with high emotional tension; (2) supportive by leadership and assurance through gratifying dependent needs, encouraging defenses, intellectual guidance, and manipulation of life situations; (3) relationship in a parental role, encouraging the patient to try new methods without setting goals too high and with a modicum of advice; (4) expressive or uncovering.

Results of psychotherapy

For professionals who have spent large portions of their lives in training, in acquiring experience and in working with patients, a realistic appraisal of the results of their work is difficult and agonizing. Have we the courage to appraise honestly the results of psychotherapy, and what criteria are valid? Do changes in social adjustment (to what group?), capacity to work productively, ability to marry (perhaps with love), relief from symptoms (depression, anxiety, impulsivity, phobias, compulsions, etc.), an inner sense of identity and a feeling of comfort with self, represent singly, in combinations, or totally a successful therapeutic result? And by whose judgment—the patient, his family, employer, or friends? Are there tests that objectively reveal constructive personality changes? Finally, what are the costs—more ego constriction, different kinds of defenses, less free play of emotionality and creativity? All these are questions unanswered by patients, tests, and statistics. Claims for efficacy in treatment by a special technique are countered by equally enthusiastic claims from adherents of another method of psychotherapy. Today we have no answers to these and many more questions.[39]

Recently a few people have been taking some hard looks at therapeutic results. Strupp states:

> Ideally, there is always a rationale for the therapist's activity, so that, depending on the context, one approach is more desirable, therapeutically speaking, than another. In other words, some criterion of therapeutic effectiveness is implicit in what is considered the preferred technique. If it were true, as some maintain, that the relationship between patient and therapist is more "important" than the verbal exchange, it would be futile to speak of therapeutic techniques or to try to study them. If technique does make a difference, then presumably one technique is more effective than another. This is partly the *raison d'être* for the various schools of therapy which attempt to explain a set of similar phenomena in different terms and advocate different therapeutic approaches. From the point of view of empirical science, a first step would be to describe what techniques are actually practiced and to specify the conditions under which they are used. Such an exploratory survey might in itself suggest new hypotheses and leads, and pave the way for a comparative evaluation in addition to a comparative description.[40]

Frank[41] considers that improvement is based on two factors: (1) nonspecific expectancy of relief; and (2) dependency on amount and kind of treatment. Thus the emotional climate of the patient-therapist transaction plus a special technique are significant. But what technique and in what relationship to the emotional experience?[42] Board[43] surveyed the results of clinic treatment and found that a high percentage of patients, no matter whether the therapist considered he had been more, less, or not successful, reported improvement. What price therapists' judgment?

A patient of one of us (R.R.G.) openly boasted recently to a young colleague that she had been "cured" twenty-five years ago in one visit —had been symptom-free and happy ever since, never needing psychiatric help again. To check this miracle her record was re-examined. She complained then of many physical aches and pains for which no organic process was discovered by her physicians. The psychiatrist, on the positive side, found evidences of a definite emotional disturbance and told her that she needed psychotherapy. She left to think it over, and the next word heard from her was the above testimony of "cure." Flight into health? Change through emotional relationship? Recovery from the impact of a forgotten word or sentence? As far as the patient was concerned, one visit was as good as months or years of psychotherapy or psychoanalysis.

Because of this state of affairs—that change for the better cannot be predicted from the use of a special method of treatment even taking into account both the type of the patient's disturbance and the skill and personality of the therapist—in this book we are not talking about therapy. To do so would challenge us to validate results, for which no successful scientific technique has yet been devised. Rather, we speak of our conceptual model and transactional methods as conducive to *better* understanding of the patient's problems by both therapist and patient.

RESEARCH IN PSYCHOTHERAPY

The current recognition that scientific methods for control and validation of various psychotherapies have been inadequate has recently created considerable activity in the field. Several groups have developed various research techniques for recording a wide variety of variables during the therapeutic process, but unfortunately the amount of raw data derived by visual-auditory systems of observation will require many years of analysis. Many new rating scales are being tested to evaluate patients' and therapists' verbal, nonverbal, physiological, and biochemical responses to their therapeutic relationship. But most optimistic recently is the weakening of orthodoxies and the willingness of many therapists to destroy or at least witness the destruction of their cherished icons.[44, 45, 46, 47]

Recently Strupp[40] has developed a multidimensional system for analyzing psychotherapeutic techniques. He states that it is commonly taken for granted that the psychotherapist's personality, his theoretical orientation, and his therapeutic techniques are interrelated.

In order to dispose of the first item, we can state with a high degree of assurance that there is a wide variety of personality types among successful psychotherapists. Eventually each develops, after considerable training by a number of teachers and supervisors, his own individual life-style of therapy. Common to all therapists, however, is a kind of attitude which enables him to be reasonably successful no matter what his theory or technique might be. We certainly know that therapists usually respect their patients, their capacities, their inalienable right for self-direction, and their worth as human beings, all of which are conveyed to the patient by both verbal and nonverbal communications. These are at least the essential features for successful psychotherapy. It has been stated repeatedly that the efficiency of any psychotherapist using any method is directly related to his enthusiasm for his own therapeutic technique and his intense motivation to help another human being in distress.

Strupp states that theoretical orientation and therapeutic techniques should be interrelated. Technical differences should be attributable to variations in theoretical viewpoint. Otherwise, the significance of a theoretical framework in doing therapeutic work would be vitiated and the essential features of psychotherapy of any type would depend on the nonverbal communications which represent attitudes and emotional complementarity. In a first investigation with a highly technical method of comparison, Strupp has come to the conclusion that therapeutic techniques do vary with theoretical concepts. Thus, in his initial study he found that differences in theory do carry over into actual practice.

Strupp views psychotherapy as "a controlled interpersonal relationship which is integrated for the purpose of effecting changes in the patient's feelings, attitudes, and behavior through the systematic application of psychological techniques." With regard to the therapist's role in the interpersonal process, Strupp stresses the following implications of this definition:

(1) Psychotherapy is a planful interpersonal relationship between a trained professional person (the therapist) and a person seeking help for his difficulties in living (the patient). It is a personal relationship within an impersonal framework. It is further implied that the relationship is integrated for the patient's benefit and that the totality of the therapist's

activity throughout treatment is oriented toward this goal; thus, it precludes any participation or intervention in the patient's living which is not therapeutic in character.

(2) It is hypothesized that the patient's difficulties in living are a function of emotional conflicts, of whose existence, significance, and consequences he is insufficiently aware, and that the application or institution of certain technical operations by a trained professional person (the therapist) in an interpersonal setting is peculiarly suited to bringing about a lasting amelioration of the patient's problems.

(3) The uniqueness of psychotherapy derives from the application of psychological techniques, based upon scientific principles, in a controlled interpersonal setting. Irrespective of the ways in which the nature of the conflict is conceptualized, the following technical operations seem to be common to the major theoretical viewpoints:

(a) The therapist listens and attempts to "understand" the patient's verbal (and nonverbal) message. In contrast to the more usual forms of social interaction, he pays close attention to the connotative or symbolic content of the communications, which typically he explains in terms of certain theoretical conceptions.

(b) Sooner or later the therapist communicates to the patient some part of this "understanding." He may verbalize the feelings expressed by the patient or he may express a conjecture concerning the implicit meaning of the patient's message. In either event, he states a hypothesis or an inference, commonly called an "interpretation." The function of this activity is to increase the patient's self-awareness.[40]

Rioch [48] has written a little-known scholarly presentation concerning theory of psychotherapy which should be read by those interested in making progress in the field. He points out that theories of psychotherapeutic process are theories of method, not formulations of the nature of the process. Ruesch [49] also makes this statement. Rioch compares the theories of Freud dealing with biological instincts and energy with those of Sullivan, who was more concerned with orientation in space. Elsewhere Rioch decries this dichotomy: "The richness of human relations termed emotional is a function of the opportunity for learning temporally extended, spatially complex interpersonal transactions." Rioch emphasizes the need in therapy to work in terms of the patient's own experience through tackling his current problems which if well understood will clarify his life history.

Patient-therapist current relationships are those for which the patient's early environment furnished little or no experience, and the new requires a long time for learning and differentiation assisted by the natural principle of tendency toward growth and health. Psychotherapy helps a person in regard to his relationships with the group through transactions based on security and undistorted communications. Thus the patient is helped to resolve interfering factors in communication, to stop behaving as a response to the past or what is not there but to count heavily on existing factors as if these were all—they *are* all in the sense of being the reality of current transactions. The results of therapy are expressed in the degree of maturity of form or pattern of group belongingness and range of change over which maturity remains stable. Yet inevitably, as Rioch states, psychological alterations may one day be formulated by the nature of durable changes in the functional organization of the central nervous system.

THE SOCIAL WORKER'S PARTICIPATION IN PSYCHOTHERAPY

As the psychiatric social worker became more interested in "relationships" between himself and his patient, he searched for some helpful concepts by which to explain difficulties and from which to learn techniques. After borrowing from several dissident schools of psychoanalysis, he finally settled on at least portions of the Freudian school. Psychoanalytic theory promised application to almost every aspect of human behavior and its derivatives, it gave a sense of completeness and closure and seemed to promise a set of therapeutic principles which could be applied to "relationships" for the purpose of understanding and changing—perhaps even curing—emotionally sick people.

Such borrowing was not without precedents because social work had never developed an independent theoretical system. It had already borrowed heavily from psychiatry, psychology, law, medicine, and sociology.

Psychiatric social work as an operational discipline has kept plastic and amenable to change with the progress of conceptual thinking in psychiatry more than has any other field. Its plasticity, however, has often led to obscure thinking, ambiguities, and tolerance for incongruities and contradictions. Social workers have a rich body of observations and knowledge about people; unfortunately, all too often these are not written down for the professional public domain. The social worker also knows a great deal about persons as total or whole individuals, and, since he works in well-defined socioeconomic milieus, he is aware of the meanings of various cultural institutions of our contemporary society.

We have mentioned that psychiatric social work has borrowed much helpful theory and knowledge from psychoanalysis, but this has been at the cost of many difficulties and confusions relating especially to the problems of transference and countertransference, the essence of "relationship" for which the worker needs most help in understanding. The major processes in psychoanalysis as a therapy involve transference neuroses and countertransferences within which resistances to insight are analyzed and weakened. There is no doubt that the way in which transferences are handled has enormously influenced the practice of all forms of psychotherapy, including that done by the psychiatric social worker.

Transference is a term that has been greatly misused. Freud originally used the term to indicate that part of a patient's attitudes to the therapist which repeats the patient's reaction to persons who had previously played important roles in his life. Such transference is part of all human relations, since likes and dislikes we have toward other persons are partly explicable on the basis of their subtle or overt similarities to significant people of the past. Yet therapists and other persons are real people with their own qualities to whom we react realistically. Ordinarily the capacity for reality testing permits the subject to recognize the differences between reactions based on the past and on the present.

A transference neurosis, on the other hand, is an irrational repetition of old neurotic unsuitable behavior patterns for which reality testing is not capable of differentiation from the present. In psychoanalytic practice a transference neurosis is induced so that the past attitudes may be projected onto the analyst, enabling him as a real person to teach the patient the difference between the reality of what he is as contrasted with what he is believed to be.

The fact of being a patient tends to revive the dependency of childhood along with many of its irrational tendencies. Yet dependency is a necessarily implicit role for the explicit role of the patient who comes for help in solving problems he cannot solve himself. Such a transference is especially intense in patients who come for supportive or directive therapy. Psychotherapy aimed at insight also requires some degree of transference so that the patient's irrational impulses are not acted out in real life but are verbalized to the therapist.

On the other hand, transference neuroses may constitute a resistance to therapy, substituting reliving of conflicts as defenses against becoming aware of them. Excessive intensity of transference feelings may impair the patient's judgment or capacity to view himself realistically and obstruct cooperation and learning. It is exactly here that sometimes both patient and therapist not only are confused but also become anxious, suspicious, or hostile, resulting in termination of therapy without benefit to the patient.

Intensive or insight therapy is the most recent development in the practice of psychiatric social work. This general field includes those activities described variously as uncovering therapy, insight therapy, expressive therapy, and interpretive therapy, which have in common the goal of uncovering, understanding, and interpreting the patient's internal conflicts. Because these processes involve the patient and the therapist in transference relationships, they require the development of particular skills in practice. But as a part of current practice intensive psychotherapy has been misused and misinterpreted, resulting in much conflict and controversy within the psychiatric social work profession.

Professional training for this type of practice is not offered in the graduate schools of professional social work. Thus educational preparation has been highly individualized and uneven, drawn largely from intensive supervision and consultation, from growing experience in practice, from personal analysis, from isolated courses and seminars, but with no formal academic training designed to equip the psychiatric social worker for the practice of intensive psychotherapy.[50, 51]

Within the total psychiatric setting the practice of intensive psychotherapeutic casework has had its largest period of growth since the end of World War II. Many psychiatric clinics have developed large psychiatric and analytic training programs resulting in the breakdown of traditional concepts of function within and across the disciplines of psychiatry, clinical psychology, and psychiatric social work. All members of the team engage more or less in psychotherapy, so that no longer is there a sharp division of labor and a clear definition of professional roles. Within the clinic, technical jargon is the framework of communication, and early speculation about the patient's unconscious is the favorite intellectual exercise in which all compete. Clichés about motivation and treatability dominate the thinking; if the social worker introduces social and economic considerations, he is often depreciated by both his own colleagues and those of other disciplines. There is a dichotomy set up of treatable and untreatable cases based on evaluation of psychodynamics, and many times to meet community pressure social workers are asked to see patients, on a regular basis, who were considered not worth the time of the psychiatrist or not counted as treatment cases by the clinic.

Problems also arise within the social worker's ancillary functions. Psychiatrists are confused about the workers' specific functions and either neglect these completely or suddenly thrust impossible tasks on them. A psychiatrist treating a twelve-year-old boy left the social worker an order for the child to be moved immediately from his mother's bed when he discovered that they were sleeping together. Another psychiatrist requested that the social worker find a job immediately for a recovering schizophrenic who had not worked in twenty years of adult life, had not finished elementary school, and could not do labor or factory work because of his physical condition. Social workers feel defensive when they are confronted with requests such as these and cling more closely to their "therapy" cases. If this is what the psychiatrist sees as environmental help, then they do not want to be involved. In many collaborative cases in which the social worker works with the parents, he finds that the psychiatrist isolates his treatment of the child and is unwilling to consider an integrated approach to the family's problems.

This is the heyday of the analytic model of therapy, and psychiatric residents, too often abetted by their supervisors, are brashly placing once-a-week patients on analytic couches to further free associations and interpret dreams. Social workers do not do this, but some feel confused and envious. They compete by talking of their own analyses, by feeling rather smugly that they know more about treatment than do the residents. Although this is often the case, it is a defensively maintained position. At times social workers talk with real conviction about understanding ego operations and ego functions. Yet behind it there lurks despair that this is "all they can do" and alarm that they are being pushed out as therapists when enthusiastic residents tout analysis as the only worthwhile treatment.

In the clinic hierarchy they are the least well paid, and their own needs for growth and satisfactions other than material reward on the job are often neglected. Since World War II residents have been flocking to psychiatric training centers in great quantities, and the case load of every clinic is now at its maximum. The influence of psychoanalysis on the treatment conducted by psychiatric social workers has reached its height. In fact, the team principle by which it was understood that psychiatrists, psychologists, and social workers would have their allocated task within the group is now all but lost. All members of the team are engaged more or less in psychotherapy; no longer is there a sharp division of labor. Furthermore, each member of the team is engaged in more *intensive,* so-called *depth therapy,* than ever before. In fact, psychotherapy conducted within psychodynamic principles has erroneously been considered to be a kind of psychoanalysis with whatever modifications are in vogue at the time and place.

The psychiatric social worker, together with other members of the team, utilizes condensations of psychoanalytic jargon in reporting cases and omits the raw facts from which others may make interpretations. All these problems indicate that perhaps the adoption of psychoanalytic theory, techniques, and language, although modified in some respects, has become less advantageous to the field of psychiatric social work.

The opposite extreme has an equally frustrating effect on the worker. In some clinics the pretreatment goals are rigidly set. The type of treatment is classified into specific categories, such as supportive, encouraging, etc. In spite of these limitations, there is little definition of the therapist's role, and detailed instructions are usually lacking. It is also quite obvious that intelligent and trained persons do not relish functioning as technicians under rigid supervision without the opportunity to use their own imagination and originality.

About five years before World War II, a reaction against lengthy and essentially nonproductive treatment manifested itself in some clinics and training centers. The Chicago Psychoanalytic Institute boldly experimented with brief psychotherapy based on psychoanalytic principles.[52] Specific principles were developed, especially in regard to managing the transference relationship between therapist and patient. Brief psychotherapy was formulated for limited goals, reducing or not permitting great dependency, dealing with reality exclusively, and affording the opportunity for a "corrective emotional experience."

There were other forces at work in this period attempting to focus the psychotherapeutic process on the current life situation as contrasted with an analysis of deep and extensive early childhood experiences. These revived some basic principles promulgated by Harry Stack Sullivan [53] in his attempts to modify psychoanalytic treatment. He considered that in the current life situation—exemplified by the interpersonal relationships between patient and therapist—the most rapid learning and personality modifications could occur.

Gordon Hamilton,[54] discussing psychoanalytically oriented casework, pointed out that social workers deal first and foremost with external forces in an effort to "better the environment." But he must realize that the individual is part of his own problem and effort is required to "change the person." She emphasizes the economic, social, and public welfare interests of the worker; but in changing a person what else but psychotherapy is involved? If one tries to place the meeting ground of worker and psychiatrist at ego boundaries, it is as if one were talking about a rigid border line with inner and outer dichotomies. The GAP Report, Number 2, 1948, likewise defines psychiatric casework very much as psychotherapy except for a heavier emphasis on external reality and social conduct.

Perlman [55] attempted to define social casework as a problem-solving process concerned with ego functions. The therapeutic goal is to help persons cope more effectively with their problems in social functioning. She elucidates the multiple factors in the development of the structure and function of the personality and how persons are always "in process" with their environments, in "being" in the present, and "becoming" in the future. She indicates that these aspects of personality may be viewed, to borrow a current sociological concept, in the performance of major social roles. Perlman attempts to separate psychiatric casework from psychoanalytic psychotherapy in operation.

Towle [18] likewise has made an effort to turn the clock back and bring casework into its previous limited place in the psychiatric team which no longer exists in its earlier form. Schools of social work, however, are still teaching applied psychodynamics (psychoanalytic) as vigorously as ever; the large social agencies are therapeutic centers, and caseworkers are doing psychotherapy.[56] They are less concerned with the client's environment; poor, rich, clean, or dirty, except by report from informants interviewed in offices.

Our general overview of psychotherapy and the social worker's role in this process has led us back to the area: "modifying complementary relationships." This simply means psychotherapy viewed as transactional in an attempt to help the worker and all therapists understand their patients better, and thus presumably become more efficient in helping them, without the confusions of applying psychoanalytic theories and methods.

The following chapters are devoted to the discussion of the transactions between one patient and her social worker therapist. After each session detailed comments are appended. The reader is urged to study both the reports of each session and the comments carefully and, if possible, repetitively.

References

1. Wolberg, L. R.: *The Technique of Psychotherapy*. New York: Grune, 1954.
2. Alexander, F.: *Psychoanalysis and Psychotherapy*. New York: Norton, 1956; Two forms of regression and their therapeutic implications. *Psychoanalyt. Quart.*, 25:178, 1956; Unexplored areas in psychoanalytic theory and treatment. *Behavioral Sci.*, 3:293, 1958.
3. Dollard, J., Auld, F., and White, A. M.: *Steps in Psychotherapy*. New York: Macmillan, 1950.
4. Fromm-Reichmann, F.: *Principles of Intensive Psychotherapy*. Chicago: Univ. Chicago Press, 1950; *Progress in Psychotherapy* (Ed.). New York: Grune, 1956.
5. Rogers, C. R., and Dymond, R. F. (Eds.): *Psychotherapy and Personality Change*. Chicago: Univ. Chicago Press, 1954.
6. Lewis, N. D. C.: Historical roots of psychotherapy. *Amer. J. Psychiat.*, 113:800, 1958.
7. Frechtman, B. W.: Report of the committee on the role of the psychiatric social worker as caseworker or therapist. *J. Psychiat. Soc. Wk.*, 19:87, 1950.
8. Knight, R. P.: An evaluation of psychotherapeutic technic. *Bull. Menninger Clin.*, 16:113, 1952; *Bull. N.Y. Acad. Medicine*, 25:100, 1949.
9. Austin, L. N.: Qualifications for psychotherapists: social case workers. *Amer. J. Orthopsychiat.*, 26:47, 1956.
10. Hamilton, G.: Psychoanalytically oriented case work and its relation to psychotherapy. *Amer. J. Orthopsychiat.*, 19:209, 1949; *Psychotherapy in Child Guidance*. New York: Columbia Univ. Press, 1947; "A Theory of Personality; Freud's Contribution to Social Work." In Parad, H. (Ed.), *Ego Psychology and Dynamic Case Work*. New York: Family Service

Association of America, 1958; *Theory of Social Case Work,* (2nd ed.), New York: Columbia Univ. Press, 1956.

11. Galdston, I.: Dynamics of the cure in psychiatry. *A.M.A. Arch. Neurol. & Psychiat.,* 70:287, 1953.

12. Redlich, F. C.: Social aspects of psychotherapy. *Amer. J. Psychiat.,* 113:800, 1958.

13. Szasz, T. S.: Psychiatry, psychotherapy and psychoanalysis. *A.M.A. Arch. Gen. Psych.,* 1:455, 1959.

14. Handler, J. S., Psychotherapy and medical responsibility. *A.M.A. Arch. Gen. Psych.,* 1:464, 1959.

15. Bibring, G.: Psychiatric principles in case work. *J. Soc. Case Work,* 30:320, 1949.

16. Coleman, J. V.: Distinguishing between psychotherapy and case work. *J. Soc. Case Work,* 30:244, 1949.

17. Perlman, H. H.: *Social Case Work—A Problem-Solving Process.* Chicago: Univ. Chicago Press, 1957.

18. Towle, C.: Psychiatric case work. *SSA News Letter.* University of Chicago, March, 1957.

19. Garrett, A.: Historical survey of the evolution of case work. *J. Soc. Case Work,* 30:219, 1949; The worker-client relationship. *Amer. J. Orthopsychiat.,* 19:224, 1949.

20. Zander, A., Cohen, A. R., and Stoddard, E.: *Role Relations in the Mental Health Professions.* Ann Arbor: Univ. Michigan Press, 1957.

21. Kubie, L. S.: The need for a new sub-discipline in the medical profession. *A.M.A. Arch. Neurol. & Psychiat.,* 78:283, 1957.

22. Grinker, R. R.: "The Impact of Psychoanalysis on Training in Psychiatry." In Alexander, F., and Ross, H. (Eds.), *Twenty Years of Psychoanalysis.* New York: Norton, 1953.

23. Ackerman, N.: "Foreword." In Hamilton, G., *Psychotherapy in Child Guidance.* New York: Columbia Univ. Press, 1947; The training of case workers in psychotherapy. *Amer. J. Orthopsychiat.,* 19:14, 1949.

24. Hollingshead, A. B., and Redlich, F. C.: *Social Class and Mental Illness.* New York: Wiley, 1958.

25. Szasz, T. S.: Doctor-patient relationship and its historical context. *Amer. J. Psychiat.,* 115:522, 1958; Psychoanalysis as method and as theory. *Psychoanalyt. Quart.,* 27:89, 1958.

26. Jahoda, M.: *Current Concepts of Positive Mental Health.* New York: Basic, 1958.

27. Levine, M.: *Psychotherapy in Medical Practice.* New York: Macmillan, 1949.

28. Whitehorn, J. C.: Understanding psychotherapy. *Amer. J. Psychiat.,* 112:328, 1955.

29. Ingham, H. V., and Love, L. R.: *The Process of Psychotherapy.* New York: McGraw-Hill, 1954.

30. Diethelm, O.: *Treatment in Psychiatry* (2nd ed.). Springfield: Thomas, 1950.

31. Rogers, C. R., and Dymond, R. F.: *Psychotherapy and Personality Change.* Chicago: Univ. Chicago Press, 1954.

32. Mowrer, O. H.: *Psychotherapy—Theory and Research*. New York: Ronald, 1953.

33. Deutsch, F., and Murphy, W. F.: *The Clinical Interview*. New York: Internat. Univ. Press, 1955, Vol. II.

34. Goldman, G. S.: "Reparative Psychotherapy." In Rado, S., and Daniels, G. E., *Changing Concepts of Psychoanalytic Medicine*. New York: Grune, 1958.

35. Rado, S.: Psychotherapy: "A Problem of Controlled Intercommunication." In Hoch, P. H., and Zubin, J. (Eds.), *Psychopathology of Communication*. New York: Grune, 1958.

36. Gill, M., Newman, R., and Redlich, F .C.: *The Initial Interview in Psychiatric Practice*. New York: Internat. Univ. Press, 1954.

37. Alexander, F.: Psychoanalysis and psychotherapy. *J. Amer. Psychoanalyt. Assoc.*, 2:722, 1954.

38. Ross, H., and Johnson, A.: "The Growing Science of Case Work." In Kasius, C. (Ed.), *Principles and Techniques in Social Case Work*. New York: Family Service Assoc. of America, 1950.

39. Grinker, R. R.: Growth, inertia and shame: their therapeutic implications and dangers. *Int. J. Psycho-Anal.*, 36:1, 1955; "A Philosophical Appraisal of Psychoanalysis." In Masserman, J. (Ed.), *Science and Psychoanalysis*, Vol. I. New York: Grune, 1958.

40. Strupp, H.: A multidimensional analysis of technique in brief psychotherapy. *Psychiatry*, 20:387, 1957; A multidimensional comparison of therapist activity in analytic and client-centered therapy. *J. Consult. Psychol.*, 21:301, 1957; A multidimensional system for analyzing psychotherapeutic techniques. *Psychiatry*, 20:293, 1957; The performance of psychiatrists and psychologists in a therapeutic interview. *J. Clin. Psychol.*, 14:219, 1958; The psychotherapist's contribution to the treatment process. *Behavioral Sci.*, 3:34, 1958.

41. Frank, J. D.: The dynamics of the psychotherapeutic relationship. *Psychiatry*, 22:17, 1959; Patients' expectancies and relearning as factors determining improvement in psychotherapy. *Amer. J. Psychiat.*, 115:961, 1959; Why patients leave psychotherapy. *A.M.A. Arch. Neurol. & Psychiat.*, 77:283, 1957.

42. Glad, D. D.: *Operational Values in Psychotherapy*. New York: Oxford Univ. Press, 1959.

43. Board, F. A.: A questionnaire investigation of patients' and physicians' judgment of the outcome of psychotherapy in an outpatient clinic. *A.M.A. Arch. Gen. Psychiat.*, 1:185, 1959.

44. Murphy, W. F.: A comparison of psychoanalysis with the dynamic psychotherapies. *J. Nerv. & Ment. Dis.*, 126:441, 1958.

45. Jackson, D. D.: Guilt and control in schizoid personalities. *Brit. J. Med. Psychol.*, 31:124, 1958; Patient and therapist observations on the circumstances of a schizophrenic episode. *A.M.A. Arch. Neurol. & Psychiat.*, 79:554, 1958; Psychiatrists' conception of the schizophrenogenetic parent. *A.M.A. Arch. Neurol. & Psychiat.*, 79:448, 1958.

46. Bateson, G., Jackson, D. D., Haley, J., and Weakland, J. H.: Toward a theory of schizophrenia. *Behavioral Sci.*, 1:251, 1956.

47. Rubenstein, E. A., and Parloff, M. B. (Eds.): *Research in Psychotherapy.* Washington, D.C.: Amer. Psychological Assoc., 1959.

48. Rioch, D. McK.: "Theories of Psychotherapy." In Dennis, W. (Ed.), *Current Trends in Psychological Theory.* Pittsburgh: Univ. Pittsburgh Press, 1951; "The Biological Roots of Psychoanalysis." In Masserman, J. (Ed.), *Science and Psychoanalysis.* New York: Grune, 1958, Vol. I.

49. Ruesch, J.: *Disturbed Communication.* New York: Norton, 1957.

50. Bowers, S.: The nature and definition of social case work. *J. Soc. Case Work,* 30:311, 369, 412, 1949.

51. *Psychiatric Social Work in Psychiatric Clinics,* GAP Report No. 16, Topeka, Kansas, 1950.

52. Alexander, F., and French, J. M.: *Psychoanalytic Therapy.* New York: Norton, 1946.

53. Sullivan, H. S.: *The Interpersonal Theory of Psychiatry.* New York: Norton, 1953.

54. Hamilton, G.: Psychoanalytically oriented case work and its relation to psychotherapy. *Amer. J. Orthopsychiat.,* 19:209, 1949.

55. Perlman, H. H.: *Social Case Work: A Problem-Solving Process.* Chicago: Univ. Chicago Press, 1957.

56. Sutherland, J. D., and Davies Lloyd, A. B.: "Psychotherapy and Social Casework." In *The Boundaries of Casework.* London: Assoc. of Psych. Social Workers, 1956.

6

Modifying Complementary

Relationships

A PRECEDING CHAPTER (4) is concerned with the experiencing of role-complementarity by both therapist and patient. Under suitable circumstances, the therapist may begin to make explicit the patient's implicit roles. This is a gentle and tentative procedure which tests the patient's capacity for learning or, in psychoanalytic terms, his ego strength. If the outcome is favorable, then the transaction becomes oriented toward modifying complementary relationship in what is usually termed intensive psychotherapy. Screening and diagnostic evaluations may indicate at the outset that this type of treatment is feasible, although errors in judgment are made and the nature of the transaction requires change.

Since intensive therapy is usually more than brief, we decided to choose for study and for purposes of illustration a patient who offered a good outlook for successful therapy and who would be expected to continue with the treatment despite the revelation of unpleasant implicit relationships. We set out to search for a young female non-psychotic patient who had strong motivation for help and could work with the therapist whom we chose.

Needless to say, these criteria imposed limitations in view of the range of the clinic patient population. We screened several patients carefully, and selected our patient after an intake interview by a psychiatric social worker. The chief psychiatrist of the clinic then conducted a thorough diagnostic interview.

The therapist who was assigned to the patient saw her first in April 1956, and thereafter once a week except for vacation interruptions. The seminar considered a report of each session for 45 weeks ending in May 1957, when we decided that we had enough material for this demonstration. The patient, however, was continued in treatment by the same therapist for many more sessions after the seminar interrupted its studies. The period between sessions 45 and 150 has been summarized (see pp. 273–275) and a late session is discussed in order for the reader to learn how the total therapy progressed.

After each session the therapist dictated her notes from memory, including as many verbatim quotes from the patient and herself as possible. Typewritten copies were distributed to each member of the seminar several days before its regular weekly session. Because the seminar occasionally lagged one to three weeks behind the therapist, it was agreed that only one session at a time would be discussed. No questions could be asked or statements made about subsequent therapeutic sessions already held, and any predictive statements by members of the seminar were to be neither confirmed nor denied. These rules were slightly modified during the last month or two, when the report of the therapeutic sessions was distributed only at the time of the seminar meeting. In the later weeks of the research, as therapeutic progress slowed and transactions became somewhat repetitive, several sessions were discussed at each meeting.

At each seminar meeting there was a full and lively discussion of the contents of each therapeutic session, with arguments, criticisms, defenses, and compromises the rule. The psychiatrist (R.R.G.) took notes of these comments, synthesized them, and dictated his comments, which were distributed to members of the seminar before its next meeting. Neither the verbal discussion nor the typed comments could influence the therapist's transactions with her patient during the next session, because she was usually ahead of the seminar. This lag in "supervisory effect" can be seen by the fact that changes in the therapeutic procedures were often considerably delayed.

It is important to keep in mind some aspects of the setting in which the treatment was conducted, as well as the setting of the research and the background of the persons involved. Treatment was conducted, as usual, in a small interviewing room in the clinic building. The patient did not know that she was the subject of research. The seminar met weekly for an hour in the quiet, comfortable library of the Institute within the hospital building. This setting, one city block away from the clinic, gave the social workers a short respite from the busy, somewhat noisy clinic halls and freedom from their telephones and other distracting business. Furthermore, they had status as members of a research team lead by the Director of the Institute. They gained not only added zest for their work, considerable pedagogical advantage, but also an increase in morale from a sense of belonging to the Institute. Actually, the seminar met once weekly from the very beginning of the research; the psychotherapeutic discussions covered only one year.

During the seven years' research, changes in composition of the social worker group occurred because of resignations for one reason or another from the Michael Reese staff. The largest number was seven, dropping during the last year to a hard core of four. Requests from new workers, other supervisors, professors from the local School of Social Service Work for admission to the seminar were denied. It was thought that new members would burden the group, for the members of the seminar had become a self-educated, tightly integrated, highly committed group. Visitors were denied admission, especially professional or administrative superiors, to avoid distraction and confusion of loyalties.

The psychiatric social workers all were experienced in the field; most of them had undergone personal analysis and had been graduated from the three-year child care course at the Chicago Institute for Psychoanalysis. The therapist of the intensive treatment case was a person of considerable background and experience, having witnessed several decades of professional evolution in the field.

Many rough problems developed in the group process. Vigorous attacks, stubborn defenses, tangential arguments naturally occurred, but never to the point of disruption. In fact, one worker assumed the role of the "gadfly," another of the "doubter," and the third of the "matter-of-fact realist." The psychiatrist was provocateur and sometimes peacemaker, but usually he stimulated and condoned vigorous discussion, which often clarified issues and always brought out ideas and suggestions that otherwise would have remained dormant.

The psychiatrist participating each week was the only psychiatrist-psychoanalyst present during the entire discussion of all the cases. He is also Director of the Institute and is actively engaged in teaching, research, and care of patients. His personal evolution as related to the field of social work is a history in itself; suffice it for our purposes, he learned a great deal about social workers in his many professional years. He entered into the research with confused notions about the field, perhaps even more confused than the workers themselves, so that the seminar was a vivid and exciting learning process for him. From his comments about the therapeutic transactions, however, one can read some of his residual impatience with social service techniques, clichés, avoidance of anxiety, blurred focusing, and general slowness.

Finally, the contents and comments of the screening and diagnostic interviewers and each therapeutic session were written immediately and are presented here with little editing and only nominal distortions for the purpose of disguising identities. The reader may judge for himself the reliability of the predictive quality of each set of comments.

THE FIRST PHASE OF THERAPY

The patient is a twenty-eight-year-old single woman who comes to the clinic because she has been told by a number of people that she needs psychiatric help. She is only aware now that she is attracted to men who have no wish to get married and is not attracted to those who are good possibilities for marriage. The patient was processed through an intake interview, the intake staff, a diagnostic interview, and the diagnostic staff.

The details of these interviews and staffings need not be presented, since all of the factual material is subsequently divulged in the therapeutic interviews. For our purpose it need only be stated that this young woman was confused and had difficulty in assuming an identity that was satisfactory for her relationships with a wide variety of people. She experiences rapid shifts in roles, depending upon the exigencies of the moment, and there is a peculiar shifting orientation to ideas of rightness and wrongness. Despite this ease of establishing role symmetry, this patient was not psychotic or borderline and could be classified either as a psychoneurosis or as a character neurosis.

Our purpose in presenting a large number of therapeutic sessions in detail is not so much to demonstrate the therapeutic processes and changes within a patient, but rather to elucidate the transactional model in the psychotherapeutic situation.

First Session

THE PATIENT ARRIVED, on time, dressed informally in sweater and skirt, short sport jacket, and low heels. She began the interview by asking if this was still "part of the diagnostic." *She was told that her diagnosis had been completed and therapy had been recommended on a once-a-week basis. I was her therapist and would be seeing her weekly.* "Then I can start?" *She was told that she could start where she wished.* "Then I'd like to talk about something that happened to me last week." She then began a long detailed account in logical sequence with no demonstrable affect. Throughout *I asked for her emotional reactions and for her role in these recent experiences.* It was only late in the interview that I began to get some affective responses.

Two weeks previous the patient arrived in California to stay with her friend Paul for a vacation. On arrival she learned from his roommate, who did not know of Paul's homosexuality, that he was out with a man. She stayed at Paul's apartment all night, and when he came home in the morning she was "building up to a big scene" and confronted him with his being out all night in spite of her expected arrival. She asked where he had been and he stated directly he had been having an affair with a homosexual friend that night—a man he had met once. She has a funny feeling in her stomach and cannot look him in the eye when he talks to her of his homosexuality, but steadfastly denies other feelings about it. Paul then pulled out her letter and proved that she had not stated that she was to arrive Friday night. This always happens—he makes her feel "small and insignificant" when she tries to argue with him. She is always wrong and he is right, but she reveals no further affect about this.

They then had three wonderful days together—until Monday night when Paul again had a date with his homosexual friend. At this point she was very stirred up, could not stand to see this man, and kept out of the way until he and Paul left. She became very upset, paced up and down and was afraid of what she might do to him. She awakened his roommate to ask for two sleeping pills, slept for three hours to stop thinking, and then "knew what she had to do"—leave Paul. She wrote him a note that she was sorry, and was leaving. She called Kay (a platonic friend of Paul's who had slept with him only once, but whom she likes better than any girl she has met for a long time) and went to stay with her. The next day was spent with Kay and Paul's roommate. After a day spent with the two people most closely involved with Paul, with precautions not to meet him, and advice from both that Paul was in need of treatment, she returned to Chicago.

She denies disappointment at not having heard from Paul; says that she has felt numb, but knew she had to leave him. *Finally I state directly that she is personally involved and must have some reaction to the ending of the relationship.* She asks, "Why did he do this to me? Why did he go out with this man the night I was there?" She brings out that it is only when she sees him that she gets so involved. She expects him to be with others when she is not there.

She gives me a history of their relationship. She met him at the "lowest point of my life"—when she was twenty and was compelled to live with her father. "I finally pulled myself away from that." She then brings up her father's past psychiatric treatment and the fact that three people have told her to seek psychiatric treatment. She was *pushed for her reaction* to each one of these and was finally able to admit that she felt each recommendation arose out of some hostile feeling toward her: (1) The girl who thought Paul was a "nice, normal young man" and that patient should get herself straightened out to marry him. (2) A man friend who insisted that she needed psychiatric treatment because she did not love him. (3) A male friend who broke down, was hospitalized, and who insisted that she, too, needed treatment. *I com-*

mented that one did not have to seek treatment on this basis. With some relief she agreed—she wants treatment for herself, she knows. She is freer in the interview after this.

She returns to discuss Paul. When she asks me *I state that this is an involved personal relationship.* She knows she loves Paul, has to be close to him, has to be demanding of him—"I want to get married." I ask if she means to Paul and she replies, "No." She knows that when she is ready she will be able to fall in love with some other man. *I ask if she has ever felt that Paul had some "fatal fascination" for her.* She does not answer directly but tells in great detail of Paul's many homosexual and heterosexual affairs, ending with, "Paul is promiscuous." *I ask for reaction to this.* She indicates that for the first time she questioned him about his standards when he picks up a man in a bar and goes home and sleeps with him. He told her, "It's different with men like this." *How does this make her feel about her role with him?* "I failed him." *How?* "He just wanted me for a friend and I wanted more than that." *I point out that she has her own stake in this* and she tells how she had advised Paul to break off with a girl who had fallen in love with him and whom he did not want. He had taken her advice. She tries to deny any feeling about it and then says it was strange but she had been conscious of watching the girl. There follows praise of Paul, of his taste in art, his intelligence, his absolute integrity—patient repeats the latter twice as if she is beginning to doubt it herself, and a little later makes a fleeting reference to these "sordid affairs." At another point in the interview she tells me that she and Paul are much alike—they think alike, feel alike, have the same tastes and interests.

She asks me again why Paul did this to her. *I tell her I do not know, but that he may have a need to hurt and depreciate women now. This is something she can react to, but all we know now is that her relationship with Paul is complicated and I am not clear where she stands.*

C O M M E N T S   O N   F I R S T   S E S S I O N : The patient, in her first transaction with her therapist, assumes the explicit role of a dependent, uninformed individual needing reassurance or help on when and how to begin her therapy. The therapist, in response, rejects the assigned role of the controlling and all-knowing authority, reassigns to the patient the task of assuming responsibility for starting wherever the patient wishes. Here immediately we are able to see a transaction in which the patient and therapist do not enter into role-complementarity, since the patient is attempting to assign to the therapist a role that is inappropriate and unrealistic. The therapist's rejection of the assigned authoritarian role results, then, in the patient's reassigning to the therapist the role of listener while she assumes the role of a logical discussant. Because this "listener role" is an appropriate one at this point for the therapist, it is accepted and complementarity is achieved, resulting in the patient's disclosure of pathological sexual experiences during the vacation which immediately preceded her entering treatment. The worker let the patient go on spontaneously in order to get an understanding of the form and content of her communications. She realized that the patient reveled in telling dramatic stories and wondered if the patient would have new ones to relate at each session. Apparently, in telling these stories, episodes are revealed in an exhibitionistic manner without any concern for confidentiality. The worker wondered whether the vacation before the start of treatment was not really a last-ditch flight away from therapy. It was as if this were structured in an effort to terminate the affair with Paul prior to treatment. This period consisted of a vigorous acting-out experience, which probably was intended to be her last fling before therapy, although this behavior is her defense against emotional learning. Implicit in her story is the indication that she somehow or other managed to arrange that Paul should not know she was coming to visit and that he be caught acting out the anticipated hostility toward her. There was obviously some contriving to bring the situation to a head. Inasmuch as the patient's account of the vacation activities contained little regarding her own emotional responsibility and involvement, the worker experimentally tried to evoke some emotional reactions and to question her statement in an effort to mobilize her curiosity. Here again in a new, modified way we see the patient slipping back obediently on one level while she maintains two conflicting roles; namely, that of the dependent and needful child or the intellectually adequate and competitive woman. The patient partially rejects the worker's attempts to fathom the underlying emotional attitudes and struggles to maintain the defensive position of having no personal emotional identity. Since the therapist cannot realistically accept this, role-complementarity is not achieved. The patient and therapist continue in the treatment process with movement necessitated by patient's having received partial gratification from the therapist's rejection of her unsatisfying defensive maneuvers (which part of the patient wishes to give up) and her need to cling to these familiar childhood patterns.

The patient is aware of the fact that the people who have urged her to go into therapy have all been sick themselves and she also knows that her father's treatment was a failure because he recovered only from the acute episode. She lives in a social system of pseudo intellectuals who trade anecdotes about their own psychopathology. They are mildly delinquent without external guilt, and even proud of their deviations. Within their group they are able to revolt against authorities and need no other relationships as long as the group enables them to create a fantasy of closeness and warmth. Individuals who break away from the group usually become depressed and isolated, for this type of personality seems to be involved in a struggle against remem‑bering deprivations which, if exposed, result in depression. This leads us to predict that in the relationship with the therapist there will de‑velop, if treatment moves, a strong, dependent, and demanding hostile relationship within which the patient may be precipitated into a de‑pression. It can also be predicted, however, that there will be a terrific struggle against the exposure of her dependent needs and its conse‑quences will be flight into further affairs with other members of the group.

Second Session

THE PATIENT WAS FIVE MINUTES LATE and began the interview by apologizing, saying that she had misjudged the time. She com‑mented, "I thought about your remark that I am hurt by Paul, but I don't feel anything, I'm just numb." When *I indicate interest*, she says, "Maybe he did want to hurt me, but I'm just not conscious of it." This bland attitude of being agreeable but not involved was characteristic of the session. Patient continued to say that just this was the trouble with her, she didn't know where she stood and whether what she thought was right or wrong. She knows that she is very insecure.

She begins telling me about her art job, saying that she does not know her position in this field. This is in contrast to the previous inter‑view, during which patient was able to state her thinking quite clearly. Throughout this discussion she characteristically presented one aspect, then would deny it by advancing a different idea—each time seeming to dodge any report that indicated her emotional involvement. Patient has an evening art class which pays her as much as $150 per month, from which she saved the money to take her trip, using the salary from her daytime job for living expenses. She has special theories of how to teach her students, who are primarily working girls interested in an evening hobby. Before she left she told the director of the workshop that she did not expect him to hold the job for her as she had no idea how long she would be away. He assured her that she would always have a job with him, as her classes had always been very popular.

On her return she was told that she could continue working, and found herself in the position of being the second teacher. She has only two or three in her class "but they really enjoy it"; the other teacher has a large class "but she already has lost most of my students from last year." The department has gone in debt whereas before it always showed a profit. When the director spoke to her about it, she suggested that he talk to the other girl. They had been planning to send out publicity notices for the class, but this had not been done. She denies any emotional reaction to all this (and is not aware of her competitiveness). It would do no good to clarify her status with the director because he is insincere and does not mean what he says. She actually has accepted the status quo with no questions, although recently she has been earning only $15 per month. She is content because she uses the facilities of the workshop two days a week to do her own work.

On her regular job she has spoken up to the manager about pay for holidays, etc. The boss, who makes a big fuss and often gives vent to his anger, is really quite easily managed—"I have his number." The other salesgirl has been there much longer than she has, but has not been paid as well. She does not understand why this girl does not complain.

When I state that patient had said that she felt insecure and I was trying to understand this, she denies insecurity but laughs in a somewhat anxious way.

COMMENTS ON SECOND SESSION: The patient entered this second interview explicitly as a person who presented no feelings, when she stated, "I don't feel anything—I'm just numb." This external blandness seemed to be a defense against participation in emotional relationships, but beneath this surface attitude there seemed to be some genuine interest in her teaching and her creative work. This side of the patient's personality seemed to have integrity, was positively directed and not self-depreciatory.

The therapist assumed the explicit role of being interested in the patient's work, particularly as it related to her association with women. It seemed as if the emotional significance of women in the patient's life was negated. In this area she seemed to be rational and logical, although the therapist saw the competitiveness beneath the surface. By maintaining the explicit role of interest with understanding attention, the therapist remained passive while the patient discussed work and feminine relationships about which she could see no problems. The therapist assiduously avoided any exposure of the underlying feelings.

Thus the therapist assumed the explicit attitude of hoping that the patient would settle down and accept the treatment as an experience in human relationships. Her acceptance was calculated to elicit trust and to indicate that the treatment would not interfere with her whole life. The second part of the interview seemed to be structured toward the patient's statement of her assets and involved a discussion of her security operations.

As the patient continued to talk about her work and her relationship with women, she seemed to become more intent on denying what she had said in the first part of the interview. At that time she made the implicit statement that she knows she is very insecure. As she went on, she bragged more and more, denying her insecurity and indicating her sense of victory over men, for example her boss. In this manner the transaction spiraled. The worker accepted the role of an understanding listener to the patient's increasing expressions of confidence.

At this point the therapist shifted to the implicit level of the transaction by indicating to the patient that she herself had stated that she was insecure. Here the technique was not to interpret the patient's explicit role as shown by her boasting but to call attention to the patient's implicit role in the transaction as it spiraled by pointing out the patient's own earlier admission of insecurity. She reacted by denial, but her laugh indicated anxiety and the therapist ended the interview with this unresolved.

That this anxiety had been implicit all the time was evidenced by the fact that the patient entered the interview by talking about the therapist's interpretation that she had been hurt by Paul. Actually, in the previous interview the therapist had said only that Paul apparently wanted to hurt her. Prior statements of her inherent sensitivity were expressed in the intake interview when she talked about her feeling of rejection by her fellow holiday travelers. In the previous interview she had attempted to project the blame for the hurt in her experience with Paul, although she herself had contrived the situation, for she asked, "Why did *he* hurt me?" In this interview she states defensively, "But I'm not hurt." Thus the explicit communication in this transaction was, "Why did *he* hurt me?" the implicit notion was, "Why do I *want* to get hurt?" and this, in turn, is denied by an explicit statement, "I *am not* hurt."

In sum, the patient's disturbance concerned the feeling of wishing to be hurt, denying this by projecting the blame, and then being curious regarding Paul's wish to hurt her, and at the same time admitting some insecurity. The second part consists in a gradual building up of security operations, ending in a braggadocio, but implicit in this was even a mistrust of the boss whom she stated she could handle very well. The third part of the interview reached a spiral of bragging and victorious denial by an exaggerated statement of constructive and positive elements in her life. The fourth period in the interview developed from the therapist's interrupting the explicit role relationship which had spiraled to a peak and was no longer productive, and the transaction was turned back to the essence of the patient's insecurity.

The interview ended in a mild disagreement between the therapist and the patient, which is a necessary part of the process of therapy. If complete complementarity were maintained, there would be no work done. But the therapist shifted the transaction, and evoking a disagreement indicates the focus of therapeutic interest.

Third Session

PATIENT BEGAN by stating that yesterday it suddenly occurred to her that she could have acted differently with Paul. She could have been sympathetic, waited for him to come home that night and talked to him, "but I didn't think of it at the time. I was just thinking of myself." She thinks it was her pride that made her leave. On the other hand, maybe he will respect her more when he sees that he can't just do anything to her. She still likes him. She wonders if their relationship will be the same again, stops herself, says "what relationship?" and comments it seems that the relationship is largely in her fantasy, and then asks me "so why should I talk about it?" *I ask if it seems important.* "Oh yes, besides my father and my brother, he's the only man I ever really got involved with." She stops suddenly, laughs, and guesses this must mean it is Oedipal—"and I hated my father and my brother." When I do not comment, she tells me that Paul used to occupy all her thoughts. Now she can go for hours without thinking of him and enjoy what she is doing. She thinks that this is really better—"but I don't know what I think; maybe I'm just hiding it." *I state that both elements may be present,* and she brings out that she has to have an absolute answer before she is sure of anything.

One thing she wants to ask me, "Can you be absolutely happy with just one person?" She tells of talking with a man who told her that although he was married he was still attracted to other women, felt this would always be so, slept with them to get it out of his system, and didn't tell his wife. If she were the wife, she would be hurt. One thing she knows is that she would have been much more hurt if Paul had gone out with another girl instead of a man. She thinks that since it was a man it really did not involve her so much. Paul told her once that when he met a woman who satisfied all his needs he thought he could give up men. She keeps hoping their relationship will go back to the way it was when she first met him.

She wants to ask me, "Can you have all your needs satisfied by loving just one person?" She is in confusion about both the extent of needs and the love object. *I say that it is possible to have one's needs met by a good love relationship but that I know she needs to understand this more.*

She prides herself on not being dependent because she feels you just hang on to the other person. *I say that it is possible to be dependent in a healthy way.* She tells me that when she talked to a psychiatrist who told her that she was very insecure and the solution for her was to find a man just as insecure as she and they would get along together, she did not like his advice. She tells of how she has many dates, knows how to get along socially, etc. *I state that we know this is not why she is coming.* Here we get into some discussion of therapy—to help her understand herself. *Patient is encouraged to feel and understand* and she verbalizes some fear of this, but more awareness of the meaning of therapy. She guesses there is something wrong with her. *I point out that she is being intellectual again—that she is standing off from her problems.* Patient says that she really hadn't said much last week that was important.

She begins telling me about boy friends with some pride. She has noticed that when she is sure of their interest in her she immediately cools off and doesn't care. If she is interested but the man is cool, her interest increases. She described her relationship with two men to demonstrate this behavior. *I point out that in each instance there is distance between her and the man—either she puts it there or the man does—and so she is safe.* She is startled—"I never thought of that before."

She is quiet for some time and tells me, "One thing I can't stand is passionate kissing. Sweet kisses are all right, but I can't stand seeing a man get worked up." One thing she wants to know, "When you feel just animal attraction for a man, do you have to understand it or is it real?" She is considerably confused about this, feels that you should know what it is. *I tell her it is all right to feel, that she needs to understand many aspects of this more, too.* Somewhere here she makes a slip of the tongue and calls herself a man in relation to Paul. She talks about not knowing what to think or where you stand. How can she ever be sure she has a real relationship? Is it really possible to love just one person? If that person dies or deserts you, will you be devastated for life? Is it just the culture that says you should love one person or is it really so? Won't you get too dependent on one person? *I tell patient that she must not expect answers from me but must learn for herself in treatment where she stands.*

COMMENTS ON THIRD SESSION: The interview began with an indication that the patient's projection of responsibility onto Paul had been reduced by the previous interview. She starts this interview with self-accusations, indicating that she should have been more sympathetic with Paul, thus testing the limits of her responsibility and implicitly wanting the therapist to set these limitations. Then there suddenly develops the idea that there will be no continuing relationship (with Paul), and it seems as if the patient had suddenly obtained some clarification as to the pathological nature of her relationship with him. Almost immediately, however, the patient turns to the relationships with her father and brother, indicating her "hatred" of them, and uses technical jargon as a provocative intellectual statement to which a response from the therapist is desired. The therapist does not respond, and the absence of her response does not give the patient any indication as to whether her hatred of men is good or bad. When she states that she can go for hours without thinking of Paul, although indicating that such thoughts are still present, there seems to be underneath this defensive neutrality a compulsion to think positively about Paul and other men in order to avoid negative feelings.

Thereafter, the patient indicates being upset about homosexuality and inability to fulfill her own role as a woman, and she wonders whether she can become completely satisfied through therapy. Implicit in this disclosure and her indication of understanding her homosexual friend is an indication that there are some doubts regarding her own femininity.

Her question as to whether one's needs can be met by loving just one person probably had some reference to the fact that her position in her family in relation to both or either parent was always in doubt. Prior to this interview she had talked a great deal about her dependency, for example, her acquaintances during her trip; she now begins to talk about her independence. Even so, she repeats the doctor's statement that she is insecure and should find another insecure person. She did not like his advice and goes on to tell how she is poised and able to get about socially, thus indicating her negation of dependency. It seems as though she is anxious about the possibility of coming closer to the therapist, vacillates, and defends herself against this.

In telling about the need for control—that is, the need to get a man in close relationship to her so that she can reject him as contrasted with the danger of being rejected—we see that there is an implicit anxiety regarding the possibility of getting too close to the therapist. The patient goes on to ask again for a dependent relationship, although she indicates that there would be a denial of reciprocity. At this point there is a confession of her real feelings and at the same time an indication of her anxieties that these might get out from under control. Here, again, the therapist does not expose the implicit meaning of the patient's role at this point. As the interview goes on, the patient becomes more confused and makes a slip of the tongue, calling herself a man, which suggests that she would like to be loved by a woman. Through the terminal part of the interview the patient expresses a wish to know where she stands in relation to what the therapist will do for her so that her basic anxiety regarding possible disappointment might be allayed.

The therapist indicates to the patient that she seems to need an absolute answer before she is sure of anything, thus attempting to make the implicit dependency role explicit and avoiding the patient's attempt to place her in a judging authoritative role. The therapist also talks about healthy dependency, which could be interpreted by the patient as permissive or as a warning. When the patient asks for assurance regarding a possible reliance on the therapist for concrete answers, an indication of her dependency, the worker does not assume a reciprocal relationship, and the question arises: Should the therapist have opened the implicit transaction more directly at this point?

The therapist explained her reluctance to indicate the patient's implicit needs and how she avoided them because of anxiety on the basis of her fear that the patient might become too dependent. Actually, the therapist's implicit attitude was a defense against her own anxiety over the patient's infantile needs, for these were felt to be so great that they might engulf the therapist herself. This implicit attitude, which prevented the therapist from dealing with the patient's underlying need, was probably derived from the pretherapeutic discussion of the case history. At that time the formulation was made that if the patient were to give up her acting out, including participation in the semidelinquent society, there would probably be a depression followed by considerable aggressive behavior. This apparently sensitized the therapist to avoid such a possible outcome.

Fourth Session

PATIENT IS FRIENDLY but says that she really has nothing to say. "It is strange, but now that I really have someone to talk to, I don't have anything to say." There have been times when she felt very upset, as if she had to have someone to talk to, but there wasn't anybody. *I ask if she has to feel very upset about something in order to talk about it.* "No"—she has been thinking about Paul and thinks she really could have been sympathetic, but knows she did not feel that way at the time. She really would not have been true to herself if she hadn't acted the way she felt. One thing she did think about last week—she is too critical.

She tells of a boy—"I mean a man"—who told her that he wanted to be with her any time it was convenient for her. She thought to herself, "ugh," but controlled her reaction and was nice to him. *I ask why she feels she was too critical.* She thinks that she used to be very unkind and would say what she thought. She feels it is possible to change and help yourself, do I agree? *I say that I do.* For the last several years she has been able to control her reactions and she feels that she has changed herself a great deal. *I inquire if she feels that her reactions are wrong.* She immediately becomes specific. "Not about this boy, because I knew I didn't want to go out with him or encourage him."

She begins to talk about Paul who was always telling her that she was selfish and critical in her reactions. When she first went out with him, they traveled on the streetcar. Paul would bring a book, open it, and completely ignore her. This often happened, too, during an entire date. He told her there was something wrong with her when she objected. *I ask for her opinion.* She is very hesitant and circumlocutious. *I point this out and again ask her opinion.* She is finally able to say that she does not feel this is the right way to act toward her on a date. *I agree and wonder why she has had so much difficulty stating it.*

She brings out that she always has to doubt and weigh her reasons before she decides what she thinks. *When I verbalize that she feels very much in doubt when she has a critical opinion,* she is uncomfortable. The therapist calls her attention to his. She tells me of three parties to which she had gone as Paul's date. In each instance he "just didn't feel like taking her home," told her to go home by herself—and she did. She is able to say that she felt humiliated, that she is very sensitive and wouldn't let any other man treat her that way. "I didn't even question it." She tells of another party that Paul gave at which he "lay down on the floor like a baby" because he didn't feel in the mood to entertain his guests.

She then appears anxious, *and I question if she is not anxious because she is telling me some critical thoughts about Paul.* She immediately denies this but feels she does not have the right to be critical, that she should be understanding. *I point out that she is afraid of her critical thoughts, afraid of her reactions, tries to stand off at a distance, and keeps doubting how she feels.* She begins to understand what I mean and tells me in some detail the extent to which she is always doubting and weighing her attitudes. She knows very well that she was constantly being humiliated by Paul but could not stop herself. She has to be sure of the truth. Why is this bad? *I say that one can become emotionally crippled by having to stay at such a distance and doubt all one's reactions.* She is frightened and startled. *I say that I have made too strong a statement for her, that I mean to help her understand what she is doing to herself at times.* She asks me if there is not a place for doubt, and *I say that of course there is but that we are trying to help her understand when she uses it against herself.*

She tells me that yesterday she bought two tickets to a show for her brother and his wife. She then got confused. Was she really buying the tickets because she wanted them to enjoy the show, or did she have some ulterior motive? Was she "selfish" thinking that they would consider her a wonderful person for doing something like this for them? If so, she doesn't want any part of it. She wants to leave herself entirely out of something like this, because it is wrong to think of yourself. *I tell her that I do not think it is possible to leave yourself out; one is directly involved in one's own life.* She sees this, says, "But how can I know what my motives really are?" *I say that she is worrying about her hostile thoughts again and that we can try to help her with this.*

Patient says that she doesn't like to think about the past, but she has felt this way for a long time. Her mother was always nice, but for years she never knew what to expect from her father. It wasn't this way when she was little. She can remember sitting on her father's lap and enjoying it. Something terrible happened to her brother and he turned to her for help. She didn't know how to help him. Patient then tells about how her brother's young wife had an affair with another man and how very upset her brother had been. Eventually things worked out between them all right. Her parents do not know about this.

COMMENTS ON FOURTH SESSION: The patient begins the interview indicating her awareness of the therapist as an understanding listener and her own difficulty in accepting her role of a participating patient. The therapist responds to this with an indication that one can establish a safe, dependent relationship without being under pressure or dramatic. The patient responds by accepting the patient role and by discussing her true feelings versus what is expected of her and reveals significant information concerning some past behavior. Apparently at an earlier point she considered herself too aggressive and too critical, and now she has adopted a very self-effacing attitude but she continually doubts her motivation. Critical thoughts about others incite anxiety. Compulsive doubts about her own role seem to dominate the patient's conscious and external behavior.

When the therapist evoked a hurt, frightened, and startled reaction in the patient—on pointing out the crippling effect of her compulsive doubts—she then also became doubtful and reacted very much like the patient—by partially retracting her statement, indicating that perhaps it was too strong. In retrospect, it seems the patient feared that her defenseless and helpless role had been accepted and that the therapist hastened to correct this. In a short time thereafter, the therapist indicates that the patient is worrying, not about critical thoughts but about "hostile thoughts." This is a deeper and more acceptable interpretation than the one which the therapist attempted to ameliorate and results in re-establishment of role complementarity, making possible the revelation of further historical material and communication of anxiety.

The communications in this session illuminate an aspect of the transactional approach. One could consider, for example, that everything the subject was saying had reference in a disguised symbolic way to her relationship with the therapist. The man who said she could be with

him any time it was convenient for her was as permissive as the therapist. Paul, who would bring a book and open it to completely ignore
her, would be as intellectual as the therapist. It could be conceived
that the patient was actually talking to the therapist about her unconscious feelings and doubts about their relationships.

The transactional concept, however, utilizes the relationship between
therapist and patient for the purpose of facilitating and permitting the
patient to ventilate her feelings regarding *all* relationships. Thus, the
therapist was permissive and attempted to judge the degree of anxiety
which the patient experienced from the feedback obtained through
her communications. When she asked why her doubtings were bad,
the therapist felt that the anxiety had become too strong and attempted
to modify the statement, because she realized that the patient was a
person whose emotions could potentially lead to or threaten an explosion. Later on in the interview the therapist recognized that the
patient had developed her defenses sufficiently and made a more direct
interpretation regarding critical attitudes toward hostile thoughts.

The actual transaction involved a relationship which ended around
the anxiety axis to which the therapist was sensitive and about which
she acted in encouraging or decreasing the amount, depending upon
what the patient could experience with safety. As this transaction maintained itself, more and more material was remembered regarding past
relationships, so that suddenly in the last portion of the interview there
was a jump from the recent past involving Paul to that of the more
distant past involving her family. Here again, although the implicit
material had to do with the mother who was "nice" but actually gave
nothing in satisfaction, the explicit material had to do with the father
and brother. Here it is clear that not only Paul but also her father and
brother were unpredictable, and toward all of them the patient had
to assume a giving role. She had to do what they wanted, to sit on one's
lap, to help in the other's domestic affairs, but at least through the con-
cession of compliance the patient seemed to obtain something real as
contrasted with the completely empty relationship with the promiscuous mother.

The transaction with the therapist was not made explicit; nevertheless, as it continued on a level at which anxiety was held to an optimum,
memories were revealed regarding past transactions. In this sense the
transaction was productive and will apparently continue at this level
until it is stalemated. This will occur when content becomes stereotyped and repetitious. Then, of course, the implicit role of the helpless
and dependent child continually disappointed in the absence of a
reliable and consistent mother will emerge.

As the memory of transactions outside of the therapeutic relationship was revived, the patient truly ventilated her intense painful humil-

iation that she endured from men. Her final statements indicated almost a nonsequential jump into the far distant past, which indicates to us the effectiveness of this technique not only in evoking intellectual memories but also in reviving emotional experiences.

Fifth Session

THE PATIENT BEGAN the interview by saying that something had happened and that she had been depressed all week. She thought about a lot of things that she hopes aren't true and made a list of them later and went over them in her mind. *When I ask if this was to get rid of the thought,* she says that it was. She knows what caused her to be depressed and thinks it was silly. On Monday night a man failed to call her and again Wednesday night another man did not call her as she expected. She felt better on Thursday for no reason except that she heard from one of them. From Monday to Wednesday she felt her job was an awful burden and she couldn't stand the boss. A friend of hers is going out West and will see Paul, so she will have a report on him.

She wonders at some length if it is all right to talk about Paul, or should she try to go on to something else. *She is encouraged to talk about what has meaning for her.* Finally, after she has ruminated for a long time, *I ask if she expects me to take Paul away from her.* She startles and reacts with feeling, denies this, says that Paul has always been in the background. She has constantly had the feeling "there's always Paul to go back to." She has let herself get involved with other people, but adds that it would go so far and then she would turn back to Paul. She has always felt that if Paul got straightened out she would marry him; in the meantime, if someone else came along, she would marry him. She feels that Paul really cares for her "in his way." After she elaborates this, *I point out that it seems he is ambivalent—in some ways he cares for her, in others, he does not.* She agrees with this. Something had hurt her during the visit. Paul had $15, spent $12 of this to buy his roommate a birthday present, and had only $3 for her visit. It is extremely difficult for her to go further with this. Birthday presents and Christmas presents are "not important for me and Paul." They do not exchange them, but send each other gifts they would like, not related to obligatory giving. She sent Paul a tie, because she knew he would like it—but not for Christmas, it didn't arrive until New Year's. He then sent her a record, not in return, but because she would like it, "and I do." After much hedging she is able to admit a little that she was disappointed Paul had spent all his money so that they couldn't enjoy going out together. Paul would say she was just selfish and insecure for believing this.

Maybe she doesn't know how to take him. When they were walking down the street recently he told her she was so ugly that everyone was looking at her. Clarification brings out that she believes this was a kind of left-handed compliment, an indirect way of saying that she looked nice. Paul has never been able to say anything nice to her directly, but always how dumb or insecure she is. However, he told another girl he was glad she would get to know patient who had excellent taste in clothes and would help her.

Paul is very striking looking—particularly his head—"You don't look at him from the neck down." He has a massive, firmly modeled head with a large nose and a mustache. People always notice him on the street. Upon first meeting him she thought his nose was too big, but she has since gotten over this. He is the only man she ever took to a party without feeling apprehensive as to how new people would like him; she didn't care what they thought.

In art school he began to talk to her in an affected way which he often has in social conversation. She responded in kind, but pretty soon they were talking seriously and sincerely to each other. He expressed surprise, because he had thought she was just a little dope, incapable of any real thoughts. She does not understand this. It is an effect she often has on people who do not realize that she really wants to talk to them, but they think she is a frivolous, empty-headed extrovert. She was a good student, too. *I clarify that to some extent patient puts up this front out of anxiety and social shyness in new situations.* She is extremely sensitive in these areas, tells me she can do better, but "knows" that sometimes she is very anxious in new situations. Patient begins talking more about Paul and the quality of their relationship (which has strong hostile and submissive tones throughout). She begins to describe how he always ended up telling her she was insecure, immature, etc. She got so confused that she didn't know what the truth was, whether he was right or she felt that way because he said so. We also got into some discussion of whether she "baited him" by her reactions. She has "thought a lot about this"—knows she was "masochistic" with him.

She has thought to herself that she was stronger than Paul. She runs away from this (*and I let her*). When she was depressed last week, she was quivering all over and anxious, and *I say that this degree of anxiety is a pretty uncomfortable experience.* She then tells me that she does differ with Paul and, after a long exposition, winds up with telling me that she thinks she is smarter than Paul. She laughs anxiously, *I slip in a comment that we can talk about it further sometime,* and then she immediately changes the subject.

She asks, "What is the difference between psychotherapy and psychoanalysis?" She met a man who is being analyzed. He told her that psychotherapy could not get at the roots of her problem and would not go into her past life and she wants to get at the root of her problem. *I tell her some general differences, say that psychotherapy can also go into the past and consider the roots of her problem.*

COMMENTS ON FIFTH SESSION: The patient recounted a depression for several days, but, in doing so, expressed some defiance to the therapist in indicating that it was not the treatment that caused the depression but what actually had happened in her life. She had attempted mastery over the depression through the intellectual process of listing the things she felt and then deciding that they were not true. The depression was apparently precipitated by both real-life disappointments and the partial awareness of her neurotic behavior. A partial recovery occurred when restitution was derived from a belated call from one of the men who had disappointed her, and by first indicating defiance to the therapist and then her needfulness.

The patient asked the therapist for permission to talk about Paul, to whom she can apparently retreat as a substitutive gratifying fantasy in the face of external disappointments. She can always evoke him when things get too tough in the outer world. It was here that the patient received a powerful interpretation from the therapist and reacted with a startle. The therapist asks whether the patient expects her to take Paul away, which, of course, hits at her most potent defense against recognition of her own internal feelings of deprivation and depression making explicit the patient's fear of the "omnipotent" therapist. The patient then goes on to discuss in considerable detail the process of gift exchange with Paul. Here it is apparent that each one uses the other as a narcissistic object and Paul is her male mirror image. Each gives to each other gifts which the donor likes and on the occasions suitable to the donor. As she talks more about Paul, it seems that she has eroticized his head and blanked out his body. At the same time as she describes his massive, firmly modeled head with a large nose and mustache, she indicates some understanding of herself acting as an empty head in response to his role assignment. This suggests again that Paul represents her masculine counterpart.

When the therapist indicates that her reputation as a frivolous, empty-headed extrovert might be due to anxiety and social shyness in new situations, and is a front that she puts up to *some extent*, the patient's self-respect is at once wounded since her defensive role is challenged. It is clear from what the patient then says regarding her "sado-masochistic" relationship with Paul that it is her own knowledge that hurts rather than the therapist's interpretation. Yet, as she describes her "masochism" in terms of what she knows about herself, no affect is liberated, since she continues to maintain the defensive little girl position.

The patient again talks about her depression and includes the fact that she also was anxious and, in doing so, exposes some hostility to Paul with a bragging notion that she is smarter than he. Within the depression is a good deal of anger, which apparently makes the patient feel anxious.

Then the patient immediately jumps into questioning the difference between psychotherapy and psychoanalysis. Psychoanalysis, she indicates, would be more suitable to her because it deals with the past life—in other words, avoids the present and its feeling content. The question also indicates a shift from childish dependency to intellectual defense as a means of dealing with her anxiety. The therapist apparently let this go because of the fear of stirring up too much anxiety at this time and because the interview was almost at an end.

In the transactional process, we see at first an implicit dependency with a request for the therapist to tell her what to talk about and with questions relating to the sacrifice of Paul, which, paraphrased, "You can't take Paul away," means, "You can't take my narcissistic defenses away." The therapist responded to her question as to whether she should give Paul up by indicating that she didn't have to. Later on in the interview the patient attempts to assert the fact that her own femininity is stronger than Paul's masculinity, which seems to indicate that implicitly there is a struggle between feminine and masculine identification.

During the current interview the patient is getting to know the therapist better. As she feels warmer, she also becomes more anxious. The therapist is more sensitive to the patient's anxiety and has a tendency to react to it with a certain degree of anxiety and attempts to dampen it down.

This interview brings out very clearly the difference between the psychoanalytic-psychotherapeutic approach and the transactional. A supervisor trained in psychoanalysis would perhaps in this interview have indicated the need for more active interpretation, especially about the patient's use of Paul as a defense. The therapist keeps the transaction going, however, for it seems likely that as the patient uncovers negative attitudes in her implicit roles she will learn why she really does not love Paul as an actual person and will recognize that Paul represents some need within herself. Here the transactional approach relies on the capacity of the patient to gain insight through a recognition of her implicit roles in relationship to Paul—if her anxiety level is held at an optimum within the transaction. Although the content of the session is somewhat confused, uncertain, and vague, because of a certain amount of drifting due to the absence of specific interpretations, the transactional process is going along and material is being divulged which the patient could grasp, and progress is being made. The therapist herself felt that the patient had been stirred up, especially at the insight of her intense hold on Paul in order to avoid the recognition of her dependence on the therapist.

Sixth Session

THE PATIENT ENTERS the office with a large package, out of which she takes a folded piece of brown wrapping paper. She comments that she is always carrying bundles when she comes to the interview. She has a budget account and finds that she needs to buy a good many things now. She is furnishing her own apartment instead of boarding, finds that many of her linens are worn out "and I have no one to borrow from—at least that I would like to." Her clothes are worn out, too, as she had "let them go" in concentrating on her trip. There are a number of things she wants to talk with me about today, which she had listed on the brown paper.

This week a friend visited her and admired something she had made. She told the friend that she planned to send it to some friends, but when the girl continued to admire it, she gave it to her. The next day the friend told her she had broken it. This is the third gift of her work this friend has broken. She describes the details. She thinks it must be significant. What do I think? *I wonder why she is asking.* It seems that both are artists and the friend generally admires her work and tells her so. But one time in the past, when she and Paul were back together, the friend failed to give her messages from him on two occasions when he was passing through town; she was not home, but the friend knew where she was. Patient would never think of doing this, but did not have courage to speak to friend about this. *Asked whether she feels she should have given friend the gift,* patient says that if friend liked it, she should have it.

She has been working hard getting ready for an art bazaar, and hopes to make a profit. Today a batch of her work was ruined by another girl's mistake. Without her knowledge, the other girl had reversed the firing cones. She was discouraged about this and about her job, too. Her boss spoke to her about her low sales record. Last week she sold about $40 and the other salesgirl, $150. The other salesgirl is up at the front, aggressive with people, makes them her personal customers, shows them merchandise when they are just looking, etc. Patient is "sincere," can't sell very well, will sell customers if she thinks merchandise is suitable and stays within the price range they can afford. Often when she walks away to let them think it over, the other girl will "cinch" the sale. Patient permits and encourages this. *I question whether she speaks up for her turn to wait on people who are not regular customers of the other girl.* She does not, and knows that she is not aggressive enough. The other salesgirl is quite brash and patient reacts quite submissively to her. Her boss "analyzed" her yesterday, to the effect that she was timid, insecure, vindictive, etc. It hurts, because they are friends and that wasn't the way to do it. She was proud of herself for being able to speak up to him and say lightly, "So I'll analyze you soon." "I thought I acted real cool." *I nod at this.*

Mentioning the piece of brown paper, she says she wants to ask me whether I feel she should make a telephone call. She applied for a job teaching art at a private school and was told they would get in touch with her. She does not have a higher degree, but would love the job. A few days later the principal came into the store and she did not recognize him at first. Should she call about the job if they promised to call her and have not? *I wonder what she thinks is wrong with call-ing?* She is able to talk a little about her possible disappointment. "Do you think I should call?" *I say that I am trying to understand what her reasons for hesitation are, if this is something she really wants.* "Then you think I should call?" *I agree if that is what she wants, but I am wondering if she feels that she is being too aggressive in calling.* She says that "in this larger use of the word aggression maybe I do. I'll call him."

She wants to ask me, too, about this summer. In the period when she was waiting to hear from us she had committed herself to be an art counselor at a summer camp for two months starting the end of June. She has done it for five years in the past, would not have done it if she had known she could start treatment. The woman pressed her and pressed her. She needs the money; her job is not secure for the summer months. She knows it will set her treatment back, but guesses she can pick up again. Do I advise her against it? *I say that I do not directly advise her against it, I will be away for a month of this time, too, and it is really her choice. We can pick up treatment again.*

Patient thanks me for the interview and as she leaves says that she had got through her whole list today. *I say that we had just got started on some of the things.* Patient was wearing an open-necked sweater or blouse. There were red marks at the base of her throat, but I did not notice any specific alteration in them during the interview.

COMMENTS ON SIXTH SESSION: The patient entered the interview somewhat gay to begin with, indicating that she was striving toward her own independence in furnishing an apartment in-stead of boarding, but implicit in her role was a pleading for help and sympathy. It was as if she were asking, "Should I take help from the therapist?" It also seemed possible that the patient felt some guilt for buying—though on a limited budget—which she attempted to explain by the "budget account." The therapist felt that the frantic looking around for new things for her apartment, because everything else had been worn out, was a kind of "building a nest" acting out, as if she were in a premenstrual phase. The consensus of the seminar was that the interview was structured by the patient as if she were preparing to ask something from the therapist.

The brown paper which the patient takes from her large package has a list of questions and items on it for discussion, to which the patient does not refer. She goes into a long account of her difficulties with her friend and colleague in the store and is unable to put all these incidents together. The therapist questions why this should happen to her, but it seems as if this question is not strong enough. Implicit in the patient's attitude is a question: What will the therapist do with her or to her? It is as if she says, "You ask me to discuss and expose my personal feelings, but what will *you* do about them? Will you hurt me like the others do?" She indicates that everyone takes from her and she gives to everyone, but the implicit attitude is the reverse: "I would like to take a great deal from other people." The therapist did not make any comment about the implicit attitude and explained to the seminar that she felt elucidation of the implicit transaction would not be advisable at this time. She felt that she should hold off but could not tell us why. Perhaps, it was queried, the therapist was afraid of the patient's explosive anxiety and thus was determined to keep her in the explicit role which she had assumed.

The patient goes on, indicating that she makes no demands and permits herself to be pushed aside, although she obviously would like to be more aggressive. The therapist encourages her to be more aggressive toward customers but avoids the implicit hostility which is denied in the transaction. Subsequently the patient pressures, although subtly, to elicit a direct answer from the therapist and at least twice openly demands positive advice.

The implicit role in this and previous sessions was clear. Why did the therapist not attempt to make the implicit hostile demanding role explicit? She felt that the patient should be permitted to go along and rest on her oars as if she had been exhausted by something. The therapist waited and by focusing on clarifying the explicit transaction hoped to strengthen the healthy defensive roles. The group felt that the implicit role should have been made explicit. The patient, who had kept her summer plans to herself all this time and suddenly confessed that she was going away for two months, was playing a game of secrets. She rationalized her decision to go on a vacation by saying that the woman begged her—it was not that she wanted to go. The therapist felt that the patient was asking her to win her over by being stronger than the other woman; she rejected this role by placing the decision with the patient. The patient reacted with a certain bragging independence, indicating that everyone really wants her. The patient obviously is an expert in being a good girl. She is sensitive to other people's needs and can get along with them at their level of role demands, but behind this is a secretiveness which will probably remain until the therapist is able to interpret her implicit roles.

The therapist knows that the group has on several occasions advised more activity which the therapist resisted. As a result, the therapeutic interviews have become more and more like the bland neutral sessions that are so characteristic of psychiatric social workers. This is in great contrast to the active, prematurely deep interpretations of the psychoanalytic tyro and certain social workers who attempt to apply psychoanalytic principles to their psychotherapy. What we prefer is something which is neither transference, depth interpretations, nor a bland "you-direct-the-interview, patient, and I'll follow you along with acquiescent nods of encouragement." The middle ground is the transactional one, in which the therapist continuously and patiently interprets the implicit roles of the patient as she at the same time continues to attempt to understand her own implicit roles in the transaction.

Seventh Session

PATIENT IS EAGER to start the interview. She begins by relating that she has discovered something important about herself. "When I do not care, I can have a good time and enjoy myself; when I do care, I don't." When she pauses, *I comment that this does seem important, what can she tell me about it?* Last night patient gave a party for her old high school friends whom she sees only three or four times a year. By now they have little in common and spend most of their time reminiscing and drinking. Actually, she is quite depreciating of their low level of culture, and tells how she caught herself putting on long dangling earrings just in time not to wear them. *Why?* Because they would think she was being "arty" and kid her about this. "I can dish it out, but I can't take it."

Much to her surprise she enjoyed the evening thoroughly. There was a boy there whom she has known for years; they necked and she enjoyed it. When she was in grade school and high school they used to have basement parties where the boys would make the rounds of the girls in a necking session. He was the only one she would neck with. She used to worry about whether she would be a social success because she refused to neck with any of the other boys. In the course of this she associates to the word basement that she and her mother used to live in a basement apartment but "that wasn't the basement where we necked." Her mother was home "except when she went out on dates." For the first time she felt that this boy actually liked her. Before she had always felt that he did not like her and was just necking with her. She tells me that although they have had many necking sessions on parties, he has never taken her on a date. "I guess I just don't know when people like me." *When I ask about this* she tells me that she knows where she stands with her friend who lives in the West. Even though she has not heard from her, she knows that when she sees her again they will be close friends. *I question if she is disappointed in not hearing from Kay.* She says that she is not, that she knows they are real friends. "It was different with my brother." She and her brother fought all the time when they were children. "But you know, I really loved him."

"Oh, and I want to tell you, I've been aggressive all week." Patient called the principal at the school; her sales at the store increased; and she spoke up.

She describes the incident and *I say that it seemed called for. I then inquire if she had felt bitchy when she was being aggressive.* She does not think so. The thing she wants most in her life is to be nice to people. She has to feel that she is being nice and is constantly examining her motives. *I ask if she feels that she is nice.* "Yes," she really feels that she is "a nice person." "Do you know, I'm not sure whether I'm beautiful, or not?" *I ask how she feels about this.* Sometimes she thinks she is beautiful, but sometimes she does not.

She touches her stomach, which is growling, and tells me that she has a hangover. A boy at the party got sick and vomited on his shirt and that of another boy. They are coming by tomorrow to pick up their shirts. She really doesn't want to see them, since she doesn't know how to talk with them like real people. They can't really talk to you. *I ask whether she can accept that she may change and not feel that she has much in common with old friends, but still feel a certain tie to them at times.* She quite seriously agrees with this; says that your friends can't all be the same.

She wants to tell me about a date she had last week. "I am the girl who has a date every night and is supposed to know how to get along with men." A friend introduced her to a new man and she felt quite shy with him, although they immediately clicked in some way. He was quite shy with her, too, but she felt real happy walking down the street with him on the way to the party, even though she felt awkward during the evening. They often gravitated toward each other in group discussions. He asked her for two dates but she was busy both nights. She did not want to tell him that she hoped to see him some other time. *Why?* Because it sounded so obvious—as if she was leading him on and she didn't want to be like that. During much of the evening she had felt just like a high school girl at her first party. The party ended and suddenly he accepted a ride home and left without asking for her phone number. She wonders what happened and why he didn't ask to get in touch with her. Can I tell her? *I say it seems that things were going in that direction, but had not progressed far enough by the end of the party.* Patient brings out her disappointment, her expectation that this should have happened immediately. "At least I'm not like a man I know. He's really a mess, in spite of three years of analysis— can't even talk to people." *I comment that naturally she is anxious and thinking of herself and her own treatment.* "I'm not really that sick— and I think I can do better than that." *I inquire, had she understood why I had said it was her own choice about coming in for the summer months?* She says, "I think I really understand it."

She wants to tell me something about herself. "You know, I'm really nasty sometimes." When she elaborates this a little and pauses, *I ask* whether she enjoys being nasty. Her face lights up as she agrees. Then she begins talking in an embarrassed way and *I tell patient this is a part of herself she does not like.*

COMMENTS ON SEVENTH SESSION: The patient entered the interview with a prepared topic which placed her in control of the interview, at least for a time. In this respect she enacted the role of the good patient. Actually, as she progressed and freely associated more than ever before. she presented attitudes that seemed to be concerned implicitly with testing the therapist. The implicit question was: "What do you think of me and my attitudes?"

The patient attempted to depreciate others and indicated that many people were lower in status and in their behavior than she. Behind this seemed to be considerable envy of other people's freedom and ability to engage in interpersonal relationships. The patient gave a party, which had some implication of giving, until it was found that this was only part of a routine matter and it was her turn. She touched on the fact that the basement was similar to the one where she and her mother lived, but brought out implicitly that, contrary to her mother, she was not promiscuous in that she had necked with only one boy. Behind this seems to be a defense against identification with the mother. This more clearly than before brings out the patient's fear of the feminine role.

In discussing physical contact without consideration of liking or being liked, relationship to this patient means physical contact alone, just as to a very young child. In discussing whether she is liked or not she reveals her insecurity, because she jumps to discuss the fact that a girl friend who lives in a distant city really likes her. Since the last interview, in an attempt to please the worker, she has been more aggressive and in some respects has also accentuated her protective niceness. This protective coloration seems to be a habitual role that the patient plays, and both attitudes at this time are the result of implicit commands from the therapist. Her discussion of whether she is beautiful indicates the narcissistic quality to her defenses. When the patient discusses her hangover, it appears to be a psychological reaction to excessive necking. However, she quickly leaves the topic to discuss the fact that the boy had vomited. She implies that she can't talk much but she can neck.

The patient indicates that she tried a new relationship with a recent acquaintance to whom she was attracted, but apparently she drew back; she did not offer to break a previous date and did not bring up the subject of another possible meeting. Her disappointment indicated her impatience for immediate results. At the same time, the patient comforts herself that she is not masculine.

As the interview ended, the therapist discussed the summer vacation again, making it clear that the patient was responsible for her own choice. The explicit response was that she understood, but then she immediately discussed her nastiness, which was how she would like to be to the therapist for forcing her to make her own decision.

The patient reveals herself as a narcissistic little child, demanding physical contact, with an aggressive reaction at frustration. Underlying this is awareness of her attractiveness and charm and some beginning understanding of her own demandingness, against which she defends by acquiescent agreement. Actually, the patient is in flight from identification with the bad feminine role into a regressive attitude which carries with it the aggressions of the frustrated little child. The patient's explicit role is that of a defensive good little obedient girl who wants the therapist to like her and has obeyed her own concept of implicit commands by being aggressive in business and nicer to boys.

The therapist's explicit role is self-assigned: to wait and to ask in a doubting way about the patient's defensive responses. Does her behavior and thinking really correspond with the accounts she gives of them? To some extent the therapist has assumed the explicit roles assigned by the patient as being the all-knowing mother when she questions and doubts the patient's explicit roles, implicitly suggesting that she knows more about the underlying motivations of the patient.

As a result of this transaction the patient becomes more defensive— that is, more embarrassed. She is more insistent and to some degree more successful in obtaining a positive response from the therapist. At the same time, she is beginning to admit her childish nastiness. Although several members of the seminar have indicated impatience at the slowness of movement and the inactivity of the therapist, the transaction seems to be productive of further revelations from the patient and some dawning insight of her implicit roles. This is all one can ask of a transaction process which has not yet come to an equilibrium. As the therapy progresses, however, the seminar felt that attention should be focused more on fear of sexuality from which she takes flight into the dependent, frustrated child role.

Eighth Session

PATIENT BEGINS by telling me that she had been sitting next to a woman in the waiting room who had a lipstick out and was twisting her hands and marking them with lipstick. It made her feel anxious and depressed. She, too, felt something like that, when, during the week, the boss asked her to assist in stuffing envelopes. After doing it for a few hours she became sleepy and thought to herself that she could not live that way.

She describes the narrow life of the woman usually doing this type of work. It was "depressing" and she does not want this for herself. *I say that it is natural to feel this way. How about the woman in the waiting room?* She brings out that this woman had made her feel anxious [woman actually was acutely disturbed] and she had no idea how to help her. *I say that seeing a very upset person can make you feel anxious. How does she feel about coming?* She likes to come but is always glad if no one else is in the elevator. *Why?* Because of what they might think. She was thinking last time in the waiting room, "What if I might see an attractive man here?" She had thought to herself that she wouldn't want him—because he comes to a psychiatrist. *Does she feel that way about herself?* No, and she wouldn't feel that way about a girl friend if she met her here, but it is different with a man. She laughs. *I say that she doesn't want a man to know she has some problems.* "Yes, I want to keep control." She laughs again.

She has kept her treatment confidential. She didn't want to get involved in discussing it—as some of her friends have done. She did tell one girl friend—"the one who broke my ash tray." The friend then told a mutual male friend. *When I ask if this was a betrayal of her confidence,* she denies this, saying that she had not made it explicit that it was confidential. She tells an associative incident of asking a special favor of C and being ignored. She is going to be more careful, and about the girl too, as they had both let her down. She wants me to know that she likes to come here. She used to forget it all during the week; now she thinks of what we talk about. She didn't like the intake worker who saw her—"She gave me a headache and that's how I feel when I want to avoid people, like the man on that boring date." She likes to talk to me.

She is worried whether it is right for her to come. *Why?* When she sees all the poor people downstairs who really can't afford anything, she wonders about this. *Does she feel she can afford private treatment?*

No, she told the real truth downstairs about her earnings; she cannot afford the private rates. But she has an apartment and pays high rent, and has certain standards of living. She wonders if she should really give up everything for treatment. *I tell her that this is not necessary so long as she is paying as much as she can afford with a reasonable standard of living.*

She wants me to know that when she called the school they told her there were two applicants for the job and they were deciding between them. She shows no anxiety. One of the girls had told her they thought she was "just darling." She laughs and *I inquire how she had felt about this.* She tells me that she can see why they thought of her as darling.

She has been "whirling" after the last interview here and noted some thoughts. Do I want to hear them? She is laughing self-consciously; maybe they aren't so interesting or important. *I say that it is hard to know but we can see.* "The first one is that I am really satisfied with myself and my life. I wouldn't change anything that happened to me, even when I lived with my father, because I learned from that, too. I think I'm really a nice person." *I do not comment when she pauses.* She tells me then that she thinks that she is in control of her whole life and everything that happens to her. *I do not comment.*

She looks at her paper. "The second idea is that I believe in fate— that fate will come along and change things." She stops suddenly, looks at me and says, "But I contradicted myself, didn't I?" *I agree.*

She really doesn't know how she feels about herself. She is not sure how to behave or dress. She doesn't own a hat or carry a handbag and feels that she doesn't know how to be a woman. She wears casual clothes and low heels. Although her clothes are of good quality and conservative in taste, she feels uncomfortable when dressed up and in high heels. When she left the session last week she went to the Loop and suddenly felt like a schoolgirl in her wash dress with no gloves, no hat, and little sandals. She is acting like a perpetual student and is afraid to be a woman. Her hair is in style, but that is because she has always worn it that way. She wears flat heels because high heels hurt her feet. A shoe clerk told her, "You'll just have to let your feet hurt." She asks me if it is important how you dress. *I say that it is important how she feels about herself as a woman.*

COMMENTS ON EIGHTH SESSION: Her initial comments indicate that the patient has some feelings about attending the psychiatric clinic. She indicates that she does not want a damaged man, but her relationship with Paul shows how fearful is the feminine role with anyone who is not a depreciated man. With women she maintains a feminine façade, for with them she does not have to be so much. Her opinion that almost everyone else leads a narrow and depressed life and is worse than she is an attempt to avoid insight into how restricted her own life has become. Implicit in this material is also the question: What does the therapist think? But the patient knows very well that, despite her curiosity regarding the therapist, her control mechanisms are working.

The patient indicates that the intake social worker was much more active and pushing, bringing on a headache. This is an announcement of a sort to the therapist that she, too, should not push the patient too far. The patient expresses confidence in the therapist and says that she likes her, but indicates at the same time that there is some anxiety about a breakdown in the confidential relationship. In doing so, she plays the nice little girl role.

Then the patient wonders whether she has to give up everything and make sacrifices for treatment. Here we see an anxiety about giving confidences and some anxiety about the apparent preferential treatment she is getting. There is danger in this because the woman to whom she is close and who likes her may possibly also hurt her. When the patient talks about her experiences with the school, she again indicates her narcissistic, childlike defenses, which, however, seem to be weakening. She wants to be left with her defenses, yet they are hollow because she recounts the compliments without any affect. There seems to be a contradiction, then, between the explicit and implicit roles. When the patient mentions that fate is in charge, she recognizes that her apparent external security is not so deep.

Finally she comes to the central focus of her problem—which we had predicted in the previous interview—fear of femininity and feeling of lack of identity. She has hidden this for a long time. Her narcissistic defenses and childlike attitudes are breaking down because she substitutes for the question, "How do I affect people? I want them to tell me how," the statement, "Now I can see for myself." She also implies a question to the therapist: "What are you going to do about this?"

In future interviews we shall probably see a working through of the development of this focus. There will be much backing and filling and resumption of narcissistic roles. The therapist will have to spend considerable time in helping the patient to deal with the central problem. Although she is in flight from dangerous promiscuous sexuality, into the little girl role, this childhood role will be abandoned through understanding.

The therapist's explicit role has been directed toward listening to the patient's statement about others and agreeing with her lack of ability to control herself and others as she questions, maintains silence, and directs the patient's attention to her own feelings. The patient's explicit role, on the other hand, is that of a controlled yet insecure child constantly questioning how to assume the feminine role. The implicit role is that of a fearful little girl wondering what the therapist will say and do, how her attitudes will affect her, and whether she will be given the help for which she is pleading. The therapist has dealt with the anxiety so that it does not attain a level too great for the patient to handle, and feels that in this interview the anxiety was really stirred up. She feels that her task is to continue to block the defensive roles, to work through the façade of helplessness, to focus on the primary problem, and to help the patient cope with the anxiety that is concomitant with insight.

COMMENTS ON THE FIRST PHASE OF THERAPY

The contents and comments of the first eight sessions can be considered as the opening phase of this treatment. These eight interviews required two months, during which time the patient and therapist got to know each other within the therapeutic setting of the clinic. Their explicit roles were understood thoroughly, they used the same language style and understood each other's cues. Communication was established and information was being exchanged.

Let us ask ourselves what was happening to the therapist. The therapeutic process was part of a research in which we were trying to understand psychotherapy as a transactional process. This meant a modification of previously used language in reporting and hence in thinking about the communication process. Some new terms had to be learned, adequate for observing and reporting explicit and implicit roles of two people within fast-moving sessions of continuous verbal and nonverbal communications.

We learned a great deal in these eight sessions. We began to focus on the transactions and use less psychoanalytic terminology. Social work clichés were slowly being erased but seemed destined to last the longest before complete eradication.

For the first time, the therapist presented the report of each session to a continuous case seminar, the members of which were sometimes impatient and overcritical. The therapist learned to endure this attitude and to avoid oversensitive reactions and retaliatory defenses. Although the therapy was ahead of the seminar, the effects of her colleagues' discussions gradually were noticeable in subsequent sessions. The therapist's threshold for anxiety in the patient gradually rose.

To understand the pattern of the first phase of therapy, we may first characterize *each session* by a sentence:

1. The responsibility for behavior (acting out) belongs to others.

2. Denial of wish to hurt. Expression of bragging self-assurance.

3. Hatred and fear of men, compulsive doubts about guilt, need for dependency.

4. Denial of hostility by masochism and compliance.

5. Sensitivity to frustrations of demands, depression, masculine role as defense.

6. Greater demands for dependency.

7. Greater demands for approval. Role of child who is nasty when frustrated.

8. Fear of feminine role, feeling of lack of identity.

Almost at once the therapist blocked the patient's denial of responsibility and imposed on her the need to take a stand for herself. The patient attempted to bolster up her courage and pretend self-assurance; however, being hurt seemed to be a role reversal protecting her against the wish to hurt. In the third session hatred and fear of men break out with the reactionary roles of a compulsive doubter, a guilty culprit, and a child in need of help. She then attempts to deny hostility by assuming a masochistic and dependent role. Within this role she is easily hurt and depressed, making increasing demands for help, support, advice, etc., and reacting with subtle nastiness at frustration. The eighth session begins to expose the patient's fear of the feminine role and her lack of self-identity as a transition to the next phase of therapy.

At this point her roles seem to be in the service of flight from the feminine role, which she fears because it represents identification with the rejecting promiscuous mother. Denial of feelings or responsibilities, hatred for men (with subsequent guilt and unsureness as to how well she behaves), and masochistic suffering are roles intended to be protective. But they all fail, more completely since therapy began, so that the patient assumes the tried and true little girl role, completely dependent and somewhat demanding on parental figures for approval, at any cost.

7

The Second Phase of Therapy

Ninth Session

To my initial inquiry, the patient says that she did well at the art bazaar and with the proceeds enrolled to take driving lessons. She does not want to depend on friends to teach her, but she felt ashamed to be in a car marked "new driver." She asks if I had gone to the art bazaar. *I tell her that I had but she had not been there when I visited her booth.* She asks if I had seen the excellent drawings of the man who had shared the booth. *I say that I had not and ask how she feels about her own work.* She can sell other people's work much better than her own. She feels that she is praising herself when she sells her own work. *You feel ashamed to do this?* She agrees with embarrassed affect. She states that her poorest work sold first and her best did not sell. *I ask if she feels apologetic at displaying her work.* Yes, she feels this very strongly. *I say that it is as if she is selling herself—she agrees.* Her work sold best when she was absent from the booth. *I point out that she can say something positive about others' work but not about her own.* She agrees with affect. *I point out her expectation of perfection for herself and her sense of shame because she does not achieve this.*

A girl "friend" whom she had not seen for months talked intimately with her about the details of the life of a man they had both known who is now in a state hospital. She is one of three people who had recommended psychiatric treatment for her. Patient found herself curious as to why this friend was telling her all these details so quickly and began wondering whether they really were friends. She used to talk to people this way because she thought it was "interesting." *When I ask how many friends she confides in,* she says that within a wide circle she confided in anyone who was present at the time she was talking. Paul used to tell her she couldn't be trusted not to tell anybody who was listening. He was right, because she had told many people the details of problems that he had confided in her. "You know, I'm not doing this much since I've been in treatment." She realized its inappropriateness when the girl talked this way at the art bazaar. As she thinks about it, she knows they are not really friends. She wonders why she does it. *I say that it is an attempt to get close to people without knowing how.*

One night last week, when she was alone and uncomfortable, she could have called a dozen people but this would not have satisfied her. She had to have someone call her. A boy called her to go out for coffee. Actually he is not anyone she cared about but she felt very relieved not to be alone. *I say that she has to be sought out, and she agrees.* She tells me the extent to which she plans all her time for a constant round of activity. *I comment that she is afraid to be by herself, and keeps busy all the time to avoid this.*

"Yes"—she had been at the studio alone late the other night. She had a feeling there was a "something" under the table that was going to come out and get her. She can't tell me more. It wasn't a man or a woman but a "something." *I point out her embarrassment.* Another thing, the light switch is placed so that she can't get to the door without walking through the dark for a short distance, and she is scared of something there, too. The building has been broken into several times; it is next to a rooming house where men come in at all hours, and there is a dark court. She knows she is taking a chance.

She had been tense all evening anyway because she had to stay late to get some work done and had to be awake at six to get her things to the art bazaar. Her mother used to tell her, "Now clean your plate and get your sleep," and she used to do this when she was little. She has noticed that she does not need sleep if she is enjoying herself but immediately gets concerned if she has to do something. Her boss was mean to her about making her conform exactly to his plans. She needed only a few minutes to set up her display; he needed a long time, but he made it clear that unless she came along she would have to carry her things from wherever he parked the truck—and "I know him. He would have deliberately parked it farther away." *I comment that she was angry.* She describes his anxious busy manner vividly, with biting sarcasm. She is being nice to him, though. *I comment that she is manipulating him to get her own way.* She agrees without guilt.

On Saturday there was a long series of irritations and frustrations. Whenever these build up too much, she gets the feeling she would "like to tear down a wall." When this strong feeling comes over her, she needs to be alone. She was tired and hungry by the time she got to dinner with "the boring date." She has found out since that he doesn't have any background and has done everything by his own efforts—so perhaps she should be more tolerant of him. She kept wanting to go home to be alone. They went to a foreign restaurant which she usually likes, but it looked dirty and the service was slow. She tried to talk to him, and he started asking her questions, not realizing how tired and mad she was. She didn't feel better after she had eaten. *I say that she had wanted sympathy.* She bridles at first, then agrees that this is what she had wanted but had not received it.

She tells me that she got the job at the school. She smiles broadly, and *I ask if she is happy about it.* Yes. *I ask if she has any reservations.* Yes, she wonders whether she can handle the kids well and learn all the things she has to know. *I recognize that she has some anxiety about doing well in a new situation.* She has other reservations. She has never had a job before "where it mattered" and she couldn't pick up and go any time she pleased. She will have fifteen weeks off in the summer and every other vacation time free. But, if a chance develops for a free ride to see Paul, she won't be able to pick up and go whenever she pleases. *I say that she is able to pay her own way and plan her own time.* "But suppose I want to go on a trip and it's during the school year?" *Yes?* "But I really have fifteen whole weeks during the summer to plan with, don't I?" *I agree.* Patient wonders what it is that makes her hesitate. Is it because she is anxious? *I say that she is hesitating to commit herself to an experience where she really has to get involved.* She agrees.

She had been thinking about what she said last week "when I contradicted myself." She really is not so much in control of things, nor does she think her life is so fine. But she feels that when you are unhappy, as she was with her father, you shouldn't let it get you down indefinitely.

COMMENTS ON NINTH SESSION: The therapist opens this interview and seems spontaneously to get closer to the patient in response to her continual implicit requests to be told about things and to be praised. Her reaction is to be pleased at this interest, although, as we shall see later, beneath this was another attitude. The therapist had made a positive effort to see the patient in her booth.

The patient's associations indicate that she had difficulty in displaying her own work, which has the meaning of exhibiting herself. She seems to understand better the implications of exhibiting her artistic productions than when she is talking directly about herself. There is considerable shame at her exhibitionism. If this defensive role is given up, her affect concerning disappointments will be revealed and disturbing to her. After the climax of the last interview, when she exposed her insecurities, the patient loosened up considerably.

In discussing the problems of confidence in her female friends, the patient is implicitly asking whether she could have confidence in the therapist. Here we see that, after the pleasure evoked by indications of the therapist's interest in her, she is suspicious about the therapist's sincerity. Actually, the patient is showing a change in that she realizes more clearly her phony way of relating to people. She seems unable to know how to get close to people without becoming overwhelmingly anxious about the possibility of rejection and disappointment.

The therapist, in making explicit to the patient the affect communicated nonverbally by her, reassures her and allays her anxiety by accepting the assigned role wherein the patient was able to elaborate her fears. There is considerable anxiety concerning her fantasies of "something" not specified, and this denial concerns the fact that the fear is related to human beings. Her associations indicate that she is afraid of men.

She talks about her mother's admonitions in the statement, "Now clean up your plate and get your sleep." This may imply a wish to clean up in terms of her past behavior; that is, to start anew again. Although she is angry at her boss, who plays the role of a father figure, she still manipulates him by being nice to him on the surface. This anger extends from the figure of the boss to the male date, who evoked her anger by taking her to a dirty place. The foreign restaurant is probably related to her father's background, and we may surmise that her anger is directed toward the father. Her uncertainty regarding the school job and her ability to handle the children suggests her implicit fear of being a failure as a woman and a mother. However, in taking this job she seems to have committed herself, suggesting that she is trying to give up her old way of life and Paul, and attach herself more closely to the therapist. Again she returns to the father when she talks about her unhappy life with him. She indicates that with him there was difficulty in controlling her anger.

The transition to this interview can be understood only by referring to the last session when she began to talk about her father. Very early in the current session she told about praising men's work, talked about the man who suggested treatment but is in a mental hospital, the need to be sought after by a boy, and finally the fantasy of men attacking her. Following this, the feelings about men and her anger toward them became more explicit and more or less directly concerned with her father, concluding with a direct statement of how unhappy she was with him.

Implicit is the indication that the patient has conceived of herself as a failure in the role of a woman in relation to men. Correspondingly, she is angry at them and feels guilty about her anger, so that she has to maintain a façade of gentle manipulation at the same time as she pretends not to care. As a secondary defense she has developed a narcissistic façade. The patient apparently is struggling with competitive feelings with women and a great suspicion concerning them. It is becoming clear that the focus of the therapeutic situation must be on her difficulties with the feminine role rather than in her regressive techniques. These, of course, must be blocked but only in terms of understanding what forces her into these regressive roles.

The therapist has maintained the transaction steady by holding the level of anxiety in proper proportions and adopting a need-gratifying attitude toward the patient. In so doing she has not permitted herself to become too important in the patient's real life. Being a woman, the therapist can in this early phase of the treatment mobilize the patient's angry feelings toward the disappointing men and indicate to her the irrational ways in which she deals with them.

Tenth Session

PATIENT BEGINS the interview with a series of rapid comments about forgetting her card today, being a few minutes late, how very busy she was all week, etc. She talks of going to camp on June 22, so that the next session will be her last until September. We discuss this a little, and she settles down.

She was so busy all week getting ready for the art bazaar that she forgot what had happened. Actually she has been feeling "very guilty" toward the other artist in the studio. Last week the work of both had been damaged during a period when either could have been responsible. The other girl cried over it, and patient felt guilty. *When I ask if she felt she had been responsible, stating that she had a lot of experience with this,* she tells me that as far as she knows it was not her fault. The girl has been saying the failure was the patient's fault. In spite of knowing this is not so, patient has found herself trying to make peace by staying late and helping the girl with her work. She knows she feels guilty, says nothing about it, but "actually I can resent it very much when I talk to someone I trust—I really don't like her." They have equal rights at the studio, but she resents being replaced when the boss had promised her the job back. She feels that he would keep the other girl if he had to choose between them, because of her dominating manner even though he talks differently to her alone. "I don't want to be competitive." *I point out that sometimes it is called for, that we are all competitive, and the problem is how to be competitive without being hostile.* Patient tells me the extent to which her colleague dominates the studio. *I point out that she had backed down,* and patient agrees.

This is something she does in this kind of situation, she knows, because she doesn't want to get involved and "can't say no."

At the art bazaar the other girl had big signs with her name all over her booth and was handing out personal cards for her teaching. Patient was handing out the workshop brochures, but after a while added her name and an arrow. *I point out her guilt feelings.* Patient sold four fifths of her work. Her booth was set up near a nationally known artist whose work is beautiful and subtle. She could hardly exhibit her work, feeling it was inferior to his, but she thought that people would like her work because it was "more feminine." She went over to his booth and was going to buy a piece of his work but decided against it. *Why?* It would be embarrassing if she had it in her house and people praised it, thinking it was hers—she wouldn't know what to say. "When I'm ready, I'll do some work like that myself. I guess all artists feel that way." She laughs and says that she just wants her own work around.

She had seen a girl friend named Peg at the show. When Peg had been hesitant in separating from her husband, patient had offered to room with her, feeling this was the extra push she needed. It proved to be so, and then patient found that Peg was not the right roommate for her. They were very tense with each other but patient did not have the courage to tell Peg this, feeling that she had to keep her promise. *I question whether patient should keep this kind of promise made on an unsound basis, but rather should be able to be direct about it.* She knows this—"can never say no in this kind of situation." Several times when patient had a date and met Peg she had been "just darling" to patient's date and patient resented this. She wonders whether she is right and *I say that it is universally accepted that one should not play up to someone else's date.* Patient had felt that they could never live together, particularly because of this trait. Peg is going to a psychiatrist and talks about it to everybody she meets. This situation came up last week and patient felt that Peg was showing off and not doing the right thing. *I agree when she describes the situation.*

Peg is supposed to be in love with one man and is dating four. "I don't know what this has to do with me. Yes, I do, it has a lot to do with me." She does not see how Peg can be in love and still date four men—"Isn't that right?" *I agree.* Patient comments that Peg must really not be involved with this man, and *I agree.* Patient wonders if you can ever date a number of men. *I say that when you are looking and not involved with one man it often happens.* Patient tells me this has been happening to her recently. She has gone through long periods with few dates but right now she has so many dates she is turning them down simply because she wants some time at home and "I'm so busy getting ready to go away." *I ask if she thinks it is because she is going away*. "I know what you mean—that I'm letting this happen because I'll be going away and I won't have to get involved. That could be me all right, but it seems that there are other circumstances too." Patient describes two of these and then tells me that she had been "aggressive" about telling her friend who had introduced her to a foreign boy that she would like to see him again at a party. *I say this is all right*. "I think you're helping me. I don't know just why, but I feel different." *I say that she is making progress in treatment*. When I end the interview, patient says, "and next week will be the last time I'll see you until September." Patient was carrying a purse for the first time today.

COMMENTS ON TENTH SESSION: The patient states that she is very busy and indicates some anxiety regarding the separation during the vacation period. The therapist, recognizing this, reassures the patient concerning continuation in September. She then goes on to talk about her guilt feelings which implicitly indicate hostility to her friend. The therapist condones her competitive feelings and attempts to allay her guilt.

The patient tells about her competitiveness with another girl, and her consideration that the feminine attitude is one of altruistic surrender which she attempts to deny. For her there is no subtlety in competition. When competition seemed to arise with Peg, the patient avoided the issue and went away. The patient does not seem to be deeply involved and actually plays with numbers of men, bragging that she has so many dates. Her friend Peg is a caricature of herself. The patient either retreats or becomes aggressive.

In discussing her sense of feeling different since her therapy began, the patient seems to be coming closer to her feelings. Although her anxiety is lessening and she is getting more involved in treatment, she is also using the therapist as a means of determining and prescribing roles, and is constantly seeking the therapist's permission and approval. The therapist takes this assigned role, indicating frequently "that it is all right," and does not point out the implicit roles at this time, maintaining the transaction at the current level.

Anxiety seems to be increasing slightly, but at this level of the transaction it is still compatible with revealing information as complementarity is continued. The passivity evidenced by the therapist indicates that the patient is still in control of the rate of her own movement. In addition, in the relationship with the therapist there is still some testing of her trustfulness. Frequently implicit in the transaction—especially because the therapist is a woman—is the statement about her relationship to substitute objects, but the patient apparently gets the connection between these and the therapist. There seems to be a better way of living and a more competitive attitude, but this improvement would hardly be permanent if further therapy were not obtained. We question what the summer experiences will bring and wonder if a blowup of her apparent stability will occur.

Eleventh Session

PATIENT WAS UNUSUALLY PROMPT and began the interview by telling me that she is on time only for important things like doctor's appointments and visits here—in other words, "for people superior to me." *I question if this is how she really feels,* and she laughs somewhat sheepishly. She is often not on time for ordinary things, like finishing some housework before going to work one day last week. "It didn't really matter, but I usually try to be on time." She was late last time here, actually less than five minutes late. *I question what she thinks this means.* Patient says that she really had wanted to be on time, and laughs somewhat sheepishly.

She has heard from Kay to the effect that Paul is "happy" and has gone into treatment. Kay wrote that she had seen little of Paul because his roommate has become attracted to her and Kay does not want to encourage him because he isn't the kind of man she could love. Kay also wrote that Mary, with whom Paul had once been involved, has passed through town and Paul had not been interested in her although she had tried to get their romance going again. Patient states that she got a thrill out of knowing this. Mary isn't any competition for her. *Why?* When she saw Mary, she knew that she wasn't good-looking enough to compete for Paul. She does feel sorry for her, though. *Why?* Because Paul has never let Mary know where she stands with him. He likes to have lots of women interested in him. Patient then states, "Here I am talking about Paul again," and laughs. *I wonder why.* She thinks that the letter brought it up, but she really didn't feel involved. She adds, "I'm still trying to find a reaction for you." *I question this,* and patient asks what I think. I state that she is *really thinking about herself and her part in this.* Patient asks, "Do you think it has to do with me?" and *I state that I do.* Patient says that she did feel a tingle of anxiety when she saw Mary's name and was relieved that her plan hadn't worked.

Paul is nice and she has many good memories of him. Last week she was strolling with a man along the lake, and they had taken their shoes off and were walking in the water because it was such a warm day. A Negro child came up to talk with them about the coldness of the water, and her date disagreed, saying that he had been swimming in it for a month. It spoiled the mood of the moment. Paul was never like that. She describes a similar incident with him which was "just wonderful." She could always count on him to respond to her mood and feelings. Don't I think this is important?

I say that patient has told me of many times where she could not count on Paul, when he let her down. She asks, "But isn't that because Paul is neurotic? Does it have to do with me too?" *I state that it does, that her feelings about herself are involved.*

Patient says she thinks that Paul combines the worst traits of her brother and father. When she gets mad, she feels about him the way she used to feel about her brother—wanting to hit him—or her father. It made her physically sick the first few times she broke up with Paul. The first time was when she was living with her father and had been going with Paul only a short time. She had been very upset about living with her father and wanted to leave. Her father met Paul at the door and said, "Young man, what are your intentions and stay away until you say." Paul had said, "Will do," and left. "My father is like that, he never wants any man to like me." It was not until she met Paul again on the street that they went together again, but he would make her very angry. One time when she broke up with him, she went to a party with another man. Paul, who was not invited, crashed the party, got drunk, took off all his clothes and put a towel around himself. Later she abandoned her date and left the party with him. She had felt ashamed of the way he was acting and actually couldn't believe it when he showed up at the party. Even though she left the party with him and must have known he came for her, she really felt that she had nothing to do with it. It wasn't until a long time afterward she realized that he had come to the party because of her. This is a reaction she often has. *I say that she loses the feeling of being involved then.*

After they had made up, following another separation, she had gone as Paul's date to another party. She told him she would go only on condition that he would take her home, and he promised. They arrived separately. At the party he went into the bathroom with another girl and stayed and stayed. Patient could not bear it and hid when they came out. Everybody thought she was mad for Paul and that he didn't care for her. It was very different when they were alone. After the party Paul took patient home, announcing in front of everybody, "Well, I'll take you home now." They were walking along the street and patient paused to look in a window, but Paul walked on, ignoring her wish to stop. She got angry and screamed at him. He kept walking. She ran after him and, when she got close, took her shoes off and threw them at him. She wanted to hit him and hit him and pound him. *I ask if she had hit him.* "No, I missed. I always miss when I throw something when I'm angry." She had begun to laugh in a strange way and limped around trying to find her shoes in the gutter. Patient then asks me what made her so mad when Paul walked away from her. *I said it was the humiliation and shame she had felt at the party that had finally burst out, especially when he didn't follow her wishes when they were alone.* Patient says she really lost control then. *I ask if it had frightened her to lose control then and she said that it had.*

She had been living at her mother's house then and Paul had called her to say that he was coming over. She was running around the apartment and had drunk a lot of liquor. "You know I never drink unless it is to bolster me up at a party." She had the feeling while she was waiting for him that she was in a movie. *I ask if she had felt phony.* "Yes—like I was in a play and it wasn't happening to me. I couldn't believe it. Why does this happen to me?" *I tell her that it is because of her anger that she is afraid of.*

"I used to feel angry at my father all the time when I was living with him. We used to fight all the time and he was always mad and nasty to me." He used to criticize her housekeeping, the way she did things, the men she saw. "I used to wish he would die. I would think of him laid out in a coffin." *As if your thoughts had magic power?* "Yes, I was so guilty I couldn't stand it. You know my father has two nice children and can't enjoy either of them. I thought of him as lonely and desperate, but you know that isn't true because he married that woman." She is feeling emotional about this. *I tell her this is not true, that she has many feelings about it which she has hidden from herself and should understand.*

"You know I couldn't face telling my father why I was leaving him. I went to his office to see him. I could never talk to him at home because we would just fight and argue, and I always went to his office when I had to talk to him. I told him a trumped-up story about why I was leaving. But he said I was leaving because I couldn't get along with him. I felt so guilty I couldn't stand it. Then he told me he loved me very much. It's the only time in my life he ever told me he loved me and I just couldn't stand it. I knew I had to leave." When patient pauses and looks at me, *I ask if she had been able to cry about it.* Yes, she had cried a lot afterwards.

The time is drawing to a close and patient asks whether she can tell me one thing more, that she will hurry. She had turned to Paul when she left her father and told him all of this, and he had not reacted at all. On the other hand, when Paul's cousin Ruth got into difficulty, he was very upset about it. Ruth was beaten and knocked down. Her father never did this "but he used to slap me when he was mad." Isn't it strange that he got so upset about Ruth? *I told her that it was the other way around—that he should have been able to feel for her too when she was upset.*

"You know it's my pride that keeps me going back to Paul—I just won't give up. Don't you think so?" *I tell her that her pride is involved, but it is more than that, other feelings are involved too.* Patient says that she needs to understand a lot more. I agree and say we will work on it more.

"Do you feel I really love Paul?" *I tell her I do not feel that she does, but that I want her to feel convinced of this herself before she decides.* Patient very warmly wishes me a nice summer.

COMMENTS ON ELEVENTH SESSION: This interview opens with a statement of ambivalence indicating both the importance of therapy and a denial and a wish to avoid it. There is every indication that she intends to take flight to Paul or some similar figure. More clearly than ever before Paul is revealed as her image of father and brother about whom she complains. But these are fascinating, stimulating figures: uncertain, sadistic, rejecting, and seductive. All of them produce anxiety and stimulating, exciting reactions in her. Life is dull without this sort of sado-masochistic partner. Love, fear, and hate seem inseparably bound, yet she begins to detail her role confusions and need for further help.

What will happen during the summer? Like the last few moments of a soap opera we ask: Will the patient return to Paul? Will the patient find some female substitute for the therapist? Will she return for treatment? The patient will probably return because her transactions with the therapist have been fairly stable with anxiety kept at an optimal level. Explicit roles have been maintained, and the patient has slowly grasped that her confused and disturbed life is less related to reality than to images of past transactions.

Twelfth Session

AFTER THE PATIENT RETURNS she asks me if I had enjoyed my vacation. Patient immediately tells me that she missed me but had been able to "keep herself in check" all summer because she knew she would return to see me and have more treatment. Her manner is childish, bright-eyed, rather brittle, and conveys a strong attachment to me. I am surprised at the openness of this statement and the lack of some initial reserve in relating to me again and absence of hostility because of the separation. *I comment that she wants to return.* She tells me that she does; she had been keeping lists and controlling her feelings all summer. She had been able to do this because she knew she would return to treatment. "I have so many questions I want answers for and so much I want to tell you." *I say that she had missed seeing me,* and there was a hint of tears as she said yes. *I ask if she felt she had to control her thoughts.* With a quick sigh, she says that she didn't know if they were normal or not. Patient conveys to me that she wants to recite her story at this point, to let me know what happened to her.

In her characteristic fashion the patient began to describe her summer at camp. She starts out with a summary statement that in general things had gone well for her; for the first time at camp she had let herself get involved (giving me a significant look—referring to my earlier interpretation of her fear of involvement) with a boy, but "I goofed." She does not know why this happened and then describes the details. She was attracted to a boy named Bob who is several years younger than she. There was a nineteen-year-old girl named Alice whom she never liked in previous summers. The patient describes in detail a triangular situation involving Bob, Alice, and herself. Alice was aggressive with Bob, openly seductive, and he dated her, while talking to patient as a confidante. There were several brief shifts in this, but each time patient retired because she did not "wish to compete." *When I point out her hostility which she has denied in describing Alice and her behavior,* she freezes up immediately and shows a strange detached air. *I point out that she is afraid of her feelings and has reacted by being detached from the situation.* Patient accepts this rather dutifully —*which I point out*—and then asks for my opinion of Alice's behavior. *I say that it sounds outrageous, that Alice was her rival for Bob, and she must be angry about how it went.* With noticeable relief, she agrees. Her mother used to tell her that every woman was a rival when it came to a man. *I ask if she believes this. I point out that she has said yes, but sounds hesitant.* She tells me about Irene, a girl friend at camp. Irene was jealous and made patient feel like a heel whenever she did not include her. She kept trying not to do this but could not stop. On one occasion she included Irene and made it a general party with Bob instead of a date; when he wanted to drive her home at the end of the season, she refused because she knew Irene, who has a car too, would look at her reproachfully and cry. *I interpret that patient had to be submissive to women because of her fear of hurting them,* both her rival Alice or her possessive girl friend Irene. Patient gives me a free and hostile description of Bob's leave-taking from camp with Alice, who wore a very low-cut dress and kept leaning over to show her bosom. Patient knew she should be competing but remained frozen on the sidelines.

She then talks of her family. Sometimes she used to feel like the saddest child in the world because her parents were separated and she had "no real home." Other times she would feel, "Isn't it wonderful that mummy and I are together and so happy because if daddy were here no one would be happy?" She could feel sorry for herself at times and neither one was actually the whole truth. When she came back her friends paid her a lot of attention and she has been very busy socially.

I say that she was glad not to be lonely and felt relieved to have friends who sought her out when she came home. She agrees and tells me of three men who are dating her but do not even kiss her goodnight. She is surprised because she thinks men expect at least this much of a date. She is not physically attracted to any of them. While she was at camp she wrote a letter to the foreign boy. She started out by saying that she was sorry to have waited so long to write, and it dawned on her after she mailed the letter that she had been at camp only three days. She denies any reaction beyond this, telling me that she had looked him up when she returned. When he seemed interested, she withdrew and now is no longer interested—in her characteristic fashion. She wonders what makes her like this. *I tell her that I cannot give her "the answer" in the way she seeks it; she will have to find her own answer.* She is silent and then tells me that her problem can be compared to an octopus—you have to kill the center of it because if you just cut off one of the tentacles it will still be there. *I say that she is afraid of hurting (others). Her main problem is her detachment from her own feelings and actions which she avoids because of her fears.* Patient appears relieved and tells me that she has been putting off getting prepared for this fall term at school, finds herself reading novels instead. She has been drifting, too, in her social relationships which are not really quite the gay paradise she has portrayed.

She apparently has preserved her dependent attachment for me by avoiding any situation which would involve her in competitive or hostile feelings with other women. Then comes the wish for gratification as the dependent good girl. *I interpret that she does not have to be submissive to women, and when she seeks further permissiveness from me I point out that she will have to seek her own answers.* She reveals her fear of engulfing me and appears more ready to deal with reality when I interpret her fear of hurting me.

COMMENTS ON TWELFTH SESSION: The patient enters the interview in a childish role, wanting the therapist to be pleased and approving of her keeping herself in check. Again the patient structures the interview, although she wants to talk freely, but she compulsively recites the details of what happened during the summer. She seems to be so narcissistically bound up in her summer's experence that she conveys no feeling regarding the separation from the therapist. In this portion of the interview the therapist uses a nondirective technique and encourages the patient to spill out what she wants to say, for she seems to need to talk very badly.

When the patient is reminded that her description of her girl friend's and her own competitive attitudes seems to point to hostility, the patient becomes detached, as if withdrawn from reality. The therapist makes a crucial error in this portion of the interview when she agrees with the patient that Alice's behavior sounds outrageous. It seems that the patient wanted to compete with Alice but was prevented by her own inhibitions. In her concern about Irene, she identifies with her and therefore is much more sympathetic to her problems. The patient does not permit herself to compete, is ashamed at her failure, and is angry at others who do compete. She still needs to be a pleasing girl and submissive to other women.

The patient herself makes the transition from the discussion of the rivalry with Alice to her own submissive role within the family. In this bit of reconstruction the mother and the patient were presented as not rivalrous as long as father was away. There was no man to create trouble between them, and the patient was very happy in her dependent role.

The patient indicates her need to get to the heart of the matter. She wants to know what makes her like this. It is at this point that perhaps she is more ready to know of her implicit hostile rivalry with women, but the therapist brings the patient back to the dependent role relationship which relieves the patient of her anxiety over her hostility and prevents the current transaction from progressing in this direction. Thus, the patient is encouraged in her role failures as a woman, and the therapist partially accepts her in this dependent position in the transaction until the expectations shift to open demands, which are then blocked.

The implicit role of the therapist in this transaction was as if she were telling the patient: "Don't be like Alice who is competitive and hostile." This protective attitude is in some part based on her own anxiety that the patient's ego is not yet strong enough because she becomes withdrawn and detached at being confronted with her own hostility. The patient, on the other hand, used the therapist as her conscience, and the therapist accedes to this ascribed role. Thus the patient is able to say: "Listen to me, how good I've been," and the therapist agrees with her.

Thirteenth Session

PATIENT TALKS about "something I forgot to ask you last week." She is wondering how to help her sister-in-law, who is not getting along in her marriage to her brother, is cold to him, and says that sexual relations hurt her. Patient suggests I might see her sister-in-law and offers one of her appointments for this. *When I inquire about this,* it develops that when patient had urged sister-in-law to get help she was not interested. Patient adds that sister-in-law's own sister behaved similarly in her marriage which ended in divorce and "it would just kill me if my poor brother got a divorce." She adds that if her mother were here she would straighten this out. When I ask how, she indicates that her mother has "a way" of being direct and doing things herself. Mother makes people do things. Patient had been unable to make any headway with sister-in-law, who talks very openly about the problem with no concern at all. *I say that it is possible to see sister-in-law here, but not by me because of possible complications to patient's own treatment. Everything she has told me leads me to believe that sister-in-law does not want help.* Patient agrees with this, and *I say that sister-in-law will have to feel under more pressure than this if she is to be helped.* Patient indicated that she could not possibly talk to her brother about it. She feels strange talking with him about intimate things. *I say that patient feels the need to play the role of rescuer in this situation and that I am disappointing her in saying that her sister-in-law must first see some need for help.* Patient talks about "my poor strait-laced brother" who really could not tolerate the idea that patient necked with her boy friends and who now has a wife who rejects him sexually.

Patient then tells me a good deal about the sexual adjustment between her brother and his wife, the wife's refusal to have intercourse for the first few months of marriage—"my poor brother must have been frantic"—his wife's affair with a lover which "almost killed him." *I tell her it is quite possible that the wife may have been sexually responsive to the lover and not to her husband.* Patient is getting more and more fascinated in the details of this, saying all the time that she "never would think of discussing it with my brother." *I say that she feels involved because of her attachment to her brother.* Patient says that she knows she has been "just terribly attracted" to him and couldn't even look him in the face or bring up the subject. She has been considerably freer in sexual expression than he has, but has always concealed it from him. She adds, "You know, I really shouldn't be involved in this and try to rescue my brother, but let them work it out." *I say that I agree, and she had discovered when she started to talk about it that she was quite involved in her own sexual attachment to her brother. This has disturbed her own ability to relate to men.*

Patient cannot imagine her brother being able to deal with this. In talking, she gained some recognition of this as his problem too, and tells me that this attitude of not trying to get help had been characteristic of him all his life. *I say that perhaps brother may become uncomfortable enough to bring up the problem openly with his wife as he needs to do.* Again she recognizes the degree of feeling she has and identifies it as a real problem.

At home they never dared talk about sexual matters with or in front of their father. "I could never go to him about anything like that. I wouldn't even go to him about something physical that was intimate."

Patient is blushing and showing strong feeling. *I say that she has sexual feelings about her father, too,* and patient agrees with much feeling. She begins to talk freely about this.

She cannot remember much about her father when she was little except that she was "just wild about him." Her parents separated when patient was five, six, or seven years old. Although she tries for some time, she cannot remember exact age. She used to pray every night that her mother and father would get remarried because she thought her father was lonely. *I said I thought she really prayed to have her father.* Patient says that her prayers got frantic when she discovered her father was going to remarry (she was five, six, or seven) and she felt that this was the last chance she would have to get her parents together again. Father did remarry—a "terrible wife" in contrast to present wife who is "good for him." All during this period of childhood she could never count on father visiting when he was supposed to, and she felt uncomfortable when with him. Only once did he praise her openly and she remembers this clearly. She, her brother, and her father were eating, and patient offered brother a choice of food on the serving plate before she chose her own portion. Father praised her for letting her brother come first. *I comment that patient must have felt her own wishes were not important to father, and that she could not have what she wanted.*

She agrees and says that she always avoided asking him for things because he made it so clear that he did not want to give to her. On one occasion she made up her mind to ask him for something. She had been invited to a dance in Michigan and her mother had no money to buy a formal dress. She asked her father, who refused, putting it on the basis that she should not be permitted to go to the dance. She was about eighteen at the time. *I say that her problem with her father was more intense when she began being interested in boys.* She agrees and tells in some detail the extent to which father was openly disapproving of this. Also, father would never kiss her although he expected her to kiss him. He would bite her on the cheek, rub his beard on her face, or pinch her. She always felt funny about it. Father never gave her birthday or Christmas gifts, but he always expected to be remembered, even though he made a pretense of not caring. She feels sorry for him and is always trying to figure out the right thing to do or say to him. *I point out that she sees herself as meeting his needs, giving to him, that this is part of the attachment which has bound her to him. In addition, she hasn't been able to count on him because of his own disturbance.* Patient says she is very conscious of her father when she is with him, acutely aware of how he is feeling, of what he says or does. She avoids seeing him much, but usually calls him every week. She feels it is something she must do, although nobody makes her and nobody seems to care. She talks again of her childhood feelings of wishing father were dead, and *I point out that this arose because of her feelings of both attachment and deprivation which she had had no chance to work out.*

Patient begins telling me of her mastoid operation when she was about twelve. She was sick and father came to mother's home and had been treating her for what he said was an upset stomach. She adds, "My father's a good doctor, but not for the family." After several days with no improvement, mother took her to the receiving ward of a hospital, where they admitted her at once and called an ear specialist who said she was in need of an immediate mastoid operation. Father wanted a consultation first and brought in an elderly ear specialist, whose hands trembled so that he could hardly examine her ear. After he too said patient needed the operation, father confronted her, "Well, which specialist will you choose?" She answered, "The other one." She told me that she knew that her father was terribly hurt by this, but she just could not let the old man operate on her. Father walked out and later blamed her fifty-per-cent hearing-loss in this ear on the fact that she chose the other doctor. *I told her that no twelve-year-old should be put in this position; she had needed to be helped and protected at this point.* She had felt she couldn't possibly let this man operate because of the way he fumbled so. *I told her that if she did have to choose for herself and her own welfare this was the right thing to have done.* Patient again mentions that she doesn't know what she would do if she had something "intimate" wrong with her; she doesn't think she could go to her father or even have him look at her. *I tell her that it would be advisable for her to see someone else if this ever occurred, but I think it is really further evidence of her confused attachment to her father.*

COMMENTS ON THIRTEENTH SESSION: When the patient talked at great length about her sister-in-law's troubles, she was explicitly talking about her own feelings regarding her brother. It is as if she denied her own problems of sexual inhibition and talked about her sister-in-law's problems instead in order to test out the therapist's reaction. She implies that the therapist should let her go and take her sister-in-law for treatment instead, thereby testing the reaction of the therapist to her role as a sexual woman.

It is interesting that this discussion comes immediately after the last session, in which she alluded to repressed sexual fantasies about her father. Here she would like to take her sister-in-law's place in relation to her brother. The patient openly admits that she was "just terribly attracted" to her brother and could not discuss any dangerous sexual matters with him. Some implication that the brother and the father are linked together in the patient's mind is indicated by her switching to her intense feelings for the father. The patient also discusses her image of the male as being more important than the female; the female is expected to serve the male.

The patient discloses protective devices against her feelings toward her father in the anecdote about her operation. Her hostile wishes toward her father are attempts to get him away so that she would not be sexually tempted.

The implicit communications seem to flow satisfactorily and bring the patient closer to recognition of her sexual feelings toward the forbidden brother and father. There are some errors in technique, one of which should be emphasized. The therapist is still alerted to the danger of permitting the patient to become anxious. She, therefore, interjects reassuring remarks, often by agreeing with the patient and returning to her in other words the substance of what she had previously recounted. This might be called a somewhat delaying form of nondirective therapy. It tends to reduce the tension in the interview and to delay the patient's recognition of her implicit roles. It is pointed out that if any reassurance need be given to allay anxiety it should be in connection with the interpretation by the therapist of the patient's implicit role. The therapist would have done better if the patient had been reassured that her sexual feelings toward brother and father, which seem to underlie both her positive and negative attitudes to them, are ubiquitous and to be found in most girls at one time in their lives. This brings to consciousness the conflictual attitudes toward men at the same time as it makes them more acceptable. This technique generally is a more anxiety-allaying procedure than the repetition of the explicit role with understanding and sympathy.

Fourteenth Session

IN SPITE OF A BAD COLD and stuffed nose, the patient states that she is getting lots of rest and is not upset. She begins to talk generally about the first weeks of school, the schedule, the poise and sureness of many of the children, the teachers' meetings, etc., stating all the time that she is not upset. *I tell her that it probably does upset her and we should try to understand why.*

She tells me first of an incident that happened at a teachers' meeting. One of the students was called in to discuss an activity program. He spoke with great ease, in fact conducted the meeting, calling on teachers to make comments or contribute ideas. She thought of her complete inability to do this sort of thing when she was a child. In fact, just last summer she was able for the first time to make announcements without severe discomfort and she had been pleased with her progress.

I interpret her envy of the ease with which the boy had done this. With some hesitation she agrees.

She had felt that she would start off differently in her new job. She has felt it necessary for all the children to like her and that it was a personal defeat if a child did not like her. She had decided: "If they give to me, I'll give to them." *When I ask more about this,* she says that if the children treat her right she will treat them right. She has them for only 45 minutes at a time and started out with a firm hand, telling the children they would get out of the class what they would put into it. She provided projects and noted the casualness with which the children accepted or rejected them. *I say that it made her angry because the children did not appreciate what she had given them and did not give to her in return.* She replies with much detail on how she has to be firm, provide work for them, and maintain discipline. *I point out that she feels guilty because she is angry at their responses and is feeling that she has to justify her handling of the children.* She says she wants to be fair, etc., and *I tell her it is all right to be angry and want to swat children.*

She tells me of one boy who created a general disturbance in class and refused to work on a project; she spoke to him after class and told him not to return unless he intended to work. She took a dislike to this child, which was a rare feeling for her. *I reassure her that this is all right.* The child came back to her the next day and said he would work. He began boasting to her in exaggerated terms of all the projects he would do. She said she felt uneasy and sorry for him because he was promising things which were beyond his ability. He was boasting to get himself out of trouble with her, and she ended up feeling guilty.

I say this reminds me of her relationship with her father, who made boasts and promises to her he did not keep and she ended up feeling guilty. Her face lights up in recognition of this. Her voice, which had been hoarse, clears as she begins to talk further, and there are no more signs of the heavy respiratory difficulty of the first part of the interview.

Patient begins talking about her father and how she tried to make him happy and not expect anything from him. *I state that she really wants to take from her father.* She talks more of her father, of Paul, and of several other men in an anxious, guilty way and describes how she tried to satisfy each and deny her own needs. *I tell her that she believes men are weak and must not be taken from, that she must deny all her own wishes to get close to them.* Patient begins telling me of an incident that happened last week. She had gone to her father's office to get a polio shot and had been determined to ask him to visit her apartment afterward. In preparation she has cleaned the apartment thoroughly for two or three days—"he hates dirt." Father has never been to her apartment. Even though she has invited him many times, he has always refused to come. In spite of all her preparations, she really expected a refusal. *I say it sounds as if she felt father ought to refuse and she should not let father get close to her.* She tells me that much to her surprise he accepted her invitation. Furthermore, he was "nice," by which she means that he did not attack her or criticize her housekeeping or apartment as she had expected. He sat talking with her in a pleasant and friendly way, making her feel uncomfortable, at a loss to know what to do or say. *I say she felt that she shouldn't get close to him, that she should protect herself from such a wish.* She asks me why she does this. *I tell her it is because of her belief that she will hurt men or damage men if she takes from them or gets close to them.* Patient comments that all the men she has ever been close to have been weak and she has had to give to them. *I tell her that she has sought this out herself and set up her relationships with men so that she avoids getting really close to them.*

She tells me that it was different with her mother. She could get close to her and take from her—used to "unload" and tell her everything. She felt that mother was strong and could take it. Her mother would take over her worries and figure them out for her. Mother told her once, "You unload your problems on me, and then I lose sleep while you go happily on your way." *I ask how this made her feel.* After considerable circumlocution and further description, she is able to say that it made her feel "small" and depreciated. *I say that she feels she can't be given to freely but must take by force from a woman who gives grudgingly and takes over completely.*

Patient tells me, apologizing that it is silly, that her whole family had completely forgotten her birthday which was last Sunday. *I tell her that it is all right to feel upset about this* when she continues to protest about it being silly and she finally accepts it. *I say that it is all right to need to be loved and remembered and to get angry when you are forgotten.*

Patient did not hear from her father on her birthday. He never remembers, and she knew that he wouldn't, but she can't stop hoping that he just might remember. *I say that she is angry because he forgot, but is afraid to express it because she believes it would hurt him to do so.*

She tells how she waited all day for her mother to telephone her as she usually does. After all it wouldn't hurt her mother to telephone her. She had resisted an impulse to sit down and write an angry letter to her mother, telling her off for forgetting. *I tell her that she feels her mother only gives to her because she is weak and she wants to be given to for herself.*

Her brother forgot the birthday, too. She went to their house for dinner and, after debating with herself about whether or not she should do it, told them it was her birthday. They had not remembered and were surprised.

Patient begins talking about how she always tries to be fair: to her family, who are absorbed in other things; in her job; and to her school children. *I point out that she feels guilty because she has had some angry feelings and some wishes to take things for herself.* "But how can I be guilty if I always weigh these things and try to figure out the right answers?" *I tell her that she is holding court hearings with herself because she feels her wishes are sinful and wrong. She does not have to do this.*

COMMENTS ON FOURTEENTH SESSION: The therapist immediately recognizes that beneath the patient's explicit statements of confidence about her teaching there was considerable anxiety. The patient admits that she felt incompetent and ill at ease and envied the boy who could do so well. She had decided to act a different role and not have to be a sweet child liked by everyone. She was going to give only to those who gave to her. Nevertheless, she could not follow her decision. In relating the story of the boy who promised too much and boasted to get himself out of trouble, she was really telling her own problem.

The therapist erred, however, in connecting this behavior pattern at this point with her relationship to her father. The patient's anxiety cleared because the therapist shifted the focus. Here we see that the clearing of anxiety is no indication of the significance of an interpretation. It may give the patient a sense of relief because she becomes aware that the therapist is not going to touch on a sensitive spot, her own wish to be aggressive like a boastful child.

In the following stream of associations the therapist concentrates on the patient's relationship to her father, which the therapist herself had suggested. It was here that the transactional process should have been emphasized in that the patient could have been aware of her demands from the mother and her feeling of being rejected. This, however, was too closely related to the patient's anxiety, which the therapist apparently wanted to avoid. In the transactional process one does not need to stick closely to statements about one or another of the parents because either father or mother can be represented in the patient's associations to the current transaction with the therapist, whatever the sex might be.

The therapist's statements regarding the patient's fear of hurting men seems to be out of context. However, the patient then moves on to talk about her mother and her use of her mother for her dependent needs. This crops up again in another context and exposes her anger at the rejection of the mother, which could have been discussed in the context of the current transaction. In the last portion of the interview, the therapist's interpretation of the patient's guilty feelings was misunderstood, for the patient responds as if the therapist were talking about real guilt rather than irrational guilty feelings and she rightfully says, "How can I be guilty if I always try to find out the right answer?" This problem of guilt feelings will require further work in future interviews. The patient apparently always attempts to find someone who will give her satisfaction for her emotional needs and in her past life has sought out the father. She has insured that she will be accepted and given support by acting the role of the good and meek child and often by reversal of roles. In this process she does for others as she wishes them to do for her. Thus she is able to avoid insight into the great feeling of frustration she has developed in relation to an unsatisfactory dependence on her mother.

Fifteenth Session

PATIENT TELLS ME she had felt resentful when she left last week. *When I inquire what about,* she says, "Am I supposed to believe what you say whether I agree or not?" *I indicate that she will believe only what clicks for her anyway and she should tell how she feels so we can understand further.* With a good deal of circumlocution, patient says that she knows she felt hostile but she didn't feel guilty about anything, particularly about being hostile. She is finding it hard to speak, is barely able to look at me from time to time, and is quite rambling and unclear in her comments. *I ask, "Is it because I said you felt guilty that you felt hostile toward me?"* Patient answers, "Yes," looking at me directly. *I say that she had felt I was pointing the finger at her, accusing her of something.* She agrees and apparently is testing my acceptance of her "criticism" and appears somewhat surprised that I discuss it openly.

She "plunges in" to say that she doesn't know if she's getting anywhere. She has so many questions, and at first she had thought she would ask questions and I would give answers. Now she sees it differently. She is beginning to wonder if there is more to this than she thought. *I ask if some of it is getting under her skin,* and she answers "Maybe I'm not as nice as I thought." She used to know just what she wanted to talk about but is feeling unsure. For example: Was her cold last week psychosomatic or not? *I say that she feels it is like magic, that she discovered there were some aspects to the cold she didn't understand and which weren't under her control.* She said, "Yes."

She wants to tell me today about her menstrual period. She had pain today which is unusual for her and doesn't know if it has anything to do with treatment or whether it is a problem for a regular medical doctor. *I tell her she is bringing this up for the first time after she had been talking for two interviews about her father and how she was thinking about going to him with intimate things.* She catches her breath in response and begins to describe her period. She woke up very depressed this morning. This happens to her at the beginning of some periods but not always. She does not keep track of her cycles or know when to expect them except when she has physical signs. "That's because I don't like it." This morning she went back to bed and the period began about an hour later. She had bad cramps, cannot describe them except to hold her abdomen when I ask. After school (which lets out early on Friday) she went home, took some medication, fell asleep, and felt better. She always feels better when she takes a nap if she has a headache or cramps. *I ask her if she suspected there was an emotional basis for her cramps.* She agrees with hesitation and again states that she does not like to find this out about herself.

"And speaking of intimate things," she tells me about a sore on her back just above the buttocks on the end of the spine, which is often open and raw and itches badly at times. She has been thinking of asking father about this. There are two little cystic places full of water. It always seems that when there is something wrong with her it is intimate. She perspires profusely between her legs. Patient then tells me that she is afraid she has gonorrhea. Last year she had intercourse with Paul and he found out the next day that he had gonorrhea and told her. He had suspected it before, but had not informed her. She was really mad about it, but he has done other beastly things to her like that. They have never used contraceptives. She has thought of getting a diaphragm, but wonders if it would stay in if you were sexually active. She went to a gynecologist in Chicago who told her she did not have gonorrhea. She went back to him four months later, told him directly of the contact, and he again told her that she did not have gonorrhea. *When I ask about a smear, she remembers having one taken but is not sure if she had a second.* She has no discharge or pain other than occasional menstrual pains. She did not feel sure that she did not have gonorrhea. *I tell her that from her description it is impossible for me to determine whether it had been adequately determined physically. I do know that she is considerably worried about it, and that many of these symptoms can be on an emotional basis.* Patient asks me if she could ask a doctor directly if the smear shows gonorrhea, and I tell her that she could. When she asks, *I tell her that it is possible for her not to have contracted gonorrhea.*

She describes Paul's penis at that time—red, sore, and discharging pus. She still doesn't know whether she loves him. "You said I would have lots of feelings about it I can't understand and I don't see that I have. I feel like I came out on top when I left him, because for once I wasn't doing what he wanted." *I said that she felt the only way to win an argument with him was to leave him.* Yes, and she hopes he remembers her as the most important person in his life. She knows that he is the most important person in her life. Do I think she loves him? *I said that her feelings are complex, being attracted to him and repelled by him, wanting to help him and wanting to hurt him.*

Patient tells me that something like that happened to her, too, with a man last week. He had called her at school for a date. She had felt flustered by being called to the principal's office, but had agreed to the date. They went walking, and the man had tried to hold her hand. She had thought she really didn't know him well enough and besides she didn't know whether she wanted him to hold her hand. Yet she kept smiling at him. *I asked if she felt her smile was strange.* Yes, because it wasn't how she felt—actually she was angry. Then she asked him up to her apartment. She knew how this might be taken by him, and really didn't want him to come. She couldn't stand it if he kissed her, yet she found herself smiling and being nice to him. *I said that maybe she had wanted this,* and patient denied it flatly. In the apartment he came and sat on the arm of her chair. She felt revulsion inside, but smiled and asked him to leave, always smiling. She opened the door and was ahead of him all the way out to the elevator, actually forcing him out. He asked for her telephone number which she gave him and, still smiling, said goodnight. I said that maybe she had wanted him to stay. No, she is sure she didn't. He hadn't called her and she has been hoping he would all week so she could refuse him and show him she came out on top in the encounter. *I say she is telling me that she really wanted to hurt him.* Yes, and she has begun to realize, too, how often she smiles when she does not mean it.

COMMENTS ON FIFTEENTH SESSION: The patient opens the interview by expressing some resentment, particularly over the therapist's interpretation about guilt feelings. She cannot accept the concept of guilt because she has spent her life being a nice and good girl and the therapist's meaning is not clear to the patient. The therapist recognizes that the patient cannot look at her directly because she feels guilty about her anger. The patient acts the role of a guilty person because she is angry at someone on whom she is dependent. But she has some justification, and here the therapist should have brought to the patient a clarification of the difference between guilt feelings and actual guilt. In many situations the patient acts out roles which are contrived to evoke her own guilt responses and thereby avoids knowledge of the primary guilty feelings which are derived from past experiences. Thus, in the first part of the interview the therapist missed an opportunity to bring into consciousness the implicit guilt feelings that were part of the transactional process.

The patient spontaneously explains to the therapist that she thought her role was to ask questions and to receive answers. That means to be dependent on the therapist and be fed information. Here again we see her frustration in the dependent role, and, although she does not respond with angry feelings about her frustration, she attributes affects which are not conscious to herself as bad in her phrase, "Maybe I'm not as nice as I thought."

In a transition phase she talks about her menstrual pain which leads her back to a discussion of her father and her interest in his advising her about intimate things. She divulges more of the intimate aspects of her life and discusses some of her sexual problems. Here again the therapist became dubious about the correctness of the gynecologist's diagnosis and suggested another examination. The patient's phobic attitude seems to be a defense against the *desire* to be infected, and the therapist deals only with the *fear* of infection. When we hear the description of Paul's condition, despite which she accepted intercourse, we have a good example of the patient's persistent attempt to get hurt and to suffer as punishment for guilt feelings of which she is not aware.

Her story of the man she brought up to her apartment and practically invited to attack her, although she says she did not want him to remain, indicates how she really wanted to hurt and be hurt. This role pattern appears over and over again in many anecdotes of past behavior. When the therapist interprets that the patient wanted to hurt the man, she is dealing with only one facet of the patient's several implicit roles. In this transactional process, opportunities for presenting the implicit roles discernible in the patient's verbalizations are overlooked in favor of a more literal interpretation of her explicit behavior.

We might diagram the dynamics at present in the following way. For some unknown reason, about which we do not speculate now, the patient has many guilty feelings. These push her into role behavior characteristic throughout her past life, and currently, in which she prostrates herself and practically pleads for some kind of suffering. These demands are met: she receives punishment and complains bitterly. But the reciprocal relationship between acting out and punishment maintains an equilibrium which avoids her insight into the implicit guilty feelings and their source. The therapist's focus, which was adequately suggested by the patient in the first paragraph, should not have been interpretations of the explicit behavior which created guilt and the need for punishment but, instead, should have been focused on uncovering the inner sense of guilt unrelated to current behavior situations. It is the guilty feelings which are related to some antecedent cause that must be made explicit. On them has been built a lifelong pattern of need for suffering, acting out, punishment, and regressive childlike behavior.

8

The Third Phase of Therapy

Sixteenth Session

PATIENT TELLS ME that she "wants to talk about the foreign boy to-day." Until last week she felt neutral toward him; then she began to feel attracted to him. He invited her to a dinner party at his apartment this coming Saturday. She always has trouble dressing up for a party or a social event. Last week she was invited to a wedding and knew she should dress up for it. She has a black velvet suit of a dressy type which she made some time ago. There have been many times when she should have worn it, but she let it hang in the closet waiting for "just the right occasion." For the wedding she forced herself to wear it, adding attractive white accessories, and the wedding party went off all right. On the way back she dropped in on the foreign boy, who lived in her building. They were talking generally and patient became aware of disappointment that he had not remarked on her appearance. She asked him how he thought she looked and he made an offhand crack in reply. She was angry, and said "Oh, you're arrogant." He said he hoped not, took her remark seriously, and talked to her sincerely. She then goes into an involved discussion that she was "not nice," she had called him arrogant, she hadn't made him happy. She feels that you should say only nice things because the world is a bad enough place as it is. *I question her directly as to why it is not nice. Why can't she tell him what she feels?*

Patient says he made remarks just like Paul did, and she lashed back. *I point out that it had ended differently and seems different from her*

194

*relationship to Paul. When she was frank in her feelings, he had re-
sponded by being frank in return and it had ended very well.*

At the same time that she found herself suddenly angry at him, she
became conscious of being strongly attracted to him sexually. *I said
that when she had expressed her feelings directly she had been able to
get much closer to him. It didn't hurt either of them to get angry, in
fact it had cleared the air.* Patient tells me in a confiding way some of
the things she likes about him: the way he talks, his appearance, etc.
She had played a dirty trick on him, too. Another man, whom both had
known in the past, recently moved into the building. He said he was
going to have patient select the decorative scheme for his apartment.
She had met him on her trip and traveled with him for two weeks.
During that time she made all the decisions, after he stated openly
that he wanted her to do so. The three of them met in the foreign boy's
flat for a drink, and this man again asked her to make all his decorating
decisions. She "left him flat," said she was tired and went home to bed.
She feels she should not have left the boy to deal with it, and *I ask why
not since he had invited the man.* Patient comments that this man is
like the girl friend who "expects you to do everything for her." *I say
that patient is becoming more aware of her own needs and asserting
them.* Patient says, "Some day you and I will figure everything out."

I ask her what she wants from me today. "I want you to give me
courage so I can dress up and go to that dinner party and enjoy myself." *I say that I hope I can give her courage and that she will develop
more and more courage within herself as time goes on.* The remainder
of the interview is spent elaborating this point. She talks first about
clothes. She can wear or select new clothes for herself without particular difficulty, except party clothes associated with "getting dressed
up." *When I ask what would happen if she got dressed up and walked
into the party,* patient tells me that she likes to go early, get herself
seated before the other guests arrive, and appear "relaxed" although
tense inside. She seldom says anything. *I tell her that her emotional
energy is being channeled into appearing "relaxed" so she has little
left to talk or enjoy the party. Has she ever wanted to be the life of
the party?* Patient tells me that sometimes she has wanted to be, but felt
that she couldn't keep it up. She compares herself favorably with Alice,
the girl from camp. *I say that she had backed down from competing
with Alice. What would happen if she competed at the party?* Patient
laughs and is able to talk a little about being self-conscious that people
would be watching her. *I ask if she has feelings of exhibiting herself
in this situation.* Yes, and she laughs nervously. *I tell her that it is all
right to feel this way and she doesn't have to punish herself for it by
sitting in the corner.*

"Another thing, I often feel dumb when I talk." It evolves that she has feelings of her words being loaded with intense meaning. "But I might want to change my mind after I've said something, and not agree with what I said later." *I said that she could change her mind, that to voice an opinion at a party did not mean that she was to hold it for life.* Patient says, "I'm acting just like my aunt. I've told her for five years I like tomatoes now and yet every time she has me for dinner she says, 'Oh, you don't like tomatoes.'"

As patient goes out the door she turns and says, "You know I left a package behind at Field's today. That must be significant."

COMMENTS ON SIXTEENTH SESSION: The interview in general seemed to indicate a certain vagueness on the part of the patient, who seemed not to be able to concentrate on one subject. The therapist did not pin her down, and, therefore, we get a feeling of diffuseness.

The patient starts out the interview by relating that she is able with difficulty to get dressed up and to be attractive on various social occasions, but there is considerable difficulty in exposing her attractiveness or exhibiting her charm especially in situations where there is a single male individual. She had some sexual attraction to the foreign boy, which preceded her going up to his apartment. Otherwise she would not have gone there alone and dressed in her fancy clothes. The fact that he did not comment on her appearance or respond to her assigned role made her angry, which probably followed her sexual feelings rather than vice versa. It was after the air cleared, when they were able to communicate with one another, that she noticed her sexual feelings. But, correspondingly, she withdrew in the presence of another man, whom she left to talk with her boy friend, as if in revenge or with an implicit attitude that "well, the men have each other, I'll withdraw."

When the patient asks the therapist for dependent gratification in the sense that they will figure things out together, the therapist then introduces the subject of her needs and obtains a response which is a frank and open statement of a request for courage. Here the patient assigns a role to the therapist, and the therapist assumes complementarity and accepts the role by offering her courage which does not further their therapeutic process. It removes tension and does not contain any urging toward understanding of the meaning of the current transaction, nor is there any pressure to assume a different role at a higher level of integration. One could have better handled the situation by asking the patient to consider the reasons why she needs courage from others and why she lacks so much within herself. The therapist became very much like the mother in the sense that she is used by the patient for solving her troubles but then goes on her own way, never changing.

Apparently the patient is extremely frightened of her own sexual exhibitionistic tendencies and reacts with inhibition, becoming disturbed and running away from the situation, or bringing disaster on herself. Then through the masochistic suffering she is justified in playing the role of the little child asking for dependent care. At other times, when she boasted that she was better than Alice, for example, she overcompensates and acts as if she were very competent and competitive. Actually, she was asking for permission to free herself of her inhibitions and not be afraid. This is what she meant when she pleaded for courage. When she received the courage, she ended the interview by telling the therapist that she recognized some inconsistency in herself. Her last sentence—about the significant leaving of a package behind— should alert one to the possibility that she may act out some of her sexual fantasies. We again observe the old theme that she is not a nice girl and somehow or other tries to prove it.

Seventeenth Session

PATIENT, WHO APPEARS RATHER SUBDUED, says that she has a lot to relate and tells me about her visit to father's office this week. She "happened to be in the neighborhood" and dropped in to see her father. Again he really talked, telling her that she looked tired and was working too hard. Patient indicates to me that she knows this is only part of the reason she is tired. Currently, in addition to teaching school, she is teaching art two nights a week for a ten-week fall session. When her father asked her why she was teaching, she told him that she planned to buy a winter coat with the earnings. Father offered to buy her the coat. She turned him down. "I didn't go there for a touch," but he repeated his offer. Patient told him that she could buy it for herself. "But you know, daddy, I was very hurt when you forgot my birthday." Father had told her, "You know I'm like that about birthdays," and then told her that he wanted to give her the coat as a birthday present, and urged her to start looking. Patient had told him that she wanted a nice coat and he urged her to look. Patient will let him know when she finds a coat and he will pay for it.

Patient tells me that she expects he will not give it to her, as over and over he had made unkept promises. *I ask if she is able to test out whether father really means to give it to her.* She tells me she has not been able to bring herself to start looking for a coat. She feels so guilty about it that she can't force herself. She tells herself her father can't afford it. *I ask if she believes this.* No, father has a Lincoln, a very nice apartment with wall-to-wall carpet, etc., "I guess he can afford it." *It seems that he can afford it and it is patient's feeling about this that really concerns her.* Another thing, she tells me, a friend had given her a coat which is five years old, so she really could get along without a new one. *I say that she is again avoiding this because of her guilt in taking from her father—has she been more aware of this lately?* Yes, she wanted to be sure to remember to tell me a story about her father today so I could see the other side of him. He's really wonderful in some ways and she is quite attached to him. *I say that she feels guilty because she has been talking depreciatingly about her father.*

The story concerns how father helped a friend to deal with her child and spent more than an hour with them in his office. She and her brother were very proud of him for that. "And you know he was able to charge for that visit. Usually if we ask him to see someone he won't charge, and he puts them under such a feeling of obligation that they aren't able to come back and see him again." Patient says she has been wondering whether it is her fault or his fault that she feels so guilty toward her father, and how do you do anything about it if it is his fault? *I tell her that we are talking about the uneasy guilty feelings she carries around inside her which color her way of looking at things; we are not trying to fix the blame.* Patient says she is aware of these guilty feelings and adds, "So I shouldn't punish myself for feeling that way about the coat." *I say that patient should test whether father will give her the coat.*

She tells me that she did not get to go to the party Saturday night. Saturday morning the foreign boy knocked at her door, told her that the party was called off because most of the guests were unable to come. She told him, "Oh, all right." He walked away, said no more. Her friend Joy had been staying with her overnight, and she and Joy went shopping and to several art galleries, etc., so the day had passed without her getting too upset. Joy is jealous of her and once had a crush on her. She thought she got through the week without being too upset, but she is getting upset as she is talking about it now and says, "At least I didn't snivel in front of him like I always do. I wasn't able to get angry at him or assert myself like you want me to do, but at least I got halfway there." *I wondered whether she was disappointed in me because it hadn't worked out for her.* Patient says she had "expected it." Whenever she counts on anything, she expects to be disappointed. *I tell her that this is because of her guilty feelings.* Patient tells me that she had had "a flash" about this during the week. "Why should everything happen to me?" and she thought to herself that she made it that way usually. "I'm going to be different. Why, why am I so guilty? I've tried to be nice to everybody. I have a nice personality but things never work out for me." *I tell her that she feels no matter how hard she tried or what she did, her parents didn't really love her.* "I know that but I'm not guilty about that." Patient tells me that when I said it it was like a blank wall or a curtain coming down. She shut her mind. *I tell her that she can't stand to think about it right then and shuts me out.* Yes, and "sometimes I look out the window and why is that?" *I tell her that she is under considerable tension at times talking about herself.* She tells me that she has "flashes" at times, too. *I tell her this is progress and so are those blank-wall feelings.* Patient asks me again about feeling guilty, and *I explain in some more detail.*

She tells me then of two times during the week when the boy had approached her, looking guilty, etc. She had been very formal with him. *I tell her that it seems the boy wants to apologize and make up to her, yet she has frozen him out.* She admits this. He had told her some time ago he was in love with another girl. She could stand it if he went to see that girl last Saturday night, but not if he was just playing around with the boys. *I tell her that she can compete with the other girl, too.*

COMMENTS ON SEVENTEENTH SESSION: The patient seems to be seeking for her father, because, although she states that she happened to be in the neighborhood, she lives only a few blocks away from her father. Now she tries to see him more often and in her last meeting did not provoke a rejection. The opening remarks of the interview sound like a script in which each person knew his part very well. When the patient says she did not go for a touch, there is a temptation to interpret this literally as meaning that she wanted to get into closer physical contact with her father, an attitude that probably lies behind many of her problems. The father offered to give her money for the coat, and the patient was torn in conflict and tentatively rejected what she really wanted. The coat probably represents the covering warmth of masculinity, which indicates that behind this contact was a renewed sexual interest in her father.

As the patient tells the story of her father, it seems that she, like the family who brought the child to him, is unable to take anything from her father because of her guilt feelings. Likewise, she can give him nothing, for this would disturb the equilibrium. It seems that the patient's sexual feelings for her father and her anger toward him are the sources of her guilt.

In this transaction the therapist, as if she were the mother giving advice, gives permission for her to remain close to the father and test him out. In this sense she attempts to force action rather than to continue the transaction on a verbal basis. It is questionable whether this was a sound technique, whether it would not have been better to reconstruct the source of the patient's guilty feelings rather than to force action, but about this matter opinion may be divided. Certainly it is necessary to take a stand at some time in therapy to separate clearly in the patient's mind those things which she uses as evidences of guilt and for

which she seeks out punishment and the guilty feelings which are behind so many of her actions. The patient continues to complain that her
father doesn't give, which seems to indicate material things but actually
she means love. If one removes the rationalizations concerning the material stinginess of her father, one may perhaps develop a deeper insight into the source of the guilty feeling.

The patient's rejection by the boy caused her to be frustrated and
angry, but she used her girl friend as a substitute. The patient seems to
think that her behavior is a role assigned to her by the therapist and
hopes that she does not disappoint her. In that respect we can construe
mistrust and expectations of being disappointing and disappointed. She
has the usual plaint of the person who seeks out suffering, "Why should
everything happen to me?"—then goes on to say how she atones for her
sense of guilt by attempting to be nice to everyone.

Again there is need for clarification of the difference between guilt
and guilty feelings, which the patient apparently does not recognize.
The therapist made a big jump with the statement that her parents
didn't really love her and permits the patient to externalize blame onto
them. The therapist, accepting the fact that they did not love her, gives
the patient an alibi. In this sense, then, an old role pattern is re-created
without the opportunity for insight into her own destructiveness of
good relationships.

The patient indicates that she not only can stand rejection by men
but even seeks it out by her choice of male companions and that the
greatest wound, however, is if the men get together. It is as if she can
stand rejection by the father, but not if the father gives his love to the
brother. In spite of the fact that the patient has reiterated that she has
difficulty competing with other girls because of her sense of guilt, the
therapist insists that she can compete.

In summary, in this transaction we see that the therapist behaves
like the mother, pushing and urging her into closer sexual relationships.
In the patient's mind this is a role of badness, both because the mother
was promiscuous and because her primary love object was the father.
The patient, in turn, continues to reiterate the fact that she cannot
succeed, meaning that her guilty feelings regarding her sexual attraction to father and to some extent to brother, plus her hostility to the
mother prevent her from coming between them and succeeding in any
mature sexual relationships.

Eighteenth Session

PATIENT BEGINS the interview laughingly, "I'm mad, grr!" She
was at the library just before coming here to get some art pictures and
books, for which there seemed to be plenty of time. The librarian de-

layed her in order to replace her dirty card. Patient left before getting the books because it was getting late and she became very nervous about being on time. She laughs, "I could kill her." *I say that she is not really mad but anxious about getting here. Is there anything else she is mad about?* (She is caricaturing anger rather than expressing it.) "Yes," she was mad at a teacher at school. When she started teaching, this person, who is the homeroom teacher for one of her classes, did not speak to her in the halls or in the lunchroom. She begins to tell me a rather confused story about some of the students and, *when I wonder how this is related to the teacher,* she answers, "Now wait." Twice during the week patient had disciplinary problems with two boys in the class. In both instances the boys did not calm down and get to work until she threatened to send a report slip to the principal's office. In one instance, patient had recognized that the boy was provoking her to hit him by mocking and depreciating her. She actually had done quite well in handling a difficult situation. She also was able to recognize her difficulty in firmness when she had to "lay down the law" to the students and to see that when she felt more comfortable in being firm the children responded better. Patient again brings in some associations as to how these children remind her of her father in their boasting.

She then begins to discuss the teacher from whom she wanted advice about handling the children. She had held off "because the teacher was not nice to her." When I question this, patient brings out that she had made no overtures herself. She had had a good opportunity one day in the teachers' lunchroom when this teacher was sitting alone at a table; she had wanted to approach her very much but had deliberately avoided it. *When I ask why,* she tells me that the school authorities had told her she was doing a good job. *I say that she feels it would be an admission of failure to ask advice from this teacher.* Patient keeps hoping that it will all work out and the children will recognize her as a good teacher whom they like. After six years she has become one of the outstanding teachers in camp. *I told her she was bolstering her pride in thinking about this.* Her face falls—"Yes, dreams of glory, I always do that." Patient, talking intensely, tells of her hope that she could walk down the hall in school and everyone would really like her. She knows life isn't like that. She knows when people really like her; but many times when she is "nice to people" and they to her, she is in confusion as to their sincerity. *I ask her what it means to have people really like her.* Patient wants "absolutely" to be sure of how people feel and to know they are not just being nice. *I say that she is setting high demands on her relationships.* "Yes, I'm possessive. I always ruin things. Paul used to tell me that." *I ask about the school.* Patient says emotionally that in spite of herself she is trying to make the kids like her and think she is a wonderful teacher. In fact, she wonders how she can teach at all. *"Now you're beating yourself and you don't have to do that."* Patient says that she does it all the time; how can she stop it? *I tell her by understanding and working on it more.* She tells me she really wants me to help her.

Last week she was reading Paul's love letters again. They are wonderful love letters, and she had thought to herself, "My therapist would tell me to burn them"—"but I didn't." *I say that she had turned to Paul again, when she was disappointed in the foreign boy and in me.* "Yes, I always go back to Paul." *I ask if she feels that I would tell her to burn the letters.* Patient doesn't know. *I tell her I would not—that she is seeking another way to suffer when she is unhappy and disappointed.* Patient says it always ends up this way for her when she begins thinking of Paul. She had the fantasy this week that he was in treatment too; both would be cured and then would be married. *I told her that Paul was like home base for her when she was unhappy.* Patient asks me if it could be that she was enjoying suffering over Paul and *I tell her this is true.* She begins to berate herself and *I point out that she is beating herself again.*

Patient wants to ask me about a dream. It is a dream she had some time ago and has thought about it. *I say that we do not have time today but can come back to it.* Patient says she has thought a lot about it and wonders if this dream might be important even if it was so long ago.

COMMENTS ON EIGHTEENTH SESSION: In this interview the patient does not mention the coat discussed at the termination of the last session. We noticed that the patient had repeatedly assigned the therapist the role of giving her directions or permission about procedures or forms of behavior which she did not carry out and does not mention again.

Instead, the patient enters the interview angry or, as the therapist notes, caricaturing anger, and the therapist rightfully understands that the patient is angry at something other than the situation in the library. She permits the patient to choose another subject to talk about, however, instead of focusing the anger in the therapeutic transaction. Thus we see that the patient's demands for information, consent, and direction and then not carrying them out as a subtle way of expressing defiance are not touched at all. Instead, an external situation is utilized as the focus of her anger. This of course enables her to maintain an equilibrium of anger through which she destroys relationships, feels guilt, and is not sure that people like her. As she says, "I always ruin things." Later on the patient sets up a pattern (similar to that described at the beginning of these comments) when she thinks that the therapist would tell her to burn the letters and she does not do so. Even in fantasy there is a defiance.

She retreats to fantasy in rereading Paul's letters and thinking of a happy ending; but reality indicates that the relationship with Paul is an unhappy one and, therefore, a certain enjoyment in the suffering is her prime purpose.

The therapist in this case is a person with considerable experience with personality problems. She is able to grasp the unconscious meaning of the patient's associations but handles them in a way which for her has been tried and true over a long period of time. It is a psychotherapy based on psychoanalytic principles. The therapist is concerned with the avoidance of overwhelming anxiety and permits the patient to pace her own progress and arrive at the essential processes of her neuroses without too much direction or pain. Hence we have a slowly paced therapy and an expectancy that the patient has the capacity for generalization from interpretations concerning real life situations outside the therapeutic transaction. These comments are made because we have repeatedly pointed out the nontransactional nature of this therapeutic process and have asked the therapist to focus on the current transaction between herself and the patient in order to make clear the patient's implicit roles and to avoid accepting the roles that the patient ascribes or assigns to her for the purposes of allaying anxiety and avoiding insight. This apparently is a difficult process for the therapist to accomplish, probably because she has developed a specific technique which has in the past fed back to her satisfactions from successful results. Thus the therapist resists modification of techniques which are oriented toward newer methods that we are investigating in this work. This should be pointed out, because it is probably easier to teach our ideas of therapy as a transactional process to neophytes who are just learning therapy than it is to get people who are already trained to change their methods.

Nineteenth Session

PATIENT BEGINS by telling me that she had a dream this week. She wonders why she gets so involved in movies and books and why these emotions seem so real to her. When I ask why she had immediately brought this up after mentioning the dream, she says this is something else she thought about during the week. *I tell her she is resisting telling me the dream. Does she know why?* She feels embarrassed because it has some material in it about herself and adds, "I analyzed it, too." *I wonder if she is hesitating to tell me.* No, she was pleased that she had a dream. Patient described waking up frequently at night and early several mornings during the week, which is surprising because she ordinarily sleeps well. *I inquire if she had been aware of dreaming earlier in the week.* Not really, but each time she woke up sharply and had a sense of struggling with some thought, but felt blank. Patient tells me the dream occurred two nights before the interview.

> I was in a bus on South Avenue and Paul was there. I was sitting astride his lap, facing him and kissing his chest many times. He was very thin and his skin was ochre (its natural color). There were people around but they were in and out of the dream. A woman got on the bus and sat on one of the seats facing forward. Paul and I were on one of the side seats at the back. Then a Negro man got on and sat down beside the woman. The woman began to attack the man verbally, yelling at him. He got very angry and glared at her. He got off at the next stop and walked away.

Patient tells me she had figured out that Paul was really her father and she was expressing her sexual feelings for him which were "innocent"; she "was sitting like a child." She stumbles over this—*I ask if she believes they were innocent.* She gasps and recalls that she was tonguing him when she was kissing him. "So my feelings weren't so innocent." Her affect, which had been one of excitement up to this point, shifts to embarrassment and then to a serious tone. Patient says she is aware that she has been seeing her father a lot lately, but did not realize her sexual feelings for him. *Like the coat?* "Yes." *I ask her how she feels about these sexual feelings.* "They really aren't right." She would like to feel that she is modern and can handle sexual relations but she knows that she really feels bad and ends up unhappily with every man. She had no idea she had feelings like this about her father. *I ask if she believes it now.* Yes, she has found out why the dream upset her. *I tell her that she is carrying over these feelings to other men. This is what makes her feel that she should not get close to them and causes her to end her relationships with men unhappily.* Patient asks me if Paul in the dream is not then her father and also her father in Paul and *I agree this is right.* She says, laughing ruefully, "That is all I could do with the dream," except for one more thing. She describes the phenomenon of participating actively in one part of the dream and being a bystander in the second part of the dream, of having an audience of the people in the bus and having them drift out of the dream, which she knows has something to do with what people will think. *I ask her about the woman who got on the bus.* Patient does not know, she was not anyone patient recognized. Could it be myself? *I say possibly, but what about it as a representation of the therapist?* She feels I've been telling her to talk back. Patient registers strong amazement and *I tell her this makes me feel this must be right. What was this woman like?* She wore a magenta dress, a fur around her shoulders, and a big floppy hat. She was yelling and acting as if she were crazy. Patient links this to the psychiatric clinic. Something happened on the bus last week which is the reverse of this situation in the dream. Patient was on the bus and a woman was reading some religious literature. A man got on the bus and sat down beside her, and with no provocation suddenly began yelling and screaming at her in what seemed to be a crazy way. He got off the bus at the next street, continuing his behavior.

I wonder what patient thinks about being more sure of herself; it seems to me that the woman in the dream ended up disastrously too. The man had become angry and deserted her. Patient agrees and *I wonder what she thinks.* It seems that no matter what she does, it ends up wrong. *I say that this is her expectation of what will happen to her and she keeps making it come true.* Patient begins to talk apologetically and *I stop her.* She catches on herself—"Now I'm apologizing again." *I agree and ask whether she knows what she is doing to herself,* "I'm depreciating myself again." *Does she think I believe she is a depreciated person?* No, she knows I don't and "I sent a report slip to the principal this week so I can be different about this." Her friend Joy had made some comment about being glad patient was in treatment, implying that she had many problems. Patient was able to fend off leading questions about her relationships. She did not answer Joy's questions about whether she had slept with Paul. She is again apologetic, and *I point this out.* "Yes, I'll say just what I thought. I knew I couldn't trust Joy with this and I didn't let her make me tell. I know I have pretty good judgment about things like this even though I get mixed up about men. I have problems, but I'm getting help. Joy tells me she can't afford treatment but she could if she wanted to. I do and I don't have to apologize to her." *I agree and wonder whether the patient feels she has to apologize to me.* "Well, I respect you very much." *I wonder about this and what it means. Does this depreciate her?* Patient sees this and says that she should be able to get over feeling apologetic. She knows she pities herself and spends days in that state. She is not going to do that any more. *I ask if she believes I pity her.* No, she does not believe this. *I ask her how she knows.* "Because then I would be depreciated and you don't do that." *I tell her this is exactly right, that we have to help her get over these feelings about herself.* Another thing, patient tells me "I can't cry. I can cry when I'm sorry for myself, sob and sob without stopping, but I can't cry ordinarily. Usually I get mad in a crisis or back down. I know I do that with men." *I tell patient that the dream is a statement of her problems with men.* She feels that no matter what she tries it turns out disastrously for her. Men either turn out to be forbidden sexual objects or they walk away and desert her. Patient recalls that she had a dream this morning which she tells me is a continuation of the first dream. She recalls when half asleep trying to put many "fairy tale endings" on it, but it wouldn't work out.

Patient was at an art show of paintings at the home of a friend. Many people were there. She met a single man who immediately repelled her so strongly that she wanted to go up and hit him. She went up to him and

they began exchanging blows (verbally). During her anger patient suddenly became aware of feeling strong sexual stimulation for him, wanted
to abandon the party and spend the night with him. "I couldn't end it.
I tried and tried but it wouldn't work out."

I ask patient if she knows why. It was those people in the dream.
They were all watching me and I couldn't do it. *What about the people?*
They were all married men. Patient realizes that this is further refer-
ence to her father and again talks of this.

She recalls something else from the dream. At the beginning she was
looking at some paintings. She was intensely busy with this, and not
looking at the people. *Like your interest in the movies?* "Oh, yes." A
few days ago a friend had asked her to store some paintings in her
apartment, prior to a show. In the dream some empty frames were
stacked and behind two or three of them was a yellow and green painting. She bent down at the beginning of the dream and looked in the
empty frames. *I said this was something of how she felt about herself
—a kind of depreciated object.* She answers yes, but there really was a
painting behind it. *I tell her that she feels this way, too—she can see
herself differently, too. Actually she does not have to suffer and be hurt
or fight and drive men away.*

COMMENTS ON NINETEENTH SESSION: The patient
begins the interview by telling the therapist that she had a dream, but
then avoids recounting it. The patient tells the methods by which she
attempted to avoid dreaming and finally comes to the point of telling
the dream in its entirety. The reason for her reluctance becomes apparent when the sexual nature of the dream is revealed. She associates
to the fact that her position in relation to Paul is part child and part
adult and quickly reveals that she recognizes her father as the fantasied
sexual object. The other part of the dream suggests that the woman is
more like the mother figure and chases the father away. The dream
seems not to be related to sexual feelings except as they concern mas-
turbation fantasies which are frequently associated with the possible
punishment of insanity. In this she uses the therapist as a representative
of the mother and caricatures her as if she were a madam in a house
of prostitution. Here reference to the scene on the bus seems to indicate
that even when she is trying to be good—that is, religious, she is open
to sexual feelings. Since the therapist had encouraged her relationship
to the father, in defense she has to be placed in the position of rejecting the patient.

The second dream—with the empty frames—indicates the patient's
feeling of emptiness and could possibly represent a feeling of contrast
with the mother when she was pregnant with the younger brother. The

sado-masochistic interpretation of sexuality in which men and women attack each other corresponds to real life in which the mother and father quarreled a great deal. Married men are all around, and it is only with single men that she fantasies the actual attack. Our attention should be called to the remnants of foreign culture in this home, in which the father could be seductive to the daughter up to a point, but the brother must not.

The patient is apologetic in self-depreciation in the transaction, which is somewhat similar to the pictorial representation of an empty body, as in the frames without pictures. Yet this is a defense behind which are various sexual fantasies that are disturbing to the girl. She outwardly respects the therapist who, however, like the mother, as a madam, encourages her sexual fantasies, especially in relation to the father. Here the patient is in a dilemma in that identification with the mother and competition with her are both involved in the primary family situation.

The patient is moving in therapy and has the courage to express her dreams and fantasies and associate freely about them. She reveals, although in considerable disguise, the nature of the transaction in the therapeutic setting and her reactions to it. We can sense, however, that the struggle of the patient with her mother will become much more obvious in repetition as the transaction progresses. We already see that the therapist as the respected, encouraging, and stimulating helper is also the depreciated madam with whom the patient cannot identify and against whom she has much deeply organized hostile competitiveness.

Twentieth Session

PATIENT BEGINS the interview by telling me that one of the two men she is dating has become serious. She would like me to tell her what to do. *When I ask about this,* she says she is much less upset than usual about this. The man has not actually asked her to marry him, but she does not want to lead him on. She feels if I would tell her what to do she would stop being confused about it. *I tell her that her inability to know what to do is the result of her confusion and not the cause of it. If I am to help her, I must help her find the cause of her confusion.* She is silent, and then says, "Oh, I see." She refers to the dream, "Shall I tell it to you?" *I tell her that she has been holding off telling it to me.* She smiles, and suddenly becomes serious. She is afraid of the dream which is the most vivid one she ever had. She remembers it clearly even though it took place one or two years ago.

The first part of the dream takes place in a bedroom she shared with brother in an apartment patient lived in when she was in grammar school.

(This was a third-floor apartment and bedroom faced the street.) There was a tiger, a big stuffed tiger like they have in the toy stores; their bedroom was a cage with bars on all sides and the front facing the street was glassed in, too. The tiger was pacing up and down in the cage and the people could see it directly from the street as if it were the first floor. Patient remembers school children watching the tiger. She was both a spectator and a school child.

In the next part of the dream, patient and the tiger were walking in the park. The tiger was walking upright and had his paw linked in her arm. The paws were like velvet pads and patient kept patting them and saying, "Now there, there, you're a very good tiger and it's all right for you to be out walking if you behave." She knew the tiger was very fond of her and would do as she asked. (The paws reminded her of a reference to *Androcles and the Lion,* which she had read about that time, either just before her vacation trip or after.) The claws did not show. She and the tiger were walking downhill. She looked up and saw two "Polacks." She hates herself for dreaming this—hopes she does not have prejudices. They were a man and his wife of her own age group. The man used to visit them when patient was living with her mother. She thought to herself that the tiger would kill the man if she didn't stop him. She talked to him, "You're a nice boy and you don't want to get into trouble." The tiger obeyed and she was proud of him.

In the next part of the dream she and the tiger were walking down the street. The tiger was going home. He lived with her mother and mother's second husband. In the dream patient had an apartment in back of the same building. The tiger had to go home alone and so did she. She doesn't know why, but the tiger had to cross the street alone and she was afraid of what would happen to him. She kept telling him to behave himself, not to growl at anybody, that there wasn't anything strange about a tiger being out for a walk. When the tiger was crossing the street, a police car approached and a policeman got out. She woke up feeling very upset and is not really sure that the tiger was shot or arrested.

After telling the dream patient continues to worry over what happened to the tiger. *I say that she feels a great sense of responsibility for what happened to the tiger. Can she tell me why?* "Oh yes, the tiger was dependent on me. I could control all his behavior. He was wonderful when he was with me." *I say that patient feels she deserted the tiger.* Yes, but she kept telling him how to behave and warning him of what would happen. She could hear him begin to growl. He let out a little growl when he saw the policeman. *I say that patient must be concerned about this—telling him how to behave hadn't worked. I say that she has been asking me to tell her how to behave toward this man now; I knew that wouldn't work either.* Patient asks, "Well, how do you make things work?" *I tell her you don't, you have to be involved yourself. What does she think about this?* Well, one thing that embarrassed her in the dream was that she made the tiger get up on his hind legs to walk with her in the park. As soon as he left her, he went down on all fours again. She thinks she was dominating him and that she is often dominating in her relationships. It seems to be one extreme or the other. *I inquire about her relationship with me.* No, she doesn't feel she is dominating me, or I am dominating her. *I say that patient has been thinking about women who control or dominate. It came up last week in the dream, and now it has come up again.* Patient felt in the dream she had to manage the tiger. *Yes. Now she is telling me of a man she has to control herself so he won't get out of control.* Yes, it always happens to her that way. There had been a man interested in her some time before the dream who had told her that she had to have her own way. She had been like this with him, too. Patient gives some details of how she had lost interest when she took control of this relationship. It was different with Paul. Even when Paul acquiesced to her wishes, he did it in such a way that he mocked her—like putting her coat on and giving her a significant look at the same time. *I ask her what she thinks I feel about Paul.* She thinks I am really neutral. She would like me to be a third party with her and Paul so I could arbitrate what would happen. She is too emotionally involved with him and wants someone else to take over and decide for her, because then decisions could be made with a clear head and her emotions would not have to be involved. *I tell her that she wants me to control this.* "Yes, no matter which way it turns out." *I cannot do this, I tell her. It is an emotional decision in her own life.* Patient is quiet for some time and *I ask her what she is thinking.* She is "blank." *I say that she would like to avoid emotional involvements.* Yes, she knows it. "But, you don't like to hear me say it." Yes, the dream had upset her too, like the one last week—although she has been sleeping better. There was a time when she used to have all kinds of physical symptoms which she knew were emotional.

I ask whether this dream refers to that period. It must, because in the second and third parts of the dream she was wearing a tweed coat she had when she was twenty or twenty-one. *I say that this was a stressful period in her life.* Yes. She and her brother were living with her mother in the apartment in the first part of the dream. Later her brother actually had an apartment back of this; he left it several years ago when he moved to a house. When patient was twenty, her mother was working and patient was working and going to art school; brother was working and going to college. Father was sending $10 a week. Her mother decided to marry again. She and her brother decided to keep the apartment and live there together. She and brother knew it was impossible for them to live with mother and her new husband; patient felt very upset. She and brother also decided to tell father the news of mother's remarriage. Patient felt "sick" about this and could not look at her father. She told him and he had said, "You'll have to come to live with me." Patient did so. It was awful. She would have the most awful waves of nausea and couldn't look at her father. Her father often was awful to her, but she would feel nauseated even if he just sat down to read the newspaper. This continued after she left his home. There was a period of several years when she could not talk to her father. If she heard his voice on the phone a wave of nausea hit her. She would avoid calling him, nag herself for weeks that she ought to call him, and then finally do it. She knows she has been seeking father out since she has been in treatment and their relationship is much changed. It is only recently she has felt this way. Her father has changed, too. Actually, father's personality changed when he had his accident and entered the hospital for treatment. She knows that since then he has been much better.

She went to see her father again this week. She tells me of the nearness of his office to her apartment and her awareness that she is seeking him out. He asked her about the coat. She told him that she couldn't locate the one she wanted. Father had offered her the cash or a check to take with her. She had refused. *I asked why.* She did not want to carry that much cash with her. If something happened to it she would be out of luck. She stops, asks me hesitatingly, "Is it because of my guilt again?" *I press her to answer this for herself and she does with affect. I ask her how she feels about paying for her treatment here.* This is one thing she doesn't have trouble with. She uses the envelope system and puts away the money for her interview first. Two weeks ago she was quite short but she managed. She and the butcher have a joke that some day she'll come in and order a rib roast and he'll fall over dead. Usually it's a pound of hamburger. She follows a good diet and often is taken out to dinner. She can manage money. One thing though —when she went to live alone, she opened a bank account. She didn't want to leave her money around, but so far as she can see that was good judgment. There was something about this in the dream. The man used to come to visit them frequently. Her mother never locked her door and people would drop in frequently, often strangers as well— a kind of continuous open house. Patient and her brother noticed a number of things missing—money, patient's watch, a pen, etc., and figured out it had happened when this man was there. They confronted him with this and the man admitted stealing, said he couldn't help it but denied taking patient's watch. Patient told him she wanted it, her mother had given it to her and now that mother was leaving to get married she wanted it in order to remember her. He still denied it. Some time later she met this man on the street with his wife (the woman in the dream who used to come to the house at times, too). He stepped in front of his wife, but not before patient spotted her watch on his wife's wrist. She wanted to snatch it off her wrist, but did not do so—did not do anything because she was so startled at it.

At the time of the original stealing incident, patient told her mother about it. Mother told her to be more careful and lock up her things. *I ask her what she thinks of this.* She feels you shouldn't have to lock up things in your own house. Then she becomes aware of the implied criticism of her mother and wants to take back her statement. She really doesn't like watches much anyway. *I point out her discomfort at being critical of her mother.*

COMMENTS ON TWENTIETH SESSION: The patient enters the interview asking the therapist again to give her direct advice. Apparently she is prepared to tell her dream but needs some urging. She tells the dream as if it were from the previous evening, with every detail in its proper place and without hesitation. A dream remembered so clearly from two years ago must have considerable significance to the patient.

The setting of the dream seems to be early in life, with the bars representing the slats of a crib and the teddy bear indicating a childhood experience. There is a great deal of looking and gazing, indicating a voyeuristic form of satisfaction. In addition, there is considerable aggressivity associated with the watching. The patient seems to be quite proud of the tiger in his upright position when his genitals are in view; whereas, on the other hand, she depreciates the man and woman walking together.

All put together, the patient's associations indicate her role confusion. She seems to be confused as to who lived with mother because of the large number of people who went in and out of the house. She is confused about domination and being dominated, about sadism or masochism, and about maleness or femaleness. There is a very strong conscience reaction as evidenced by the policeman finally making the arrest, and we see the struggle going on between her aggressive and sexual impulses embodied in the tiger and her rather severe conscience.

It seems that the father and the brother are condensed in her associations, but at present we can only conjecture that the father was the most significant person. The nausea in relation to the father may connote either her infantile sexual feeling or some disgust at what she had seen her father do in a sexual act.

The watch is significant in that she was warned by the mother to lock it up, preserve it, and see that nothing happens to it; whereas the mother left herself open to any kind of theft. This probably refers to the life pattern in which the mother was promiscuous while at the same time she warned the patient not to be. The crowning insult, of course, was that the man who stole her watch gave it to his wife, which may have a connection with the patient's sexual feelings.

The transaction seems to be spiraling rapidly, with the patient bringing in considerable emotion in connection with her dreams and fantasies. In the transaction the therapist is asked to be controlling—as the mother was and in the way the patient controlled the tiger. If she lets the tiger go—that is, her aggressive sexual feelings, then she will be punished. Therefore, she must control them even though in the process there is considerable vacillation between the sadistic, aggressive component to her sexual feelings, as demonstrated by her excitement on getting angry, and the masochistic, self-accusatory, self-punitive behavior. The primary focus of the patient seems to be the role conception of the therapist as portraying, like the mother, an admonishing, controlling, but self-indulging person. Thus she wants to be told what is right by the therapist and at the same time she fantasies her as being a madam in a whorehouse.

Twenty-first Session

PATIENT GREETS ME "Hi" in a talkative and "bubbly" manner, conveying immediately that her controls have lessened considerably and there is a quality of freedom in her associations throughout the interview. She tells me that two things happened, and she has remembered another dream from at least a year ago.

Kay had come up in her thoughts this week. She felt mad at Kay for the first time this week because she had not heard from her. *When I ask about it,* she does not know what set it off, "But I can tell you what I thought." Patient then tells me her fantasy that Paul and Kay had gotten married; that is why she had not heard from her. *I interpret that she fantasies this as a punishment to herself for having angry thoughts about Kay.* She is apprehensive at first, "But it could happen," *and I point out that her fear has no current reality basis.* She goes back over the material and sees what she is doing to herself.

She tells me of a "strange incident" that happened to her this week. She had met and talked with a girl who works at the art school. As she was talking with her, she got a strange feeling like floating off into outer space and then recovered and got her feet on the ground again. "You could go crazy if you felt like that all the time." She does not know why or what they were talking about. The girl wears very artificial make-up even though she is an artist and should be aware of it. *When I say "like a painted doll,"* she says, "Oh, yes." Girl has only four outfits of clothes and prides herself on having no personal possessions. Patient tells me of her own full closet, her records, and books. Girl prides herself on not being involved with anybody and has reduced her life to the simplest terms possible so that she can live an uncomplicated existence. She has no close friends and you get a sense that she is off in her own thoughts. *I tell patient that for a moment she had lost herself in the girl's identity when she was talking with her and then came back to earth again.* She laughs, "Oh, yes."

She says that it would be wonderful if you could live like that—just an uncomplicated existence with nothing to worry about. Has this been a tempting thought for patient this week? "Yes, I know you can't live this way, but I've been thinking about it." *I ask if she knows why.* Well, one thing, she has been thinking about Christmas and buying presents. She realizes that she invests a lot in this. She likes to pick out just the right present for people and puts far too much feeling into it. She doesn't feel she has any problem about receiving presents. I say, *"Oh,"* and patient catches herself. She knows she has lots of feelings about presents from her father, we have been talking about that. She adds, "And my mother, too, she has horrible taste in gifts." Patient tells me that she gives mother a list so mother will pick out something she likes. When she is silent, *I ask what she is thinking.* "Well, I'm the favorite of both my father and my mother." *I ask how she knows.* Her father told her once that he loved her more than anyone else in the world, that she should never forget that. Her mother—and she hesitates a great deal—really prefers patient to her brother. Her mother really thinks of her when she picks out a gift for her. *When I ask why she feels her mother prefers her to her brother,* she tells me, "Because I was less trouble."

Patient begins to tell me of the period when she, mother, and brother lived together. Mother worked. Patient did many household chores. She could never get her brother to do anything. She used to beat him with her fists to get him to help "so things would be nice for my mother when she came home tired from work, and I ended up by doing everything. We used to fight like cats and dogs. I was stronger than he was." From about thirteen on they punched each other instead of fist fighting. Then one day her mother took her brother aside and told him not to fight with her any more—he might hurt her. This happened when she was fifteen, after an incident when she hit her brother with a broom. Brother came home, brought in his friends, and stretched his feet out on the living room carpet which she was trying to sweep before her mother got home. He didn't think she would hit him, but she did. She says she enjoyed fighting with him. She never got into any trouble, was good in school, got good marks and did well. *I ask how she felt about doing this housework.* Well, she didn't like doing it so much. She complained to her mother twice about it—"This is snitching on my mother." Patient complained bitterly one time to her mother that she couldn't make her brother behave and mother should do something. Mother lost her temper and beat her brother. He was stony-faced and hard like a rock, she couldn't make a dent in him. She then turned and attacked patient, "You see, I can't do anything with him. Why do you bother me with him?" Patient adds that she was worse off because her mother was mad at her too. *I say that patient felt she had to look after and take care of her mother.* She agrees, "Yes." *I say it was as if she didn't have a mother for herself, she felt more like she had to be the mother.* Patient's tension rises immediately. She tells me how tired and unhappy her mother was with the responsibility of two children; she couldn't have enjoyed it. *I comment that patient is telling me she felt responsible for her mother.* "Well, yes, but I never thought of it that way before." Patient tells me that mother had a man there for several years. "He was a dunce." She and her brother didn't like him at all and were relieved when he finally left. They were afraid mother would marry him. *I say that patient felt she had to be good and do the housework and also keep her brother in line so mother wouldn't leave them.* "Well, yes, that's true." But it was different with her brother. Even though they fought like cats and dogs and she hated him, she loved him, has always loved him. *I say this is like her feeling for Paul.* "Why, how did you know that? I never thought of it but it is right—it's exactly how I feel. Oh, I'm sure you would know things I hadn't thought of. That's why I'm here." *I tell her it wasn't any magic that made me say that— I had noticed the similarity in her emotional feelings when she described her fights with her brother and her fights with Paul. I am also wondering whether the tiger in her dream last week wasn't reminiscent of her relationship with her brother.* Patient agrees that it is in some ways. She and her brother have always been very close. *I ask whether they had a bedroom together.* Yes, when they were smaller they slept together in a pull-down bed in the living room. Then they got bunk beds and patient had the bottom bed. She does not remember the age, but it must have been when she was twelve or thirteen, because she remembers that she had to sleep in the top bunk for a period then. They were in an automobile accident. She was not hurt but her brother's leg was broken. "I really loved him then. I felt really sorry for him." Brother used to call out for water at night and patient would hop down quickly from the top bunk to get it for him so her mother wouldn't have to be awakened and get up—she looks at me significantly, and *I say that this is another time when patient felt she had to protect her mother.* She nods and wants to know if there is time for her to tell me the dream—it is another scary dream.

It is night out—it must be just before dawn because the light has that quality. I am in an alleyway which really is a space paved with brick between the backs of houses. The house on one side is my father's and (also) the house where I was born. Across from this (back-to-back diagonally) is the house where my mother is living. There is a third little house, but I don't know whose house that was. I am standing all alone in the dark near a light pole. I feel so terribly lonely.

Patient stops and looks as if she can't go on. *I say that she didn't know which house she belonged in or where to go. She felt all by herself.* "Oh, yes—that's it."

As I was standing there I saw a man wearing a blue shirt the color of the night crouching behind a garbage pail. I was terrified and wondered whether I could yell for help. It is strange because I don't know if it was happening to me in the dream or if I was watching myself dream the dream. I kept wondering whether I could yell for help if the man came toward me. He came toward me. I woke up and was calling for help in a whispered voice and holding my throat.

Patient is holding her throat and whispering "help, help"—she is still living in the dream. *I tell her she had found out that she was able to call for help.* She comes out of the dream and says, "Yes, but it wasn't very loud." *I say that I know these dreams are very vivid to her and she is afraid of being locked up in her dreams.*

COMMENTS ON TWENTY-FIRST SESSION: The patient discusses her fantasy that Paul and Kay had gotten together and been married. Contrary to what the therapist suggests, in addition to this fantasy being a punishment for her having angry thoughts about Kay, she is also angry at her because of the fantasied competitive frustration. The notion that she is doomed to frustration is a natural sequence from the previous session in which rivalry and incapacity to compete were central themes. Since we know, however, that this patient has a great deal of trouble in knowing her identification vis-à-vis sex, we may surmise that she is equally disturbed regarding the frustration of homosexual fantasies with Kay. It is not a question of one or the other; that is, turning away from one unsuccessful relationship to another, but both are present at the same time.

We see that the transaction follows a logical trend in that she begins to talk about her feelings toward her mother or the therapist. Here we see a closeness to the mother and a desire to be in her favor, which is the prototype of her later homosexual feelings. At the same time we can see in the playful aggressiveness with the brother the beginning of primitive adolescent heterosexual feelings which she feared could not be controlled and asked her mother for help. Her jealousy of the other man was a jealousy that someone else would have her mother's attention.

Following this, the patient seems to have difficulty with her mixed feelings which she cannot synthesize and so makes an attempt at regressive associations. In her dream she expresses clearly that she needs help, and it is interesting that this dream occurred at about the time she decided to go into therapy—although it was necessary to wait for an appointment. Nevertheless, the dream indicates that she does not know where she belongs. She is in between and is watching, but the houses are back to back, not front to front, indicating her attempt to desexualize her confusion regarding her role. The figure in a blue shirt the color of night; namely, a nightshirt, crouching behind the garbage pail is the object that she interprets will make an attack on her, thus revealing her masochistic sexual fantasies. Her choking up and inability to cry out seems to be representative of her life pattern of being choked or stymied by her defenses.

We see again that this patient's relationships are all sado-masochistic. The difficulty in recognizing her sexual role, whether male or female, is quite prominent. She seems to exist in a kind of undifferentiated role area without much discrimination, veering back and forth between being masochistic or sadistic, being feminine and homosexual or masculine and aggressive.

Although this session indicates that the patient is progressing in insight, the therapeutic process which has lately accelerated is not interrupted enough by significant interpretations except for the purpose of allaying anxiety. Much of the transactional nature of the patient's productions is clear despite the reassuring and incomplete interruptions by the therapist. The transactional interpretations are lacking, and the patient has been permitted to indulge in reminiscences of the past in a regressive fashion instead of focusing on the present and current therapeutic relationship. Nevertheless, there is a pressure from within that keeps this girl on a straight track toward divulging more and more details of her difficulty in role discrimination. We would assume that this pressure will continue for some time, and the working through or understanding of her difficulties will make the problem clearer. As this continues, however, the transaction will be maintained on the same plane unless the therapist takes the initiative in focusing on the immediate aspects of the patient's role relationship with the therapist.

Twenty-second Session

PATIENT TELLS ME that she has a holiday today. She felt uncomfortable about last week because she was attacking her mother. It is different with father. She was at her brother's last night for Thanksgiving and father was there, although they kept saying he wouldn't come. He came and was very nice, pinched her cheek, held her hand, and talked to her. The subject of Christmas came up and patient kept quiet because mother is coming for Christmas and father blows up when mother is mentioned. When she was in grammar school mother would send her and brother to father for Christmas dinner. She doesn't mind telling me about her father but she does about her mother. *I ask about her feeling toward me in talking about her mother.* She had been talking with a friend who is in treatment also and found that she too had the feeling of telling things more and more. *I say that perhaps she feels critical of her mother, that she (the patient) should be attacked.* She says, "my poor mother," and then tells me I am right, she is critical of her mother.

Patient tells me a great deal about her mother with awareness of what she is saying although she did not put many of these things together until recently. At the time she was confused, blotted them out of her mind. She knows that she was afraid of what the neighbors might think. She knew this would come out when she got into treatment and wants to tell me.

When her parents were living together, they fought terribly. Father accused mother of having men around but patient can never remember a man around then and thinks her father accused her mother falsely. They separated and divorce proceedings were under way. Patient is never sure of the date, thinks she was seven. She remembers mother coming into the children's room, sitting in a rocking chair, sobbing, and she knew mother was unhappy over father. Patient knew "like a woman would" that the mother was unhappy over father. Father broke his leg just before the divorce proceedings went through and she hoped then they would get together. Mother went to visit father in the hospital and patient was sneaked up to his room. Father kept insisting there was a pin sticking in his toe. Mother looked and said this was not so. Mother stood against the wall in the hospital room and mother and father looked as if they loved each other. She had thought there was a chance but the divorce proceedings went through. Father kept saying he was trying to prevent mother having the children because she was unfit.

Mother took the two children to live in a building where a woman who was a "crumb" took her in even though she had no money. During this period mother had two women friends who were "crumbs"—you would not speak to them on the street, and neither would mother today. For about three years mother "went to the dogs." She was a 26 girl, a hooligan, played the horses, had parties in the house, and slept with many men. Patient remembered first seeing a naked man when she and brother were supposed to be asleep. Two of mother's men friends molested her. When she was about eight, one man came into the bedroom, reached his hand across her brother who was sleeping in the same bed, and rubbed her genitals. This happened several times. She did not know what to do, finally told her mother and the man never came to the house again. The men mother went out with were all low types and had strange foreign accents—like Polish. There was one man who sounded Polish although he wasn't. (Patient herself made the connection to the "Polack" in the dream, although the actual man in the dream was someone else.) This man used to kneel down and put his eye to the door when mother went to the bathroom. Patient and brother had a bedroom at right angles to the bathroom so could see what was going on. There wasn't any keyhole and patient later went and looked herself, but couldn't see anything. The man used to feel her breasts, which were budding, when he hugged her. She never told her mother, because she thought mother would get mad at him and he at her. For a while they thought mother would marry him. She and brother liked this man much better than most of her men friends, although they were relieved when mother did not marry him. Patient also was molested by a boy in the neighborhood, never told her mother about this either. *I said that patient felt she could not depend on mother to protect her.* She tells me that she had seen her mother having relations with one man. Mother was having a party and moved the children to her room. Patient got up later that night and saw her mother having intercourse. Mother must have been hurt and annoyed at this; she told patient to get out and go back to bed. This was also the period when father would promise to visit and never turn up to see them.

Mother then went to secretarial school, completed the course, took a secretarial job, and got better and better jobs. She had better men friends, too, though patient thinks she slept with them. They were not left alone and mother did not have parties like she used to. Then mother met her present husband, of whom brother and she approved. *I add, but mother deserted you when she married him.* Yes, that was true. Mother has been very different since she married him—like her earliest memory of her. She can remember that when she was little mother bought her prints of paintings. She told her that even though she didn't appreciate them today, she would some day. She also bought symphonies, although they were just the standard ones, and played them for her—took her to some concerts too. She could be charming. *I say that patient is telling me of the other side of her mother which she admires. She has conflict about her mother because there were both sides to her.* "Oh you make me feel so much better already—knowing that you understand both things. Actually she was terrible in some ways but there was the other side to her." *I then question patient closely as to her reaction to telling me about her mother.* It is hard to talk about, not like the dreams which she loved telling me. She couldn't bear to talk to her mother about sex. Not so long ago her mother asked her whether Paul ever made love to her. She pretended that she didn't know what her mother meant. Actually she was shocked at her mother's questions. *I say because of these experiences she had told me about today.* Yes, she never put them together before, but that is right. Like the list—she looked at it a few days ago and discovered her questions all fell together in one big category—"my apologizing." *I said that patient had been using the list to keep from talking about things.* She wonders why she ever had any doubt of needing treatment. She knows why, she couldn't face it. She wants me to know there are "even more personal things" she has to tell me. She knew they would come out when she got to it. *She will need to be able to tell me these so that I can help her.*

COMMENTS ON TWENTY-SECOND SESSION: In this interview the therapist is assigned the role of the good mother who, in terms of time, antedates her memories of the bad mother. Since the therapist accepts the role of the good mother, the patient is able to recollect and to confess many of her memories of the bad mother. When she says that at the age of five or six she knows something about her mother as a woman would, she reveals that at this time she was in the height of her earliest sexual feelings. Recollections of her mother as a prostitute are associated with the identification of sex as being both fearful and fascinating. There was a good deal of early sexual stimulation by the men whom the mother permitted in the house and in her bedroom. This added to the patient's difficulty in obtaining a healthy view of sexuality, which added to the disturbances in her early sexual feelings. She was stimulated to look and listen for sexual incidents. It reveals the conflict in identification. She does not want to be like the mother, who is identified in her mind as a prostitute. Nevertheless, the identification with the mother has resulted in her prostitution fantasies, some of which she has acted out. The incident in the hospital with her father indicates her close attachment to him and her sexual feelings for him. But at the same time she recognized that there was something wrong with the father and developed, probably through the course of years, the notion of the queer and crazy aspects of men.

Twenty-third Session

PATIENT SAYS that many things have happened this week, including one big thing. An unknown man has made obscene phone calls for the past two mornings. *Is this the big thing?* No, but she can't stop thinking about it and wants to get it out of the way. *Why does she do this, I ask.* She just has to get little things off her mind before discussing the big thing.

It will take lots of time. *I tell her that is a reason for not postponing it. Does it have to do with her feeling about talking to me?* Well, when she told me about Kay she stopped worrying so much about it. These are all things she has been anxious about and needs to talk out. Won't that help her? *I tell her not to any extent. For instance, about Kay, we must help her get at what causes her to get anxious. I think she is anxious about telling me what is worrying her today. We must get at this.* Patient says she can't help it, she has to do things this way. *I say she is making herself go through a ritual.* She discovered what I meant in the dream when I said she was lonely. You can be lonely with people all around you. She discovered that it takes about two weeks for what I say to sink in. She thinks and thinks about it and pretty soon she understands emotionally what I'm getting at. *I tell her she can understand it right here with me and this will help her the most.*

Well, the phone calls made her feel "sick" for two days and she finally called the police. She wants me to tell her how to stop them. *I tell her she did the one thing to stop them herself. Why does she need my help to stop them?* Well, she thinks the man was sexually stimulated by her. *I point out that she is taking these calls personally.* Yes, she felt responsible for his talking that way. In a fantasy she had wanted to meet him, with the police in the background, and claw his face and beat him for feeling sexually attracted to her. *I tell her that she is describing the perverted approach of a sick person rather than sexual stimulation. Why does she respond to it in this way, as if she felt responsible and then had to attack him?* Patient is considerably disturbed by this. "Well, I did think I had to beat him up myself to show it wasn't my fault. I think it is because of my father. These calls reminded me of my father some way."

She had been very upset about the coat and her father anyway. She finally purchased a coat and today sent it back because the sleeves were too short. *I asked whether she had picked it out herself.* Yes, but if she had had the money in the bank and could shop leisurely it wouldn't have happened. *I say that father had offered the money.* Yes, but father made two remarks to her when she picked out the coat and was very attacking. He kept asking her if the coat was warm enough, and told her not to leave it on the floor and walk on it. She had responded flippantly to this last remark.

Patient then begins "the real problem" with a long, circumstantial account of her relationship to a man and his wife. *I interrupt her to say that everything today has been about men and how they attack and depreciate her* (there were three or four additional incidents mentioned). *She has wanted me to protect her and I have been pointing out her own responsibility and questioning her as to why she had difficulty with this.* Patient tells me more about Joe and how his wife had let him down and he had turned to her last Friday night. *I point out that she had taken on the roles in which his wife had disappointed him.* "Yes, but I don't know whether I could resist him." She had necked with him until 4:45 A.M., refused sex relations because of his wife, and sent him home. During this she felt "sick," too, partly because of the gin she drank earlier. She would like to think of it as an isolated incident away from his marriage as he begged her to. He had been mad at his wife that evening because they were interrupted just as they were about to make love by guests coming, for which his wife took no responsibility. Then patient had called them to speak to the wife, who was remaining in bed, and when Joe said he was bored and mad, patient impulsively invited him to come to a party where she was and they went home from there. She had held out, couldn't prevent him from coming up—which she has got to learn to do. He kept calling her and Sunday she told him that she was mixed up about men and was in treatment, that she couldn't sleep with him. *I say that patient wants me to protect her from getting involved with this man.* "Yes." *But why is she doing this to herself? Why is she letting him use her this way when he has told her he had no serious interest in her?*

I end the interview quite abruptly, as the time is up and the cleaning woman opened the door. I also felt that patient must take responsibility for coming to grips sooner with her major concerns. Patient kept saying, "I can't hurry," and *I pointed out several times quite firmly that she was keeping me from helping her. Maybe this was what she wanted.* "No, no, I just can't hurry."

COMMENTS ON TWENTY-THIRD SESSION: When patient recounts the story of the man who called her on the telephone, she reveals more than just the actual happening. When the therapist challenges her, she admits the fact that her own sexual impulses disturb her. Patient apparently has to arrange her statements in the interview in order to accomplish a certain amount of self-justification for what she is about to say. She would like the therapist to accept her projections and to act as a control over her own dangerous sexual feelings and accept her concept of not being responsible for what happens to her. These roles, which are not accepted by the therapist, are made explicit in the transaction. In a series of ensuing hostile fantasies, the father becomes one of the men from whom she refuses to accept material things. Nevertheless, she acts out repeatedly her desires to take a man away from his wife, as she probably wished to do with her father. The continuation of her contact with the man until the early hours of the morning perhaps reflects the repetition of the early hours at home when she heard the sexual affairs between her mother and other men.

Twenty-fourth Session

PATIENT BEGINS by commenting on her difficulty in talking except with a systematic plan. She thinks there is a place for a list in life but realizes what I meant about it not being the way to go about treatment. She is going to try to stop herself but finds it very hard. *I say that she feels she has to be fair and present all sides. She wants to be sure I have all the facts and then judge. This is not going to help her with her own feelings.* She had been thinking of Kay as an isolated incident and from what I said she thought I saw Kay as a woman who was her rival. Then every woman was her rival. Does it have to be that way? *When I ask,* she is very aware that she thinks of Kay as a rival. It seems that everything she ever thinks about has some emotional meaning.

Like Joe, she would like to think of that as an isolated incident, but she can't stop thinking about it. *I ask if she feels a fascination for thinking about it and she admits this.* Joe had kissed her once this week but she didn't feel any sexual attraction for him. She hadn't felt any real sexual stimulation from him when they were necking either, even though she was fascinated by it. In a way it was like being in a play. Every time he complimented her she kept saying to herself, "It's not true," and yet she had to keep on listening and felt he believed every word he said to her even though he really loves his wife and she knew they had a "beautiful marriage." "Now you're not going to tell me Joe is neurotic?" *I wonder what made her say that.* Well, Joe is a Catholic and doesn't believe in treatment and she doesn't think he really needs it. She had told him that "when I get through treatment you and I will both be cured for my $5 a week." *I say that patient has included Joe in her own emotional reaction to treatment. Is this part of her own reservation about treatment?* No, not really, she can't explain it. She has a feeling in a way it is unreal but she can't keep away from it. *I say this then is the fascination she feels.* Yes. *I think she has been stirred up by talking about her mother and is now playing and acting like her mother did.* She says that she is not consciously doing this, but has the feeling that she can't help herself. In fact, she has not fallen in love with him yet, but has the feeling that if she talks about it here it might happen to her. *I point out the threat toward me implied in this.* Yes, she resents that you can't have an isolated incident like this without any other meaning. *Does she believe this, I ask.* "No, not really." *I point out that she is also angry because she can't have things on her own terms. In a way she and I are fighting this irrational part of her-*

self which she does not believe in either. Well, what can I do? *I say that right now she is setting up for herself another relationship with a man which will end disastrously for her, and rather than let her propel herself into it we are trying to help her face what is happening to her.* "I didn't use to feel that way toward him. It is only recently." *I say this is because she is stirred up about her mother.* Well, it is hard to sit in a vacuum with nothing to do. She catches herself here and comments that she always has to make things turn out this way. "I always get hurt." *I point out that she hurts herself.*

Patient begins to tell me about Joe's comment to her—which he really meant—that she had a beautiful soul. She is serious about this, tells me what a wonderful person he is, with such fine thoughts. Finally the name of his wife creeps in and she suddenly falters in her presentation of him and is quite hesitant. *I say that she liked to hear him say that she had a beautiful soul.* "Oh yes." *Does she feel this is romantic?* "Oh, no, it is very real, he would never put it on in this way." Then she begins to hesitate and finally tells me, "I didn't believe it anyway. I knew it wasn't real even when he was saying it." *I say that she was carried away with her fascination for it though. Would she have been intrigued the same way if he weren't married?* Her reaction is strong surprise and she then admits this is right, she knows she wouldn't be intrigued with him at all if he weren't married. *I point out this is not a real relationship then, it is an acting out which we are trying to help her understand.* "Yes, but I resent it. I don't see why I have to do things like this. I always end up this way." *I say that in treatment we aim to stop this and help her see what she is doing to herself.*

Patient tells me about a male teacher at school. They are the same age and he is a nice guy. She is attracted to him and is aware that he is beginning to be attracted to her. She passed him in the hall today and they smiled and spoke. She wants to "do something." *I ask what.* Well she just has to do something about it. *I tell her that the one thing she has to do is control her anxiety enough so she is not driven to* "do something." Yes, she sees this. "I drive people away that way." She tells me that the other day she was talking in a natural conversation to this man in the lunchroom. Suddenly she thought to herself, "Why, I'm actually talking in a natural conversation." She then felt scared. *I say that she scared herself when she realized she had been able to forget herself. This is just the point. We want to help her be able to do more of this and not be so propelled by her own impulses.* "But he might get away before I can get cured." *I say that now she is pushing me to act fast, too.* Patient says that maybe she is making some progress "because I could at least talk to that man. I know what you mean."

Patient comes back and knocks on my door to ask that her card be renewed and sent to her. It was on the secretary's desk inside the office and the secretary had left. In other words, she inhibited her own curiosity to peek inside the office.

COMMENTS ON TWENTY-FOURTH SESSION: The patient's list of items and orderliness in presenting her story seem to be controlling defenses against anxiety and the divulgence of unacceptable attitudes. She places the therapist in the role of a judge and attempts to be fair. Actually, she is sorely torn between her drive toward sexual acting out and the role of a dependent child. In dealing with her rivalry with other women and other aspects of her sexual impulses, the patient has a tendency to isolate incidents as if they were separate and required understanding as different patterns. She attempts to separate them as a defense against observing the repetition of the total pattern. The background setting in the transaction is one of great dependency. In the foreground is the sexual rivalry in the fascination for married men. In the transaction the patient reveals, in recounting her acting out, her sexual feelings for Joe, but this fascination is not so significant as is the hostile identification with the mother. The therapist has a tendency to deal with the manifest content of the transaction and with the explicit roles in rational language. In this way there develops too great a digression away from a central focus. The therapist is seduced to respond to her pleas to do something and to act in an authoritative way, but at the end of the interview she attempts to reject this role.

Twenty-fifth Session

PATIENT BEGINS by telling me that she is taking things too personally. She had a lot of difficulty in school this week. A boy had told her he didn't like drawing, which is the current subject matter of his class. She told him to get a transfer if he didn't like it because he wouldn't get anything out of the class. Another boy had asked her why he had to take art, he didn't see how it helped him. This morning her class did not arrive and she kept waiting for them, wondering what happened. She found out later they were rehearsing for a school play. She dreads to go to a school faculty party and does not know how to talk to people and does not think they like her at school. "I told you I wasn't so worried about people liking me. Well, it's much worse now. I just feel that everything is mixed up and I'm so mixed up. I wonder if treatment does help."

I say that she is angry at me. Yes, she felt "real hostile" to me for two days. On Wednesday night, when it was so stormy, patient and her brother had gone to the downtown terminal of the airport to meet her mother. The plane was late and brother went home but she stayed and waited to see her mother. When she finally had news of the plane arriving, she called the airport and spoke to mother on the phone. Mother did not come downtown to see her, but took a cab directly to brother's house where she is staying for the holidays. Patient invited mother to meet her downtown for dinner on Thursday, but mother thought she would be too tired and busy with brother. Mother is meeting patient for dinner tonight. Patient was wearing drab casual clothes, obviously not dressed for dinner downtown. "Why my mother has been in town for two whole days, and I haven't seen her yet." *I wonder why she is angry at me.* Well, when she was talking to her mother on the phone it suddenly flashed into her head, "I'm not the favorite. You know I told you I was the favorite and I thought you questioned it and doubted it. I told you how Mom let me do the housework and you thought it didn't mean I was the favorite. When I talked to her I thought she liked my brother better." *I say she felt it was my fault then.* Yes, if I hadn't put doubt in her mind she would never have had these thoughts. *She cannot tolerate not to be the favorite, then.* Well, she doesn't know. She was surprised at what her mother said. *These were her own doubts that had come up in her own mind, weren't they?* Yes, but I never had them before. *I tell her that she had been hiding them from herself for a long time.* Yes, but I don't like it. Patient then talked a good bit about how mixed up she is, questioning everything now, and wondering what will happen as a result of treatment. *I say it is understandable that she is stirred up meeting her mother right now. It is tough on her because of these feelings she is just now facing. I then ask specifically about her doubts of treatment and me.* Well, there is a girl at school who is the child of a psychiatrist and a psychologist, and as far as patient is concerned she is one of the worst-adjusted children; she sucks her thumb all the time, etc. *When I say, "Oh,"* she begins to laugh a little. *I then comment that she is attacking me, isn't she?* Yes, and sometimes she doesn't like the words I use; for example I said "repress" a while back. When I told her she was hiding something from herself she understood, but when I went on and said repress it wasn't the same. She is apologetic, *and I point out that she should tell me her reactions so we can understand further. I ask about "repress."* Well, that was psychiatric and it was like I was talking to an equal, and it made it seem worse or better; she is undecided about this. *I comment that she isn't sure. Does she have doubts about treatment?* She denies this and *when I am openly skeptical* she admits doubt and *I encourage her to tell me about it openly.* "Well, sometimes it is wonderful and then we go along for a while and I can't see I'm getting anywhere. I guess it's like that. I've never felt so conscious of squirming and wiggling or felt so much emotion. It upsets me and sometimes I wonder if you get a wrong idea of me and what I'm like. I wish I smoked. I'm so conscious of not having anything to do with my hands. Paul used to tell me I wanted to be an infant because I don't smoke or drink coffee. He's usually right even for the wrong reasons." *I ask how she thinks I feel.* Well, she wonders whether I think she has any talent or ability. *I press her quite hard on this, point out her marked self-depreciation. I then state that I feel she has talent and ability, pointing out further her self-deprecia-tion when she cannot take this. I ask her what she thinks I feel about her being emotional.* She berates herself further. *I point this out and state that I am capable of understanding that she will be more emo-tional in the sessions here. In fact, I am pressing for it so we can get to those feelings she can't handle in herself.*

Patient tells me that she has been very depressed this week. She knows it and she knows everything has gone wrong because of it. *Does she know what set it off?* "Was it my mother?" *When I ask her what she thinks,* "Yes." *I tell her that she had some angry thoughts about her mother and couldn't tolerate them. She turned against herself by beating herself down.* "Yes." *She also got mad at me.* "Well, I thought you felt my mother preferred my brother, didn't you?" *I say no, actu-ally not. I am not sure about this yet. I felt sure that mother was so occupied with her own needs that she couldn't give to patient. I don't know whether she could give to brother or not.* Patient tells me Mom always did have a hard time traveling. She gets tired and then won't put herself out for people at all. She never had it dawn on her like this before—"I need reassurance very much from you." *I tell her she needs to understand how the feelings she has been hiding from herself have been affecting her.* She wonders what she is coming to treatment for. Will I ever get married? *I point out her provocation.* She is quite seri-ous and asks me the same question. *If she means we will guarantee that she will get a wedding ring, then the answer is no. If she means that we will help her become emotionally ready to seek marriage, then the answer is yes.* Patient says she knows what I mean. She knows she is like a little girl in some ways and one of the reasons she can't do better is because of this.

COMMENTS ON TWENTY-FIFTH SESSION: The patient, through her recounting of several incidents in her present life, is talking about her hostility to the therapist for not accepting the assigned omnipotent role. She has developed a masochistic attitude toward her experiences of being mistreated. She attempts to use her talent and ability as a substitute for love and, in failing, places school, the brother, the mother, and the therapist together in a pattern of re-jection. The rivalry with the brother seems to be secondary to her feeling of being rejected. She apparently does not like what the therapist has done in bringing her insight, and actually her anger—which she has difficulty in experiencing or ventilating—is displaced to the therapist. Whatever anger does approach the level of awareness produces feelings of guilt and additional self-depreciation. Again the patient questions herself regarding the dichotomies of: "Am I better or worse?" "Am I a child to the therapist, or am I an equal?"

Twenty-sixth Session

PATIENT HAS A COLD and comments first that she is eating liver and onions for breakfast every morning for her health. She then states that she feels the cold is on an emotional basis, links it up to her mother's visit and spends the rest of the hour talking about this.

Mother seemed different to her this time than ever before. She thinks it is because mother is going through the menopause. Patient does not know mother's age, perhaps in the early fifties. As patient talks, she realizes that problems in her relationship with her mother are long standing, and abandons her original feeling that mother is upset primarily because of the menopause.

Mother went to brother's house where she immediately was quite critical of her daughter-in-law, particularly about the way she cared for her baby. Mother kept saying that she had brought up her own children well. Patient expressed surprise that her mother would act so much like the traditional mother-in-law. Her mother has usually had very good sense about things like this and she was really way out of line in the way she was behaving. Patient had spoken to her about it, and mother was hurt. She is very sensitive. Patient dropped the subject, feeling that she did not want to get any more involved as it was not her problem. Gradually the picture evolves of the mother as a self-centered woman threatened with growing old. Mother left her husband alone to come to Chicago for Christmas, plans to go back for New Year's. Mother's current husband is described by patient as somewhat odd in that he does not like classical music, unless others take the initiative to present it to him. He is also withdrawn at times. As patient talks about this, she begins to see something of her mother's demands on this man and switches to defending him with some warmth.

About the middle of the week mother moved in with patient for the rest of her visit, saying that she could not stand the noise at brother's. Several things happened which were quite disconcerting to patient. Patient has an army cot for an extra bed, sleeps on it when she has visitors. Mother kept insisting that she wanted to sleep on the cot, acting like a terrible martyr. Patient had to insist that mother sleep in the regular bed and felt very uncomfortable at the fuss mother made. Then one morning patient slept later than mother and woke up to find mother had not eaten or had coffee. Mother said she would not dream of opening the refrigerator to take out grapefruit, etc.; she didn't feel it was right because she was a "guest." Patient was startled about mother's feeling of being a guest and being unable to help herself to food in her own daughter's apartment.

Mother had asked her directly whether she had seen Paul and wanted to get involved in a long discussion. Patient cut her off by saying, "No, mother, and I don't expect to hear from him." Mother told patient that she knew father had made patient unhappy and caused her to have an unhappy life. She then asked patient if she had ever done anything to make her unhappy, clearly expecting a negative answer. Patient told her that she had made her unhappy, adding that she guessed mother herself was pretty upset and unhappy for a while. It is the first time mother has ever alluded even indirectly to the past and patient was surprised that mother could slide over it the way she did and believe it wouldn't affect the patient.

Mother constantly uses two phrases with her: "Oh my darling, oh my darling"; and "You're so beautiful, you're so beautiful." She used to love hearing this, but now it makes her distinctly uncomfortable and she found she couldn't stand it. She shows guilt which *I point out to her*, and she is then able to talk of mother's possessiveness. Mother had come "home" for Christmas and patient had realized that it had been many years since there had been a home. She begins to see mother's clinging and demanding personality, and *I interpret this to her*. Patient had not told mother of her treatment, as it was "too intimate."

Patient had always thought they had a perfect mother-daughter relationship with so much understanding. Do you think it will ever go back to this? *When I wonder what she wants*, she brings out a longing for a close, dependent relationship. *I point this out to her*. She then talks about feeling really critical of her mother for the first time in her life. *She is told that all daughters feel resentful of their mothers as they grow up, that this is the first time she has been able to face her critical feelings.* She guesses this is another illusion which will have to go. She again brings up her awareness of her childishness and her discovery that you can't go back to this for happiness.

COMMENTS ON TWENTY-SIXTH SESSION: At this interview the patient arrives with a cold which may be related to the frustration of her dependent needs. She is apparently ready to observe and interpret her insight regarding mother's personality and the fact that mother has been a rejecting mother most of her life. Yet in defense of this, we see the evidences of an intimate, clutching, dependent relationship which the patient can observe only in her mother rather than in herself. She has some insight that, as far as her dependent needs are concerned, she cannot go home again.

COMMENTS ON SECOND AND THIRD PHASES OF THERAPY

The ninth to twenty-sixth sessions constitute the second and third phases of this psychotherapy. Their central axis is the patient's vicissitudes in understanding and acting a feminine role. Consciously she tries hard and outwardly is partially successful in pretending to be a woman—psychologically, behaviorally, and sexually. Yet her implicit roles interfere with the successful execution of femininity and often direct and control the actual behavior. The end result, aside from her intentions, is a series of vacillations among many roles, none of which is stable for any length of time.

The ninth session concerns her feeling of failure in the role of a woman, followed in the tenth session by a beginning competitive attitude, but in the next several sessions we see an overwhelming fear resulting in flight to sexual fantasies and masochism or to childish dependency. In session 13 there is recognition of incestuous feelings to father and to brother, followed by regressive retreat, guilt, and need for punishment. In fact, her guilt associated with competition with mother instigates a pattern of forcing her own rejection. The nature of her fears aside from the above becomes clearer as her image of the feminine role emerges as being sado-masochistic. Playing the female role indicates a difficulty based on her image of the promiscuous mother. She vacillates between the seductive prostitute role and the good little dependent girl. But in the latter role she experiences rejection, anger at frustration, and depression.

Thus we see that the vacillating roles which keep the patient confused and not knowing where she stands, and dependent on others' opinions, start with her earliest conflicts over sexual feelings. Femininity is incestuous, promiscuous, masochistic. What else to be but a good little favorite child? But this was not and cannot be true, resulting in angry frustration, guilt, and depression. At times she behaves like a sadistic person taking revenge on the men who apparently cause her to feel a failure as a woman.

The therapy has not always gone as we anticipated, in spite of free discussion. The heavy weight of previous psychoanalytic orientation showed through the transactions. Too many anxiety-allaying comments were verbalized by the therapist and too much of the authoritative role was accepted by the therapist and remained unclarified. Yet the patient moved on in therapy, gained greater strength to expose and endure her feelings and to some degree change her pattern of behavior.

Is this the result of learning some intellectual formulations, or is there some realignment of role structures and internal identifications? For this question we have no ready answer at this time, as is the case in any form of therapy. Yet we may conjecture, from the anecdotes of her current behavior in life and in the therapeutic transaction, from the flow of associations and dream material, that changes are occurring in this girl's psychic life. We are particularly impressed with evidences that the patient is becoming more aware of her own role identities.

9

The Fourth Phase of Therapy

Twenty-seventh Session

THE PATIENT OPENED THE SESSION with the statement, "A lot of things happened"—patient met Kay at the airport, her mother left this morning, and she is managing a store in the suburbs which will prevent her from keeping her appointment next Friday.

Patient begins telling me of Kay's visit. She met her at the airport and talked for an hour or so and Kay gave her all the news. It left her feeling upset. Paul has had two homosexual affairs this fall, has made two attempts at psychiatric treatment but backed out each time with a flimsy excuse, is now in Cleveland visiting a homosexual friend, has no job or money, borrowed money from Kay to whom he has talked frequently in a platonic way about his troubles, has not slept with a woman for months. There are many sordid details which really upset her. *I agree with her reaction.* When she told Kay how sordid it all was, Kay tried to make her feel that this was nothing unusual and patient should accept it naturally. She found that she couldn't and knows that she is right. She figured that Paul is bent on self-destruction in every way possible and is getting closer and closer to the gutter. Nobody can help him until he is ready to be helped. Kay herself is involved with a homosexual man. *I said that patient may have begun to have some doubts about her friendship with Kay.* "Yes," she had. She had told Kay what I had said about being able to take or leave the friendship. *I meant that she herself as well as Kay had a full share in deciding whether or not she wanted her friendship.* Patient tells me some more details about Kay, including an illegitimate child and homosexual affairs, winding up again with her sense of estrangement from all of this.

Kay had asked her whether she was a homosexual, too. Patient said she has worried about this, wondered if she is hiding it from herself. She has never had any homosexual experiences, has never wanted them or been in love with a woman. She knows she is fascinated with watching beautiful women, but this is all she knows about herself that is unusual. She knows you can be too disgusted, for the sake of hiding from yourself what you feel underneath. She will admit she was very curious one time about Paul, but when he told her the details of one affair, she felt it was sick rather than interesting. She knows Paul went out with the homosexual man that night to get rid of her and she can face it. Don't I think this is right? *I tell her I agree but that it must make her pretty upset and angry.* Paul told Kay that he is responsible for getting patient into psychiatric treatment, and she was surprised at this. She wanted to go on her own. Paul came into her life when she was desperate about her father. She still has some fondness for him. She has been wondering what it means when you like a man who is also a homosexual. Do I think she really is a homosexual? She knows that everyone has a little bit of this in him, but do I think she is really a homosexual like they are and hiding it from herself? *I tell her she has some problems with women but this does not make her an overt homosexual.* She expresses relief, saying that she thought she was right about this but had to hear me say it after Kay attacked her.

After she saw Kay, she didn't sleep well. All these things kept racing around in her mind and she was thinking how complicated they were. In a way she is glad she was upset. It felt "right" to her and she was not drawn into all of this in the same old way.

The patient then recounted a long and involved dream, the details of which need not be reported. Her associations were all to the manifest content brought out spontaneously and in response to the therapist's questions. They may be summarized briefly as centering around homosexuality and sexual perversions from the frame of reference of the adult.

COMMENTS ON TWENTY-SEVENTH SESSION: In the twenty-seventh session we see emerging the patient's confusion of sexual roles: a boy, a girl, an identification with the promiscuous mother dealing in stolen goods, and her conscious reaction against the latter role. In the main transactional focus the patient is becoming more aware of her disguised homosexual role which centers around her relation to her mother. This protects her from feeling anger toward her as if she says, "I am not angry at my mother, I love her." Actually, on her mother's last day in town the patient felt so mad at her that she was tempted to hit her. She says, "I never felt mad at my mother like this before." But the mother's visit ended with a giggling session and gales of laughter so that the anger was neatly covered up again as far as outward appearances were concerned.

Within the interview the therapist's ready acceptance of patient's initial role assignments (herself as the anxious patient and therapist as listener) permits elaboration of homosexual concerns ostensibly around Paul, which, when not reacted to with anxiety on the part of the therapist, spirals to a confession of her homosexual fears about herself. The therapist's matter-of-fact clarification of homosexual problems as opposed to overt homosexuality results in the diminution of the patient's anxiety.

Twenty-eighth Session

PATIENT STARTS TALKING about a New Year's Eve party which ended with her feeling depressed and unhappy, wondering whether she liked anybody because she was so critical of everybody. From this she relates her inability to express anger except in three situations in the past. One was a day after a man had brushed her off; two others after going home after other incidents, writing down how she felt, and reading it off over the phone, checking off the words as she said them.

I ask directly about anger toward me. She denies this. *I ask what she was doing this time last week.* "Well, I did have a reaction. It was about stealing." Patient then tells me that during her week at the store she had sold half as much as the owner had sold the previous week. Perhaps the owner will feel that she has stolen from the store. Immediately she recognizes this as an irrational reaction.

What does she feel she is stealing from me, I ask. Well, the last time she came in, a little boy had a present for his psychiatrist and the psychiatrist had one for him. She had been startled because it had not occurred to her to give me a present, although I am the kind of person to whom she would like to give something she had made herself. She thought about it, but decided it wasn't spontaneous and didn't do it. Then she wanted to send me a card or call me up, but decided not to. She wanted to ask me whether or not she should call Paul but knew that she just wanted to talk to me, for she knew there was no point in calling Paul and she was just making up something to be concerned about. She always thinks of the wonderful times she had with Paul when actually she should remind herself of the many difficulties. She feels empty and has to keep busy. Last week a friend hinted at this and it really got under her skin.

I say that she wanted a gift from me. She denies this. *I tell her that she felt angry about it and wanted to steal from me.* Well, she doesn't know what category I'm in. I'm not a relative and not a friend but in a special category of my own. She thinks of me but not in a personal way. She likes me but it is not the same as ordinary liking. When she worked at the shop, psychiatrists used to come in to buy gifts for their patients at Christmas and when they were sick. "It didn't come up until I saw that boy with a present and then I wondered why I didn't think of giving you a present." I know I was mad at you that time about my mother but it really wasn't in a personal way like that. *I say that she really wanted something from me and got mad and depressed about it.* Yes, she had felt superstitious at New Year's because she was crying. *What did she expect of the New Year?* Well, she had thought she could stop working so hard trying to get a husband until she got through her treatment. She has no serious responsibility to get a husband while she is in treatment. *When I ask her what she means by serious responsibility,* she tells me that her mother writes in practically every letter, "For God's sake, hurry up and get married." When she was away she realized there was no one in the world she really wanted to come back to. She describes how at the party she was looking at all the married men. She had felt disgusted by one who was nibbling her neck when they were dancing. She doesn't see how a psychiatrist could ever enjoy himself at a party, knowing so much about people. *Then she feels this knowledge is hostile, another way to attack people. Does she feel she is stealing knowledge from me to use against people?* After a good bit of circumlocution, she admits feeling guilty about this.

COMMENTS ON TWENTY-EIGHTH SESSION: The general tone of this transaction from the patient's side is that of a lonely and dependent little girl appealing for help. Although she expresses this in terms of her rejection at the New Year's Eve party and her memory of being brushed off, it is apparent that the essential feeling arises from her relationship with the therapist. The patient felt brushed off because the therapist did not urge her not to miss a session at the last occasion. Here we see that her helplessness and frustration are associated with anger which cannot be expressed directly toward the therapist because it is on the therapist that she is so completely dependent. This is the formula for the dilemma of the child who feels frustrated by a mother who does not give and yet at the same time is frightened of expressing her feelings because then she will get less. In fact, this patient's mother was less giving and more demanding herself and expressed her own individuality in a selfish life. The patient has a constant fantasy of acting out the process of stealing from another woman —now the therapist, but in real life the wish to take a woman's man away from her is forbidden because of her conflicts. It is as if she says: "Either you steal from another woman, or you get nothing." Her feeling of helplessness is expressed by her pessimistic conclusion that it's no use—she will not get married, which means she will not compete with another woman. In fact, if she should get married, it is the therapist through her treatment who should get someone for her.

Twenty-ninth Session

PATIENT BEGINS TALKING about an incident that occurred on the way to the interview, saying that she became very angry about it. She had stopped to exchange four light bulbs and dealt with a woman who was very mean. The woman told her that she could not exchange the bulbs, and took two of patient's bulbs away from her without giving her any in exchange, saying that these belonged to the company. Patient boasts about how angry she was and ends up, "I fixed her. I bought four new light bulbs at the five and ten." Patient did not deal with the situation, she let this woman dominate her. *I point out that she felt helplessly angry about this and was unable to do anything.* She is somewhat deflated but agrees. *I then inquire about anger toward me.* She denies this. *I point out that she had wanted to steal from me last week and now this woman had taken two light bulbs away from her. What about her feelings of anger toward women—toward her mother, for instance?*

"Oh, no. It's my father I always felt angry toward. So many things stand out in my mind." She remembers when father had promised her $5.00 if she got five S's on her report card and then broke his promise. When father saw her new coat, which she is wearing today for the first time here, he said it looked warm but wouldn't say anything nice about it. *I tell patient that we are trying to understand her feelings of anger toward women today.* "Well, I thought fathers loved their daughters more and mothers loved their sons more. I felt very angry toward my father many times for the things he did to me without any reason." *I said that I know father did deprive her and was unreasonable, but she is aware of her anger about this; she knows where she stands and how she feels about it. I do not feel that she understands her anger toward women.* "I always fight you off when it comes to my mother. I guess I want to blame my father for my unhappiness. There are some things I know about my anger toward my mother I should tell you."

Patient then tells of an incident when she was about eleven. She wanted some party shoes and cried and stormed at her mother. There was no good reason so far as she knows why she shouldn't have had them; mother just wouldn't get them. While she was crying, her mother hit her and bloodied her nose. Patient said to her, "You bleeded me." She was too old to talk this way, it just came out. "But then I played it to the hilt like a little actress." Patient often reminded her mother of this incident. Some time later patient "decided" she wasn't going to let her mother hit her any more. When they were having an argument and mother hit her, she resisted a very strong impulse to hit her back. She folded her arms and told mother that if she hit her again she would hit back—and she meant it. Mother did not hit her again. She really cannot get mad at women, though, except Ivy, and anybody could get mad at her.

Then when she was in high school and used to have parties in the basement, she was very uncomfortable and miserable. In grammar school she was popular and the boys liked her, but at these basement parties most of the boys were three to four years older. Her mother used to entice the boys to her room to tell them dirty jokes. Three or four of them would sit on her bed and listen. Patient was not allowed to hear the jokes or to participate. She felt shut out, although she knew she should not be hearing the jokes either.

One time she got very angry at her mother. Patient had a crush on one boy, the only one she felt comfortable with. On one occasion during a party this boy came over to talk and be with her, and she felt very happy. Then her mother appeared, came up to them, and before she knew what was happening the boy was walking away from her with her mother. She cried and screamed at her mother afterward, but her mother could not see that she had done anything wrong or why patient was upset. *I comment that it was this feeling of helpless rage, wasn't it?* Yes, although her mother did not come down to the basement again. *I say that patient had the feeling that mother could take her boy friends away from her any time she wanted to do so.* Yes, she did feel that. She was looking at her mother critically when she was here visiting. Mother still has a very good figure, although she may be flabby without her clothes on. She also still has her charm. Patient felt even now she couldn't compete successfully with her. "Yes, I guess it's not a strange idea to me that my mother would come along and take away my boy friend. But she always praised me for anything I did. It didn't have to be the best, like for my father." *I wonder how this kind of praise made her feel.* She is quite enthusiastic but then begins to hesitate and ends up saying that it's no good because it really doesn't matter what you do then.

COMMENTS ON TWENTY-NINTH SESSION: In this interview patient discusses a life situation which coincides with the role relations developing in the transaction. A woman refuses to exchange her bulbs and takes some of them away from her. We learned in the last interview that the mother was constantly making demands on her instead of giving to her. When the implied anger at the therapist is pointed out, patient is defensively angry at the father, but the therapist pulls her away from this focus and asks her to concentrate on the mother. Now a large amount of information is divulged about the mother and her false promises. In the patient's eyes the therapist has taken Paul away from the patient, although indirectly. The transaction continues to be expressed in terms of the mother, who, although she gives false promise to the patient, still implies that she is not good enough to compete. She will never be good enough for her earliest object relationship, namely, the father, and feels that even now, although the mother is flabby, she is still a competitive threat. Here the capacity to compete openly with the mother is very low and the patient has over and over again acted out the role of the loser. This is also expressed in her current life situation with other girls.

The focus of the transaction is the competitive role with the mother in which there is considerable anger. She is ill-prepared for direct expressions of hostility because of her experiences in the earlier dependent relationship. The therapist cannot make the interpretation of sexual competition in the transaction itself, for there will be no occasion for this material to arise. However, the maternal background of the transaction comes from the implicit role of the therapist in the control maintained by her, which implies that the patient is not right, is on the wrong focus, is dodging the issue, or that her own interpretations are not correct. It is in this therapeutic procedure that the rivalry of patient and therapist as two women comes to the foreground—expressed by the current and past relationships with other women.

Thirtieth Session

PATIENT STARTS IMMEDIATELY with two dreams. The first was three nights ago. She has had difficulty sleeping since. Last night she had another dream. "I hope I can sleep tonight."

> I was looking in the mirror at my eye. It was very painful. There was a red spot of blood—a beautiful crimson red. There were four lashes on a little strip sideways across the white and blood was coming from the ends of them. Then I looked up under the lid and there was another red place up there. There wasn't anything like this across the pupil, and I could see.

Patient comments with feeling that this had upset her. On the other hand, last night's dream terrified her but she has not felt badly since awakening. She wanted to scream at the end but had catarrh of her throat and couldn't.

> It's about my mother. It didn't look like my mother, but I know it was my mother. She was a great big woman, tall and fat. She had a gun. At the beginning of the dream she was killing a lot of people, shooting them

down. I was off to the side. I knew who they were in the dream, but I can't remember at all since I woke up. They were both men and women. Then I was standing beside her husband in the background. I don't think they were married yet in the dream. There was a wall that had some of my clothes put on it. My mother began shooting at them. I thought, "Why, my mother's trying to kill me, but she can't because she's only shooting at my clothes." I remember particularly a plaid skirt which she shot at. Then, my mother turned and pointed the gun directly at me. She was going to kill me. I tried to scream but I couldn't.

With an abrupt switch to a markedly childish manner, patient then asks, "Do you think these dreams are important?" She doesn't know what they have to do with her. She can't make any sense out of the eye dream because she never had any eye trouble she knows of. *I ask what she thinks they have to do with me and her treatment.* "I haven't dreamed about you—yet." *I tell patient that she feels she is being punished by her mother for talking about her to me.* "Oh!" Patient tells me then that she had sort of enjoyed the first part of that dream when her mother was killing other people but she was really terrified when her mother turned on her. *I ask if she feels I'm killing her with treatment and interpretations.* "No, I'm sure it wasn't you in the dreams. I'm sure it was my mother." *I say that I'm behind it though,* and patient agrees.

I ask about the first dream and patient responds with a fuller description of the pain and the beautiful color of the blood. *I point out that there are aspects of both suffering and enjoyment in this then.* Yes. She cannot understand what the eye has to do with it. *I interpret it as a symbol of curiosity and looking. She is looking at herself with pain and enjoyment both.* Patient understands this. *I relate this to her feelings about treatment and me.* Patient does not think that she feels pain about me but is conscious of bracing herself to go through an ordeal at points. Then she realizes that she is actually describing a form of pain—says so, "I didn't know I felt that way about myself." *I tell patient that she has kept her feelings hidden from me—and from herself.* Yes. She cannot let herself go. She can weep at movies. *I say, "But not about yourself."* Yes, this is true except for one thing. At times she will say to herself, "Now let yourself go and cry—and then I can." She can never cry "naturally" and she knows this is a problem. *I say that she has to give herself formal permission.* "Yes"—and patient adds that she was feeling sorry for herself in the dream. *I tell her that the blood is a substitute for weeping. She feels battered and attacked by her treatment.* "Yes," she has been curious about many things. She tells of hearing a nurse in her class talk about a patient and she had "pricked up her ears." *I ask about curiosity about me.* She very gingerly agrees but is vague and nonspecific, and *I comment that she is wondering about me*—and then let this go.

Patient brings up the four lashes saying that she can't see why they were in the dream. I suggest that there are four members in her immediate family. "Oh, yes"—the other day she was thinking that they were all in the mess together of her life. She knows it is her life, though, and she is a separate person. *I say that we are not trying to blame anyone, we are trying to help her understand herself.*

"Then it's because I'm guilty about talking about my mother that my mother tried to kill me in that other dream." *I say this is correct.* Patient says she always tries to make her mother better than she is. "I protect her when I don't have to do that." *I agree and tell patient that I am not trying to get her to gang up with me against her mother.*

COMMENTS ON THIRTIETH SESSION: The patient recounts two dreams, both of which were quite disturbing to her. The therapist attempts to interpret the dreams, using the information obtained to bring the patient's attention to her experiences in the treatment. The therapist feels that the patient's narcissism has been shaken or battered by her experiences in therapy. In general, we can state that interpretation of dreams in the processes of psychotherapy, particularly the type that we are attempting to develop and herewith demonstrate, is not of central importance. In the first place, the patient needs to have her attention focused largely on the present reality. The bringing of dreams to the therapist for interpretation with a minimum of associations, as occurred in this session, implicitly makes her dependent on the all-knowing therapist who fathoms the answer to the dreams. Probably more important is a third reason: it tends to stimulate an intellectual interest in dreams rather than a truly effective insight.

In viewing the first dream, the patient seems to be looking in the mirror at her I (eye spelled as a pronoun). The very act of looking expresses a voyeuristic tendency, which in this case is entirely narcissistic since she is looking at herself. The therapist interprets the four lashes as possibly representing the four members of her family. Nevertheless, it is quite possible that the bleeding developing from these injurious strips may represent some deeper connection with her conception of a menstruating woman as being damaged.

The second dream very clearly concerns problems with the mother in which the distancing from the hostile relationship gradually becomes ineffective during the course of the dream. At first the patient is off to a side; the mother shoots at clothes, and then finally at the patient. At the same time it is clear that the patient is standing next to the mother's husband, watching the whole scene. It is as if there is a distortion of the patient's hostile curiosity in an effort to get something on the mother.

The last interview indicated that the patient was concerned with competition with other women, particularly mother figures. We saw that the setting in which the therapist made interpretations seemed to be the only context that the patient could use as competition with the therapist. In this session the patient experiences, behind her hostility and feeling of danger involved in it, curiosity about the therapist. It is as if she asks, "Who are you really, and what are you doing?"

Thirty-first Session

PATIENT BEGINS with three dreams. She comments that she had a feeling there was lots more but only remembered bits of them. "In one I protected my mother and got even, and the other two were about school children and Negroes." She tells the dreams in reverse order of their occurrence. The dream about the mother was first.

> I was in a big apartment building on Lake Shore Drive, like those big glass ones I don't like. I was in a room and behind it many other rooms opened out from each other with no windows. I was a schoolteacher. Then just hundreds of school children came trooping up a fire escape. I recognized some of them as boys from school. Nobody was doing anything about it. Then I started sending the children to the elevator to go down that way. I got on to take them down. Two great big Negro boys were standing just back of me. I felt one pat me on the flank. I was very surprised.
>
> Then I dreamed later that night that I cut off this Negro man's head. It wasn't the same Negro as in the first dream. I cut off one of his ears, too, and I picked it up and looked at it. I wondered if his body would work the same as before and I thought it wouldn't because he didn't have his brains.
>
> The night before I had a dream about my mother. We were sleeping in a very crowded room with lots of people in it. It was an old apartment building. I was sleeping curled up on a quilt on the floor. My mother said she had to go out and tend the sheep. She took a long stick with her. She had to go down a long dark road and there were wolves there and I knew she wasn't safe. I let her go, but then I decided to go, too, and protect my mother. I took two sticks with me.

Patient remarks that she had protected her mother. She then says she is wondering what made her cut a man's head off in a dream. She is also concerned because as far as she knows she doesn't have racial prejudice. She became aware this week, however, that she is conscious of racial differences in school. There is a Japanese child, toward whom she is conscious of being careful of what she says. There is a Negro boy who grins at her very politely when she asks him to do something, but goes ahead doing just as he pleases. She had finally been able to tell him, "I mean what I say," referring to giving him a school assignment. He had responded by doing the assignment.

She had dated two men this week who seem to want her just on their own terms. They had professed great interest on previous dates but then dropped her for long periods of time. Patient describes both of these persons as exploiting infantile men. These are not different from patient's usual dates, but she is beginning to want more from such relationships and to resent exhibitionistic behavior. She comments that she doesn't think this behavior is cute, became quite exasperated with one boy's clowning on the street and told him so. She had wanted one to kiss her—and he didn't, and the other not to kiss her—and he did. It seems to work out that way.

I say that patient must feel that she is not having her own needs gratified. What about this? "Well, there wasn't one single thing this week that was gratifying to me except maybe that school is going better." *But nothing happened you wanted for yourself?* Patient agrees with a good deal of warmth. She begins talking of the various disappointments and frustrations (dates, friends, etc.) and becomes more animated. *I wonder whether it hadn't made her angry to have so few of her own needs met this week.* She agrees with considerable warmth and begins telling me about a visit to an artist friend. This man had a sculptured head of a man in his studio. She knew that Paul admired this piece of work and thought that he had purchased it. She wonders whether this man bought it from Paul or had a duplicate of his own, but had not felt free to ask him. There are three classes of men, "Those I want to kiss, those I don't want to kiss, and Paul, who is in a special class of his own." Whenever she meets a man she wonders in which category he belongs, and usually knows, but this week she switched classifications for both men she had told me about. *I wonder why.* Well, she isn't so sure that one is as attractive as she thought and maybe there is more to the other one than she thought. *I ask what it means to put men in categories.* She wants to be told by me, and *I ask for her feelings.* She is quite anxious about this, does a lot of ruminating, and finally says it puts distance between her and the man. *I say that she is wondering how much she can depend on other people for meeting her own needs.*

COMMENTS ON THIRTY-FIRST SESSION: The patient spent most of this session relating her dreams and associating on them. We, of course, are not very much interested in making an interpretation to the patient about her dream life, but we do try to utilize the dreams for the purpose of better understanding her transactions. It seems that the patient is making demands on the therapist, who does not seem to be responding to her assignment with the complementarity that the patient desires. The patient indicates that she has the capacity to become aggressive against anyone who deprives her, and to avoid this she becomes the pleading little child who searches for the dependent relationship by being very, very good. The dreams indicate to us that one of the things she feels deprived of is related to her mother's plethora of men and her brother's possession of an anatomical structure which makes him something apart from her. She seems to feel deprived at not being a boy and accuses her mother of discriminating against her. Secondary to this we see that the patient maintains, out of fear of her aggressions, a state of deprivation which then can give her some secondary masochistic satisfaction.

Thirty-second Session

PATIENT BEGINS by telling me about a letter she had received from her mother, saying that she had dreamed about it this morning. Patient's mother had invited her to visit her new home and patient had wanted to postpone this until summer—"actually I never have a very good time there anyway." Mother had written back "come when you are ready" in an angry, rejecting way.

> I was going to visit my mother and I had $175 for the trip. She lived far away on an island in the South Seas. Actually I wasn't too sure I wanted to go and I couldn't afford it, except that I was going on a work trip with my expenses paid, so I could stop off and see my mother on the way to somewhere else. I made her three kites as a present. One was pink and white and lacy; another one was purple and yellow. I can't remember them too well. I put them in a long tube to carry them. I got off the boat in the South Seas and I was carrying the tube. My mother lived on a separate little islet which had an arched Japanese bridge you had to cross to get to it. From the bridge I could see the house and it changed several times; it looked beautiful and then it looked ugly and drab. There was a kite I had made hanging as a decoration on the open porch and it looked worn out and I was glad I had brought my mother these new ones. There was a man there and sometimes he looked like my mother's husband and sometimes he didn't. My mother saw me and came out. She folded her arms and said, "I don't want any of your god-damn kites. They're no good." I turned and walked away.

Patient says that her mother is rejecting her in alternate dreams "and then I do something for her and she still rejects me." She is then quite concerned as to whether or not her mother is really angry at her or whether this is just her own reaction to the letter. However, mother had issued her a specific invitation for April, which she had turned down because she didn't want to go. In other words, it becomes clear that patient feels guilty because she had rejected her mother's invitation. *When I interpret this* patient tells me that this last week had been awful. She had left the interview feeling as if she couldn't do anything. *I ask whether she felt I thought she was unable to do anything.* She doesn't think so, it all seemed to be about men. Saturday night she had hopes of a date for a play at school. The man is very good-looking and she particularly wanted to appear with him "since the kids place so much emphasis on what kind of date you have." He didn't show up, through a set of events which include a great deal of mutual provocation between him and patient, and she had to go at the last minute with somebody else. Patient had been very provocative in planning this date, sort of half-promising she would be home. Then Sunday she went skiing with Albert. He was "just darling" to her, paid for a ski lesson for her, was very patient, entertained her extensively, and paid all the bills— which is unusual for their group. He is still physically repulsive to her, not at all good-looking, and she didn't particularly want to be seen with him. "I like handsome men." Another evening she had met a very handsome German man at a party, was immediately attracted to him "but he hasn't called me yet—I was sure he would." She described several other incidents, all in this same vein. *When I wonder whether she feels she is missing something,* patient has only general association of not being able to make things come out. *Would it be different if she were a man?* In an excited manner she says that she would make telephone calls to men she wants instead of waiting; girls are not supposed to do this. She can call men who don't matter to her as men, but she can't call the others. Patient talks on about this, and *I wonder whether she would like to be a man.* She doesn't really think so, but her affect suggests otherwise. As I end the interview, patient comments that today she could go on talking to me for hours.

As she is leaving, patient asks me to look at some of her pupils' art work. "I wonder if you would like to see this." It is a booklet containing block prints illustrating various months of the year. I look at the pictures while she stands beside me making occasional comments. *I tell her that I like the book.*

COMMENTS ON THIRTY-SECOND SESSION: In this session the patient relates a dream which took up most of the hour. It is utilized not as a means of interpretation of her unconscious wishes and conflicts but as information for the therapist to further her understanding of what is going on in the transaction. The dream concerns the mother and the patient's past experiences with her, but it also has the elements of what is implicit in the current transaction with the therapist. The patient is hostile to the mother-therapist and has difficulty in dealing with these feelings and seeks a reaction of rejection, both as punishment for these wishes and as justification for them. Thus, the patient is provocative toward the mother. Her ambivalence is clearly expressed by the changing view of the house. It is both beautiful and ugly and drab. She fantasies it would be possible to get to the mother over an arched bridge, which is probably a penis symbol indicating that to her the only approach to the mother is through the sexual role of the male; for the mother was promiscuous and also favored the younger brother. The implicit question in the therapeutic transaction is: If the patient gives to the therapist what she expects from her, in return will she obtain the penis or be able to play the masculine role?

This session points up how much role-playing the patient does, not only because of her confusion resulting in the continuous query: "Who am I?" but also in her implicit and overtly modified behavior. All of this role-playing seems to be in the service of hiding an underlying depression. In this regard, it seems that the therapist engages in too much complementarity and structuring of roles for the patient so that it is easy for her to find the proper position vis-à-vis the therapist.

In her relationship with men she envies the good-looking ones, at the same time depreciates them, and does everything possible to avoid the feminine role which is correlated in her mind with prostitution. Although she depreciates men, she has a tendency to identify with them. In this session the therapist attempted to expose her implicit wish to be a man, which would solve many of her problems, and the patient reacts with excitement and great interest.

Thirty-third Session

PATIENT SAYS that she has a slight cold again. She is going on a skiing week end with Albert, but does not particularly want to go— "So why didn't I just tell him I didn't want to go." Patient says that she can't say what she means to men. She tells of an incident this week when a date was in her apartment and another man called up. She laughed and giggled over the phone, was unable to say that she was busy and both fellows must have felt she was foolish. She feels confused about what to wear on the ski week end. She knows it's how you feel about yourself when you wear the clothes that counts. She has been thinking a lot about what I said about her need to find out the right act. She is not sure about how anyone feels toward her, and she drives this curiosity to the ground because she has to know. *When I ask whether she is wondering about how I feel,* she says, "Oh, no. That is all right."

She does want me to tell her to relax. *I ask why.* Well, on this ski week end she can just see herself getting into one of those tense awful silences when she is so mad, and then doing something nasty. She is not going for Albert anyway, but because she might meet some other people she likes. He is really repulsive to her. He had told her they might have to go to a motel instead of the ski lodge and share a room, and that he would sleep in a chair. Patient says she is not prudish so she doesn't mind, and she also knows that Albert would never crawl in bed with her, she can control that. "I wish you'd tell me to relax." *I wonder why I should tell her to relax if she's not able to do so. Rather, I'd like to help her find out what's the trouble so we can help her.* "That makes me feel better already, knowing I don't have to relax. Now I bet you'll tell me it's really that I'm attracted to Albert, but I'm not." *Does patient know why she feels repulsed?* She can't stand the thought of seeing him asleep. There are very few people in the world she can see asleep: Paul, a few girl friends, and a few fellows. *Is she afraid of losing control?* She tells me of an incident which occurred several weeks ago. A man was visiting her and was taking a nap on the couch while she was taking a shower. She had an impulse to come out of the shower nude and "pounce on him." It was very strong. She doesn't know what she would have done exactly, hurt him or make some sexual advance. She doesn't want Albert helpless and out of control around her. *I say that the patient is afraid she will lose control.* She nods, guesses she wouldn't because she never has.

"You know I've run through more men than any girl I know and I've been a failure every time. The worst are when I still like the man and he doesn't like me. The best are when the man still likes me but I don't want him. There are some where we don't like each other or just never get off the ground." *I wonder why patient feels that she has failed when a man doesn't like her.*

COMMENTS ON THIRTY-THIRD SESSION: In the discussion of this interview, the therapist indicated that during the period of therapy the patient had had dates with anywhere from 30 to 40 men. She rejects those who are interested in her and searches for those who are not interested. This acting out is denying some essential elements in the transaction. The therapist is attempting to get the patient to understand her behavior as acting out, but this is only on an intellectual level. Sexuality is associated with so much aggression that she cannot express herself freely. As she states, she didn't know whether she should come out nude, pounce upon the man and either hurt him or make some sexual advances to him. This indicates that she has very intense aggressive impulses toward the man.

This interview, however, points out the difficulty the therapist is having in dealing with the transaction itself; for the patient deals with her mixed feelings by splitting her roles. She would like to be the little girl in relation to the therapist and be mothered, directed, advised, and told what to do, but beyond her control are her angry feelings toward the therapist, which are strongly denied and from which she takes flight into her heterosexual play. This play is not fearful to her so long as it remains on the level of play, but as soon as there are advances from the men or sexual impulses within the patient, anxiety develops. The heterosexual role has been invested with aggressive negative or hostile feelings and she turns back to the therapist. At the same time, she is repeating her mother's promiscuous role.

There can be no one-sided interpretation because the patient always takes flight in the opposite role. When her heterosexual impulses are discussed, she moves back to the dependent little girl role and then gets involved with her anger. There has to be a double-barreled interpretation indicating both roles simultaneously which will give the patient a notion of the acting out of flight from the therapist and return to her. The therapist cannot rely on the intellectual understanding that her life has been patterned in terms of artificial defensive role-playing or acting out.

Thirty-fourth Session

PATIENT SAYS that she has a lot to talk about because many things happened this week. On the bus she was wondering if she was really getting at things that were important when she realized what a list she had. Smiling apologetically she says, "You know, the list." *I tell the patient that she does not have to please me by what she says.*

She begins to talk about the boy downstairs in her apartment building. Monday he sought her out four different times during the afternoon and evening about plans for a date Wednesday night to go to a play. *I am aware that patient is describing this relationship with much more clarity and feeling than I have ever heard before.* The four meetings on Monday were unusually clear examples of patient's provocative relationship with men. She became withdrawn when he was friendly and vice versa, with much provocative double talk between them. Patient became aware of this herself after Monday evening and wanted to let herself be a woman for the date. She was in a panic about whether he would kiss her, knew that she wanted it but was scared and wanted to run away. She got dressed up, which is very hard for her, and met her date at the theater, having come from dinner at her brother's. As soon as she saw him she knew she would not have a good time. He told her that he had been harassed all day at work, and she knew that he was in a hostile mood. She tried to be quiet and understanding but he didn't respond particularly. The play depressed her. Usually she gets lost in the play altogether, but she kept wishing it didn't have to be such a sad play for a date. When he invited her out after the show she offered not to go if he had to work late. He said it didn't matter and took her to a bar where she had two drinks, feeling uncomfortable and trying to talk to him with little response, while he had ginger ale. He took her to her door and she invited him in for coffee. He refused, bade her goodbye in cold hostile tones. When patient closed her door she got panicky and upset, she wanted to call him, go down and pounce on him, throw things, and bounce something on the floor to jar him. She managed not to do these things. *I say that she must have been disappointed in the way the date turned out.* Yes, and she could see that it wasn't all her fault, "but, I'll never see him again." *I say patient must feel disappointed that her greater understanding of what is happening to her and her attempt to change had not worked out better.*

Yes, and she had been mad about the week end with Albert, too. "There's another man I'd like to murder." Patient says the first day of the week end she was an awful dud. She figured out she must be guilty and made herself change, and the second day went better. When they arrived Albert put her in a ski class. The instructor was a big blond man who kept smiling at everybody and was trying to make an impression of being very popular. Patient is very vehement in this description. The instructor wouldn't pay any attention to her or help her once, and she felt like a fool skiing down the practice hill past him and not knowing how to stop. Finally she quit the class and went out with Albert, who insisted on this even though she urged him to go off with the experienced skiers and enjoy himself. She kept falling down and getting mixed up in the simple things she knew how to do. Albert insisted that she must keep on and on and learn at all cost. He kept "making" her go up the tow rope she was afraid of. *When I comment here,* she says yes, she knows she didn't have to do it. He was giving her order after order about what to do. "Then I got real nasty. I told him to let me alone. Couldn't he see how mixed up I was? That's an awful way to treat a man. It's terrible to be so nasty." *I tell patient that I don't understand why she felt she was so nasty about what she had said.* "Oh, I was angry and yelled it at him." *I say that patient was really mad because she had let him order her around and felt she had made a fool of herself.* Yes, and especially from him. He's short and not good-looking, etc. *I point out that patient depreciated him and then is humiliated and enraged when he orders her around, but feels she has to do what he says.* "Yes, I felt real powerful though when we went to bed." They shared a motel room and she told him he could put half of himself on the bed. She thought it was funny when he put his head and back on the foot of the bed and his legs out in a chair. "I felt real powerful, but I went to sleep that instant." *I say that patient felt she had controlled the situation.* Yes. *I point out that she had fallen asleep right away, withdrawn from the situation immediately.* Well, she was real tired and she thinks that is the reason although sometimes when she is tired that doesn't happen. The next day Albert was very nice, attentive and interested. She was able to do much better, too, and felt that they had both enjoyed the day. "I might have been ruined as a good skier if that day had gone like the day before." Patient decided that she should pay part of the expenses since the cost was so high, and Albert accepted $10 from her and gave her a cute receipt. Suddenly he was angry and hostile at her on the way home. It happened after they stopped somewhere to eat and he was carrying on with one of the waitresses in a corny way. She hates this in public. She tried to control her comments but he must have sensed her disapproval. After all the time he had spent trying to please her, he changed, and she felt when he said goodbye to her that she would never see him again, either.

Then there was her father. Father has been sick so maybe she should have made more allowance for him. He called her to meet him for lunch and asked her to suggest places. This is "a game" he plays and she always ends up going where he wants to go, where they know him and he feels secure. Actually, he is so terribly insecure that he is doing well to earn a living because he is upset so easily. When he asked her how she was, she began telling him that the dentist was going to remove two of her wisdom teeth because they were impacted. He yelled at her right at the table, that she didn't know anything about this, she was just dumb. She told him it was the dentist's opinion, and he had explained it to her and shown her the X-rays. Father became furious, yelling at her that she was so dumb she didn't know that an X-ray from a different angle would show things differently. She had told him—and meant it really for the first time in her life—that if he didn't stop yelling at her she would leave the table. Father looked kind of sick and lost. Actually she can never see him except in his office on a friendly basis. There he seems to know somehow how to behave differently. "I'll never see him on the outside again."

Then patient asks me whether she had done right to get so mad these three times. *I say that she is asking my approval and permission for getting mad. She has told me of three times she got mad or the man got mad at her and she ended up losing out. She feels that the men have deserted her and now she wants my approval.* "Well, I could see each time that it wasn't just me." *I agree but wonder how she felt.* She keeps asking me about what I think and *I say that I feel she wants to turn to me because she is disappointed.* Patient begins to ruminate in a confused way about whether she feels guilty. She "knows" that for the first time she tried to express how she felt. *I say that she had understood much more the kind of relationships she had with these men, but she is running away now from men and turning to me instead. She has been telling me, "You see, men are no good."* Patient begins to tell me about having lunch yesterday with a girl who was responsible for her meeting the boy downstairs. This girl is in psychiatric treatment and told patient yesterday that she finally realized she had pushed this boy away and suggested he call patient for neurotic reasons. *When I ask patient how she felt,* she says she was very relieved that the boy was no longer interested since this girl wanted him back. *I point out that she would feel she was hurting her girl friend if this man were still interested in her.* "Oh, but I know he isn't." *I point out that she has to insist on this, doesn't she?* "You mean I'm guilty." *I agree.*

COMMENTS ON THIRTY-FOURTH SESSION: The patient talks at great length in this interview about her various experiences with men. These are repetitive patterns which have gone on for quite some time and have continued over and over again during the course of her therapeutic experiences. She seems to pick out rejecting men and forces them to reject her by acting out a castrating role. After being successful with her week end of symbolic castration, she asks for approval from the therapist. This is not completely understood or interpreted in this therapeutic transaction. If it continues over and over again after this, then the patient at most has achieved only some intellectual understanding. Deeper understanding is questionable because the implicit nature of the transaction seems to be the patient's need to play the little girl who gets approval of mother, including compliance by verbalizing her anger to the therapist. Unless this acting out with men outside the therapeutic situation and with the therapist in the transaction is repetitively interpreted, blocked, and understood, the therapeutic process will be stalemated.

Thirty-fifth Session

PATIENT SAYS that this has been an uneventful week so that she will tell me what she did not get to last week. On the day she had brunch with her father, she received a phone call from a man who wanted to come up for coffee. She had met him with the German man to whom she had been attracted, but was not attracted to this man at all. He is also German, a married resident psychiatrist. After he was there for a while, he got red as a beet, told her that he loved her and wanted to sleep with her. She had told him she wasn't attracted to him, but, when he begged her, she agreed to see him and his wife later in the week at an art gallery. *I ask why she had done that.* "Well, I knew he wanted to see me." *If she doesn't like him, why does she plan to see him again?* Well, it is with his wife. *Yes, but this is double talk in view of what he had told her. She is acting out and is getting pleasure out of it.* "Well, I don't enjoy it. He was really suffering. He looked so funny and red, and besides I didn't attract him. I was trying to get the other guy." *I point out that patient had got involved. I tell her that this has to do with me, too, since this is a psychiatrist.* Her face is red, she is angry and tries to recover herself and plead with me that she didn't mean it. *I tell her we must face that she is acting out her feelings.*

She tells me of an incident with the boy downstairs, essentially to prove I am wrong. It has to do with her leaving impersonal notes about hi-fi equipment in his mailbox. *I point out that this is double talk because she knows that she hopes for some response to these notes.* Patient admits this and tells me she has become very conscious of walking around her apartment and being in the bathroom, because he is directly under her.

She tells me of two other incidents each containing a relationship which ended up in a fight. *I point out strenuously that patient always gets involved this way, she must enjoy it.* "I know I always do this but I don't enjoy it. Why, if I gave up these fights I wouldn't go out with anyone at all." When I am silent, patient tells me she stayed home two nights this week for the first time in a long time and was quite anxious. She tells me she got real mad at me earlier in the interview because she thought I was attacking her but she must have misunderstood. *I tell her that I was attacking her.* Patient tells me that she is this way with men because she thinks she has a lewd body which is different from the rest of her. *I ask why*—because her hips are so big. She then admits to playing the fascinating woman role, and *I point out that this is enjoyment.*

Patient begins to tell me that she met a doctor of our staff at a party. He is Ivy's friend. She is attracted to him but does not like his wife. She went up to him and asked him about "that woman (intake worker) I saw first" and the doctor told her that she was competent but disliked. *I point out that she is acting out her feelings about me.* Well, the doctor told her that he worked with me on a case once. She then told him about wanting to give me a Christmas present and card, and also that she wanted to show me a valentine but had hesitated. *I ask why she couldn't talk with me about it.* Well, she was afraid it might be too personal. She then starts telling quickly about her discussion with the doctor about different kinds of therapy. *I point out that patient is telling me she had "taken in" two psychiatrists this week. This has to do with me and treatment.* As she is leaving, she laughs hostilely, puts her hand on her hip and says, "Well, I'll have to think about this one. You really stirred me up."

Thirty-sixth Session

PATIENT SAYS it has been a "terrible week." She has been unhappy about what she said to me as she was leaving. *I say, "You mean the hostile crack."* Yes, she had felt very guilty about it. She had felt I was attacking her when I saw her and had worried all week as to how she could think such a thing of me. *I state that I was attacking her.* Well she kept wondering whether I was getting after her for being involved with a married man, but she knew I didn't mean that. She resented very much my saying that she enjoyed playing out situations, and I should understand that she meant it when she said she was unable to say no. *I tell her that I do not accept this, she has to settle down and work on it instead of handing me an ultimatum that she is this way.*

Patient says a very strange thing happened last week which she does not understand at all. A man had asked to accompany her to the school basketball game. She had accepted and told him that she wanted to be on time. When he did not show up on time, she waited fifteen minutes, then called him and found he had just finished taking a shower, would be over "soon." She got angry, told him not to come, and went on by herself. *I say that she had said no, then.* She never expected to hear from him again. But he called her later in the week and asked for a date. They had a long talk over the phone with his admitting to being wrong about stalling over the date and in turn telling her about another date when she had left him in confusion as to which night. She admitted this to him also. They ended up making a dinner date. Here she was angry at a man—a feeling of which I had previously accused her—and was also saying no, as she had said she couldn't; yet he called her again. *I say that this kind of anger was open and direct and had cleared the air, hadn't it?* Yes it was true that she felt much better and she knew what I meant by this. *I told her I wanted to force her to look at the hostility she couldn't understand that made her get into one disastrous mess after another with men.* Patient tells me that she thinks she knows what I mean. Already she has been having many fantasies about the dinner date; that he won't show up, that they will fight and she'll never see him, or that he loves her. *I say that she does have these fantasies and each time she makes them come true in a disastrous way for her. She runs if a man is interested or she gets into a battle.* Patient tells me that she thinks it is because of her father. He is incapable of telling the truth. She tells of an incident that happened when she was about twenty. Brother was in school and they were living with father and were terribly unhappy. Father said he would give patient spending money, but patient was working and earning her own. She feels father really wouldn't have done this anyway. He refused to give brother spending money, saying he should get out and work for it. Brother said he couldn't find a job, and patient gave him spending money from her earnings. Finally, by falsifying his age, brother got a job delivering for a liquor store. Father found out, but pretended he didn't know, and brother kept telling father other reasons for his being out in the evening even though he knew father knew. They kept fighting and arguing in double talk and neither of them owned up to what they were really arguing about. She hates this, cannot stand this kind of dishonesty. *I say this is what upset her when I told her last week she was talking double talk with the boy downstairs when she left him notes.* Yes, she has to be honest with all these men because she doesn't know what she feels. *I tell her this isn't so, that she is carried away by these hostile feelings which she must recognize, and instead feels that she is being honest.*

Patient tells me she is thinking of visiting Paul. *I say this is because she is mad at me that she is running to Paul.* "Well, I didn't think it was fair last week." *I say maybe not, but this kind of fairness will not help. She also thinks she is being fair when she avoids positive relationships with men, but this is not the problem.* Patient says, "You know if I go to California I may not even see Paul. I hope I won't call him up. But I got into another mess trying to get there." Patient tells of trying to get a ride to California. A man she knows offered her a ride and she accepted it. She knows him only casually. When she later saw him in some group, he made a comment to the effect that he expected to sleep with her on the trip. She let it pass. Actually she has no intention of doing this. She thought she would handle it on the trip when it came up. Now she is wondering whether this is right, but how can she go back on her word when she had already promised him that she would go with him? *I ask, is this her idea of honesty?* Yes. *I point out that she let herself get involved on a neurotic basis, and if she really wants to be honest about it she should face the fact that she let the man assume she would sleep with him when she had no intention of doing so, and then she wonders why she gets in a mess.*

"Well, I'll have to get it straightened out." Patient says she doesn't understand why I felt that she was responsible for the mess with the married psychiatrist. After all, he was there for an hour before he told her he loved her and wanted her and how could she assume he meant this when he just said he wanted to drop by for a cup of coffee. *I told patient I had heard her tell the story last week and believed that patient knew immediately on the phone what the man was getting at even though he didn't put it in words.* Isn't this so? Patient admits this quite directly, and says that she just doesn't "realize" these things until later. *I tell her we must make her realize them.*

COMMENTS ON THIRTY- FIFTH AND THIRTY-SIXTH SESSIONS: These two interviews belong together because the thirty-sixth interview is really a continuation of the thirty-fifth. The patient revealed that she has been hostilely seductive and acting the role of a promiscuous woman like her mother, but her defenses come to her rescue in the end and cause her to push the men away, although in so doing she again expresses even more hostility toward them. She is angry and competitive toward women, and these include the wives of the men to whom she is attracted and the therapist as well. If she ceases to identify herself with her mother, then her hostility will become more overt and will be expressed in a more intense fashion toward the therapist.

In this interview the therapist directly attacked the patient and her defenses. In this sense it seems to be a means for the patient to justify her own hostility. She was angry at the therapist for telling her not to act out. Both of these, although in the name of therapy, were explicit attacks, and the therapist was annoyed at the patient. However, it is not a failure in technique because, although there will be some feedback from the patient justified by the therapist's attitude, the content of the anger and its degree will enable the therapist to point out to the patient her implicit participation in it.

The patient responds with a disturbance which indicates that she feels her position as the good girl in the therapeutic transaction is jeopardized. She comes back in the thirty-sixth interview and reveals how much distortion of reality is inherent in her behavior. She tells many untruths, and most of these are conscious. They are efforts to obtain a reconciliation with the therapist, promising to be a good girl if she is no longer attacked. The therapist does not accept the patient's distortions and calls her at each turn. The patient also indicates that she is tempted to run away from the therapist back to Paul, although she is untruthful in saying that she would not see him.

The patient is now confronted more directly than ever before with her acting-out behavior and its aggressive connotations. What will happen when the therapist is away for a week cannot be predicted, but from past behavior we might assume that there will be some exaggerated acting out as a further defense against insight.

Thirty-seventh Session

PATIENT TELLS ME that she is not feeling well. She is tired, has had long menstrual periods recently, has headaches, her feet hurt, she scratched her vagina inserting a Tampax, etc. The "place" at the end of her spine has been blistering and draining. She would feel embarrassed to talk to her father but wonders if she should see a doctor, "knows" that some of this is emotional. *I encourage her to see a doctor, particularly about the place at the end of her spine.* She asks me for names of doctors and I suggest two after learning that she is somewhat reluctant to return to one she had seen once before. Because her father is a doctor she gets lowered fees or is not charged. She does not like this, feels that she is then under obligation and finds it difficult to ask questions. She thinks she will not tell this to a new doctor. *I say that she likes to pay less, but then feels she is not getting what she wants.* She admits this.

She has also been thinking about summer vacation and what she will do. *I relate this to my taking next week off.* She thinks it would have come up anyway. She is tired of seeing children, has had enough during the school year, and probably will not go to camp again. She has never taken a real paid vacation in her life, and would like to do so. She has thought of getting her degree by taking courses this summer (her salary at the school is paid on a twelve-month basis), but doesn't know whether she wants to study. *I state that she is thinking about staying in town for treatment this summer with me.*

She nods almost imperceptibly and then tells me that she is no longer going to California with the man but has a chance to ride with a girl. She does not know whether she will go.

She tells me about the foreign boy who again sought her out this past week. He brought her flowers and told her he loved her, was quite intense and his accent became very marked. She begins to laugh and tells me that she laughed at him when he told her he loved her. *I hold her up on this quite hard. What is funny about it, I ask?* Well, he looked so precise and was under such emotional pressure. She could see he was nervous. *I ask why this is funny.* Patient tells me she always reacts this way in this situation. *I point out that she is being cruel.* She sobers abruptly, says that she knows it isn't funny. *I tell her we must make her aware of it if she is going to change.*

Patient asks me whether I think she is really going to California in order to see Paul. *I press her on this* and she admits it, thinks she should try not to do this. As our time is up today, she states that she will "postpone" her decision until I come back, because she wants to talk with me more about it and does not want to go ahead on her own. She knows she could have brought it up earlier today, but did not, so will have to wait for me to return. *I tell patient that she is concerned today about my being away.* She asks me what I am going to do next week and I tell her. She wishes me a good time.

Thirty-eighth Session

PATIENT ASKS if I enjoyed my vacation. She tells me she had gone to the doctor, who has not completed his study but told her that so far everything is all right. He would be glad to send me a report if I wish it. *I tell patient that if there is something I need to understand I will request a report, otherwise it is not necessary.* Patient tells me that her contract has been renewed at the school with a raise in salary.

She has a hard time living on her salary but will be better off in the fall. *I ask, isn't she pleased about having her contract renewed.* Yes, and school has been going much better for her recently. She begins to talk about her income tax. If she counts all her salary, she owes the government $20 in tax, but if she omits some of her jobs, she owes $3. If she pays the $20, she will have to dip into her savings which she tries not to touch. She is trying to decide whether or not to cheat because she resents having to pay so much. *I relate this, too, to paying for treatment.* She agrees, but says that she can manage when she has extra expenses, such as dental and medical bills. She asks me directly if I think she should cheat. *I tell her that I cannot go along with this. I know she is tempted but I cannot advise this. I think her conscience is worth more than saving $17.* Patient indicates that she "will think about it."

Patient wants to tell me about the foreign boy. She has seen him twice since I last saw her. The first time he brought her roses and violets and again told her that he loved her. Patient is describing this with a good deal of detachment and *I comment on this.* She agrees that she felt this way. They started to neck and patient began to think of ways of pushing him away. She recognized this in herself and deliberately stopped herself. He did not continue to make further advances to her and she realized that he was not going to do so. She guesses she really "knew it all along." *I again comment on her detachment and control.* She tells me that when he was leaving he made some comment that she had rejected him. She "told him" that he had rejected her by not pursuing her. She was quite specific and detailed in her accusations toward him. *I point out that this is phony—patient is again acting out her feelings of hostility which she does not understand.* Actually she had withdrawn from him and watched from the sidelines. She shows strong affect of surprise and tells me to wait for the rest of the story—that she understands it better now. She then expresses embarrassment at talking with me about it, but goes ahead. On the next date with him they started necking. She again described her detachment and her knowledge that it would not work out, while engaging in sex play. She decided to let him have intercourse with her. He was unable to, had an ejaculation without erection, and patient was "not surprised." She then begins describing his "problems" with obvious satisfaction. *I point out her phoniness, her detachment, her acting out an attraction which she did not feel.* Patient admits this and *I tell her that we want to help her form real relationships with men, that these episodes will not help her.* She thinks it is because she "knew" he could not perform that she let him try. *I say that this is right and she must recognize it as a phony kind of relationship.* She tells me then that she knew he was embarrassed. She had been able to understand this, had been able to resist and also feel ashamed of her impulse to laugh at him. She had really meant it, too.

COMMENTS ON THIRTY-SEVENTH AND THIRTY-EIGHTH SESSIONS: The patient talks about her pain and the draining at the end of her spine, along with the self-inflicted wound which seems a little unusual to have occurred after inserting a Tampax. It seems as if there is a self-destructive motive behind this. But more important is the wish to have the name of a doctor and discuss fees, which indicates some wish to see someone other than her present therapist. There is a depreciating component to this element in the transaction.

The therapist understands that the patient projects her own cruelty on to men whom she provokes, and the therapist then presses very firmly against the patient's acting out in spite of the fact that the result is apparently an increase in depression and a turn to a dependent, clinging, passive attitude. There seems to be an increasing strength on the part of the therapist and an attempt to make the patient responsible for mobilizing her therapy.

After the therapist returned from her short vacation, during which the patient missed only one session, the entire matter of cheating came up in regard to income tax. Here the therapist erred in being involved in discussing cheating within the frame of money. Cheating should have been discussed in general and especially in relation to the therapist and to men. In talking about cheating, the therapist made a value judgment and perhaps unwittingly responded to the patient's testing her moral and ethical attitudes toward the patient. At the same time there may be an attempt to determine whether the therapist herself is corrupt, but these are not the important aspects of the transaction. When the patient talks about how she managed her affair with the boy, it becomes quite apparent that she especially cheats men. She states that the sexual fiasco was his problem and she wasn't to blame, when, as a matter of fact, she had provoked a situation which would make even a strong man impotent. The therapist uses such words as phoniness but she should have repeated in the context, in which she made her interpretation, the patient's own notion of cheating.

We have here an example of the way a patient in psychotherapy is able to escape from direct responsibility of dealing with her own feelings, because in psychotherapy it is difficult to maintain relentless pressure to emphasize the patient's own participation in interpersonal relationships within the therapeutic transaction. The patient has been able to get away with a great deal of her own distortion by logically and rationally describing the men she "chooses" as if then the problem is only what kind of man she picks. It becomes clearer, however, that it is the patient's corruptness that leads her to make of men the weak and easily attacked and castrated creatures that she needs to find in order to deny her own failures as a woman.

Thirty-ninth Session

PATIENT, LAUGHING PROVOCATIVELY, says that nothing much has happened this week. *I say that I believe she is cheating me by holding out.* "Oh, yes, there was something." She had a dream ten days ago which she does not remember too well. *I wonder why she didn't bring it up last week. Was she cheating me on this?* She laughs, then suddenly becomes sober and says that she wants to tell me the dream.

> It is in the alley back of our house where I lived when I was about twelve. It's not really a garbage alley but a paved courtyard. I was out there as an adult looking in the basement of the house across from ours. The dream was in four parts although I can't remember too clearly. I know in the begining it was a horror movie and just awful things were happening. In fact I think it even flashed on the screen that it was a horror movie. I heard a woman moaning and she was on a wicker settee and I could hear it creaking. I looked in the basement window and I could just see this woman. I went in a funny little door (not to this room) and down a passageway and I was in a room where they were cooking spaghetti—just mounds and mounds of it. Someone shoved me forcibly into a tiny closet and I thought I couldn't get out. I did get out into the other room where I had seen the woman. She was sitting nude on the wicker couch and she looked like a Renoir painting. I was spreading some funny papers to sit down on the sofa, too, and then I looked down and realized the woman was me. I was startled. Then I went out up the stairs back in my other form. I don't know how it changed but there was a way out that hadn't been there before. The girl I was with was there; she was tall and dark. I don't remember what happened then.

Patient tells me that this was not a nightmare like lots of her dreams. There is nothing of terror and horror in the dream but she had this feeling all the time. She thinks it has to do with the kind of watching and looking she has been talking about. *I say that this is so, and wonder whether she had gone underground in her feelings this week since she had told me that nothing had happened.* "Oh, you would have been pleased with me." Patient tells me of a speech she had made at school; she had not felt faint and unable to perform. *When I press her on this, with real reluctance she finally is able to tell me the extent to which she did well.* She thinks this is because of her treatment here. *I point out that she is very apologetic about this. Does she think I won't like it if she improves?* No, she was really pleased, even though she finds it hard to admit it. She knows of three parents who complimented her to the principal. *I say that perhaps she resents praise, that she does not like to be judged by others or praised by me for doing well.* Well, it wasn't much she did. *I tell patient she feels it has to be a big deal before it is worth anything.* "Oh, I did something else, too, you will be pleased about." *I ask, is patient pleased herself about it?* Yes, she is. She then tells me the details of how she talked directly with the German resident psychiatrist about not wanting to see him and not getting further involved. "I felt like I was treating him. I don't really mean that but I felt like I had to have more sense than he had. I don't want to be the other woman in a messy situation and when I finished I was sure he understood this." Again patient says that treatment made this possible. *I ask how it would have been different.* Oh, she could tell that she would have let it blow up into a great big scene with her getting very angry and raging. She was able not to do this. *I say that she must be pleased but I wonder whether she is afraid of my influencing her too much.* In the dream she was afraid and it had to do with women. Patient gasps and tells me of witnessing a fight outside her window in the middle of the night. She thought a man had backed a car into a drunken woman when she fell in the gutter. She tells two other very sordid incidents, saying that she wonders why they always seem to happen. *I tell her that she is afraid of being a woman.*

COMMENTS ON THIRTY-NINTH SESSION: The previous hour had contained an allusion to cheating, and this session begins with a frank and bold statement by the therapist that she feels the patient is cheating her, which is openly admitted, and then the patient discusses her dream. The dream starts out with the notion that what is going to happen is dirty; then the primal scene of witnessing sexual relations is presented in a detached manner; namely, as a movie or painting. Following this the patient takes a regression into an infantile oral phase and into isolation; she finally is confronted with the picture of the nude woman, but here again, out of action into a fixed pose as in a painting. The next element of the dream is a kind of resiliency in which she makes fun of the situation and then finds herself in the position of the woman whom she was watching, which indicates that her identification with this woman is a crucial problem.

Thus, cheating is basically the hiding from the therapist her real feelings as she does from herself. Her techniques are detachment, oral clinging dependency, and isolation. Finally she breaks through and, in her associations, says she wishes to play fair with the man and tell him that there is no sense in continuing the relationship. She makes a confession in which she really says, "I attack men in order to avoid their sadistic attack on me." Her concept of the primal scene is that the man sadistically attacks the woman. Her sadism to men is an attempt to avoid the masochistic role of women, but, as in so many other fearful situations, she has a fascination for attempting, or coming close to, the role of which she is most afraid.

Fortieth Session

PATIENT STARTS by telling me that she decided to go to California for her spring vacation. She will ride with some people, stay with Kay, and get a chance to do a lot of things. She is very apologetic as she is talking. *I point out that she feels she is hurting and disappointing me and also that she feels she has put one over on me.* She laughs anxiously and then denies this. She knows that she will be dying to see me and will hardly be able to wait until she gets back. *I tell her that I think she is afraid of getting too close to me.* Well, she has the feeling that she can talk over "whatever happens" with me and I will help her. *I tell her she is acting out her feelings instead of experiencing them, which is the way we need to help her.* Patient says that she probably will not see Paul or call him. *I ask whether she feels she has to make this commitment to me.* Well, she has been thinking about it. She knows that she would like to hurt Paul and have the satisfaction of telling him off. She no longer feels sexually attracted to him since he has been living so openly as a homosexual and does not think she could stand to have him touch her. *I point out that patient is attracted to Paul, and repulsed by him too, and feels confused by it.* "Well, I'm not really going to California to see Paul." She begins listing all the things she is planning to do and she hopes not even to call Paul. *I say that I think California means Paul to her and just being there means she is expressing how she feels about Paul. If she doesn't call him, will it be acting out how she feels about Paul? I tell her this is right.* She tells me that she had not understood this before, she had thought that only if she got directly involved with him would it have meaning. *I tell her that I want to help her face these feelings and understand them better and we can't let her kid herself that going to California has nothing to do with Paul.*

Patient begins telling me that she had called her father to say goodbye and to tell him where she was going. "I don't know why I did that but I felt that I had to let him know where I was." Much to her surprise he had wished her a good time. It is the first time he has ever done that, even though it was abrupt and hurried. He had also remembered his grandson's birthday for the first time. Patient tells me of father's negative attitudes about her other trips, and how he abruptly turned away from her, professed no interest, and didn't care what happened to her. It was always this way except when she was directly in his sight. *I tell her I think that in the same way she has to see Paul in order to know what she feels.* She is silent and then confesses that, in spite of all her denials, she has been planning her whole wardrobe for the trip "in case" she should see Paul. She wants to look nice. *I point out that she feels guilty toward me and feels that she is disappointing me.* Well, she absolutely knows that she can trust me and talk to me—"whatever happens." She knows it has to do with Paul and her feelings. *I tell her that she is stirred up over her fears of being a woman and her acting out against men and we will have to help her further with this and not let her kid herself about this.*

Patient refers to her father again. *I tell her that I know she did not receive the emotional support from him she needed when she was younger and one of the reasons she was so attracted to Paul was the warmth of their early relationship when she felt so stranded.* Patient tells me that she has felt lonely and stranded all her life. *I tell her that I know this and want to help her, that I feel she can get over this but not by kidding herself about what she is doing.* Patient tells me of several things that she had done well and when she asks, *I say that she is making progress.* "Well, I had to hear it from you." *I tell patient that I know she wants me to tell her not to go. I cannot do this if I am to help her live her life in a responsible way for herself.* She tells me in some detail of how she is financing the trip and *I comment that she has very little money for this kind of trip.* She will "get along" on a minimum of food, etc. As patient is leaving, she turns to me—"Would you advise me directly not to go?" *I tell patient that I cannot live her life for her, so I cannot make this decision, but I want her to be able to be happy and will try to help her be happier.*

COMMENTS ON FORTIETH SESSION: The therapist has been asked to accept a complementary role to the patient's dependent role and behave like a mother or father or both. The interview points up the patient's increased demandingness that the therapist accept complementarity as the omnipotent mother. The worker said that she wanted to make the patient happy, which promises an undefinable value and should not enter into the therapeutic discussion. The patient wants to be rescued by Paul or the therapist, either one would do. The patient made a spontaneous switch after discussing seeing Paul when she began to talk about her father. It is as if then she tried to place the therapist in the father's position. Later on she again makes a spontaneous change in her stream of conversation, returning to her father and voicing her complaints. Here the therapist erred in apologizing for the wrongs done to the patient and, in that sense, entered into a complementary relationship. As the therapist states, the patient must make her own decision and not rely on the omnipotence of the therapist.

At this late date, when the patient has already decided to go to California, it probably would have been well to point out that the factors
involved in her leaving and what might occur would have to be
thoroughly ventilated on her return. Without discussing the decision or
indicating any wishes for her having a good time, one can then hope
that tension will build up and perhaps she will feel guilty enough to
reveal her true motivations on her return.

In the seminar devoted to the discussion of this session, each one of
four psychiatric social workers had a different idea of how to respond
to the patient's request for a decision as to whether she should go to
California. Apparently each one of the potential therapists received a
different message and would have given different responses. The question is: Are these indicative of different techniques or of different personalities of the therapists? The patient places the therapist in a bad
position, and she will be wrong no matter how she responds to the
advisability of the trip.

Forty-first Session

PATIENT BEGINS by describing her visit to the art school on the
way to her appointment today. She learned that some of her credits
are no longer good. She is thinking of going to school this summer, but
does not like to have so much of her time scheduled.

When I am silent, patient says, "About California, I didn't see Paul
or call him, and he didn't call me." *I ask how she feels about this.* She
said that she had almost decided not to go but had committed herself
to sharing expenses with some friends, so didn't want to back out at
the last minute. When she got there she called Kay, whom she could
not reach, and decided to go to Kay's house anyway. Kay had just come
in when she arrived. She feels that she should have been home if she
were expecting a guest. They sat up and talked until very late. Kay told
her she had told Paul that patient was coming, but he was no longer
interested in her and there was no hope. *When I ask how patient feels
about this,* she tells me that she thinks Kay was right. After all, Paul
had been living so openly with men. She then revealed that Kay sees
Paul frequently. This is a platonic relationship and Paul jokingly says
to Kay that he is going to marry her, but neither one means it as she is
in love with another man. *I tell patient that it seems to me she let Kay
take control and decide the situation between her and Paul.* She protests, talks a great deal about how a girl friend should let another one
know how she feels, and *I point out again and again that she had
handed the decision to Kay.* Finally she begins telling me with some
feeling that Kay described many aspects of Paul to her as if she assumed that patient did not know him. Patient had replied once, "Why

I've known that about him for years." Patient knew also from some of Kay's descriptions that she did not know Paul as well as she thought. *I point out that she did think of Kay as her rival, then.* She protests a good deal but finally guesses this is right, and *I point out it is a situation where she had let the other woman set her role for her.* Patient then tells me that once when she was there Paul called Kay, who said the patient was there. He had not asked to speak to her. *I say that she must be disappointed and mad at him, too.* Patient tells me, after a long protest reaction, that she guesses she had hoped she could have a real friendship with him and that they could go on in a relationship different from before and not mixed up as it was. The happiest she ever was with him was when she first knew him and they used to talk about art and life. But she knows how selfish Paul is. Even though Kay told her that Paul is not at all interested in her, she can't believe that there wouldn't be something between them. She has felt less and less for him, though. *I tell patient that she believes every spark of feeling must be eliminated before she knows how she feels about him.* Yes, I do. Oh, you mean that things aren't like this, and it isn't possible, like black and white. *I tell her that this is right. I know she is disappointed and angry about her visit.* Well, she really felt depressed about her relationship to Kay. She had startled her when she woke her up to say goodbye and had known she was annoyed and didn't want to be bothered. She had felt depressed all the way home. She tells me how much she had counted on her friendship with Kay and now she doesn't know what to think. *I tell patient that both Paul and Kay had disappointed her and she felt hurt and controlled by them and caught between them. She had let herself in for this, and we must understand this, too.* You mean I let this happen? *I agree.* Patient tells me that she saw how much she was wanting to hurt Paul by going to California and kept away from this. *When I ask,* she admits to hoping he was hurt a little, *and I point out that she hurt herself, too.*

COMMENTS ON FORTY-FIRST SESSION: Since the patient is denying feeling so strongly, this interview is concerned with attempting to make explicit what went on psychologically in California. Its manifest content reveals her passivity and masochism in her roles both with Kay and Paul. The patient kept "busy" shopping, visiting art exhibits and friends, and wondered and speculated a great deal about Paul, Kay, and their homosexual friends. It seems that the patient plays the role of failure as a woman and suggests that the patient's visit to California was influenced by the therapist's interpretations regarding her heterosexual feelings. It can be considered, at least tentatively, as an attempted flight into a disguised homosexual role away from the aggressivity and anxiety concerned with heterosexuality.

In the transaction with the therapist, the patient is not permitted to deny her emotions about or involvement with Kay and Paul and is able to reveal feelings of hurt and disappointment and finally her anger toward them.

Forty-second Session

PATIENT BEGINS by talking about missing her appointment next week. At school they are preparing all day and evening for an art fair and she doesn't see how she can get away. She feels uncomfortable about this and doesn't want to miss the appointment. *I ask if there are other possible times for the week,* but it seems unlikely. Patient tells me that she could insist on coming next Friday, but she knows she has a lot of responsibility because it is a department project. *I tell her that we can cancel next week's appointment, then.* Patient discusses summer plans. When she turned down the camp job, she was offered a much better job for just a month as a head counselor at a higher salary. She wants to accept this. *I tell patient this is her decision to make,* and she tells me that she is going to do it. She doesn't think this plan will interfere with her treatment, but she got all upset about missing next week. She wanted to see me, but she knew she had responsibility at school. *This put her in the middle, didn't it?* Yes. She wants me to know that she has enjoyed teaching this year, she likes working and looks forward to it, and knows this is because of her treatment here. *Does she think I will reject her because she needs to miss the appointment next Friday?* She laughs with relief.

She tells me that something else came up last week about which she got real uncomfortable. It concerns a party to which Edith invited her, and she was unable to go because she had other plans. Over the phone, however, Edith told her that there would be many models there and she got very uncomfortable at the prospect. Edith is always telling her that she knows wonderful men for her to meet. Twice she has arranged dates for her. Once the man turned out to be an overt homosexual and the other man was just an impossible character. She was amazed that Edith could think of them as suitable dates, let alone wonderful men. When Edith had talked about the party, she had stressed that there would be many beautiful models there, and the implication was clear that the patient would be at a great disadvantage in competing with them. Patient was relieved that she was unable to go, but found herself anxious about it. She becomes quite anxious in the interview and appeals to me to stop her anxiety, "Why should I be acting like this?" *I tell her that it is because she is afraid of being a woman. It is important for her to talk about it and try to understand.*

During the rest of the interview patient talks as if the discussion is very painful and upsetting to her. She is aware of this, and comments, "My trouble is that I can't feel." *I tell her this is so, but she is feeling now.*

Patient begins to talk about how very beautiful these models are. They are perfectly dressed and made up. Yet they are nice and talk intelligently, too. *I say that she envies them.* Yes, she couldn't dress up and be like them. She feels very inferior when she is around them. *I tell patient that this is the first time she has verbalized this feeling.* Well, she feels this way, and feels out of place when she is dressed up and in heels at a party. When she picks a party dress she always buys a party dress that could be used for more general wear, too. *I tell patient that once she had told me she thought she was beautiful.* Yes, she remembers. "Well, I could be like the models; I could wear make-up and dress like they do and carry it off, but I don't." She tells me of going home after one of these parties and making herself up very heavily. When she looked at herself it didn't look right. One thing she has noticed—she can stand to look at herself in the mirror now. She noticed this just recently when some dirt flew on her face and she was able to get out a mirror and look at it. She also can stop and really look at herself in the mirror in the apartment. *I ask what she thinks when she looks.* Well, she doesn't know. She doesn't really want to be like those models, but she doesn't feel comfortable with herself either. *I say that she feels they are bad, that they are getting dressed up to seduce men. I say that part of her wants to do this.* She tells me of a woman she had seen all dressed up as a prostitute, without realizing the implications. *I tell her that she feels like she is bad when she dresses up and this is why she picked this example. I tell her that her feelings about being a woman are upsetting to her,* and she agrees with this.

Patient tells me it used to be hard for her to wear any lipstick. Father used to say, "Take that lipstick off, and don't go kissing any boys." He used to watch her all the time. Her mother was not like this. The lipstick, the Maybelline, the mascara, and all the supplies were always out, and mother would have let her use any make-up she wanted to, "but I didn't." *I say that this is because patient thought her mother was a bad woman.* She starts—and then agrees with me.

Forty-third Session

PATIENT CALLED ME and asked whether I could see her on her regular day from which she had been excused last week. She had asked at school if she could be excused from the teachers' meeting because she absolutely had to keep an appointment.

Patient appears tense and upset, tells me that she had to see me; she couldn't wait. Both Monday and Tuesday she had become nauseated and headachy at noon and had to go home from school. She has her period, but knows it must be more than that. Monday night she heard definitely about the camp job and accepted it for July. She had not expected the call definitely on Monday night. *I say that she had been thinking about it, though, and what it meant for her treatment.* She tells me that she did worry about the therapy when she went away. *Is she worrying about me and her plan to go to camp?* She admits this briefly but feels she ought to earn her living. Finally, in a burst of confidence, she says that a man will be there to whom she is very attracted. She is going to see if she can "do better" than she did last year about handling the relationship.

Patient quickly tells me that she thinks this is not really what she is upset about. Later Monday night a friend called her and asked her whether she would like to share an apartment with another girl who has a seven-room apartment and wants a roommate. Patient got very upset, could not make up her mind. She describes the girl to me. She is like a model, but not of the beautiful type she had described to me last week. She reminds her of a Toulouse-Lautrec model and the French period of the 1890's, she doesn't know why, exactly. She knows many people but has few close friends, sleeps with many people—and patient has heard that she is not particular about whether they are men or women, although she is not sure about the latter. Patient knows her slightly. They have been in the same social groups for a long time, but she seldom sees her. She does not like her really, and whenever she talks to her it is only a few words. Of course, if she shared the apartment she could probably stay in her own part, but wonders whether she would feel free to bring guests into the house. She knows she could save money. "I guess I'll have to go and see the apartment, and make up my mind. I can't make up my mind." Patient appears anxious and distressed. *I tell patient that we had been talking about her fear of being a woman, and it seems to me that she is tempted to run into a mixed-up situation where she can hide from working on her own problems.* She says that the girl does not entertain much, but then admits that it would be a Bohemian atmosphere. "But I can't make up my mind." *I ask patient if she is attracted to her.* She is somewhat tense and quiet as she denies this, but tells me earnestly that she doesn't want to get into this sort of thing. "But I can't make up my mind." *I tell patient that she is afraid of being a woman, and is tempted to bolt and run into this sort of living arrangement. She has given me many logical reasons why it is not suitable, has told me in describing the girl that there are many reasons why she shouldn't do it.* "Yes, I know and the most important is that I don't like her and can't get through to her. But I can't make up my mind." *I ask patient what would happen if she made up her mind.* "Well, nothing really because I don't owe her anything. But I just can't make up my mind." *I say that patient feels like she would be killing her off if she refuses her.* She tells me rather frantically that she might be wrong about the girl, she might feel differently if she knew her better. *I say that patient really does feel she is killing her off if she refuses her.* "Well, I never can make up my mind when something like this happens, and I go around and around." *I tell patient that she wants me to make up her mind for her and stop her from being so anxious, but I must help her see what she does to herself by doubting and doubting and being unable to decide what to do.* Patient tells me that she has been like this ever since she can remember, just gets frantic. She thinks it is because of her unhappy childhood. She pauses, and says, "but my brother had just as unhappy a childhood and he isn't like this so it must be me." *I say that patient couldn't make up her mind about her parents, she felt that if she chose one she was killing off the other.* She objects, "Oh no, I never felt that way. I followed what you said and understood it until you said that, and I don't think I felt like that." *I say that patient is afraid of magic and she thinks I have done something wrong by saying this.* She knows she is worried about what will happen if she makes a decision. She can remember standing on the corner when she was a child, waiting for her father, and being frantic as to whether or not he would show up. She used to worry over whether her mother loved her brother more than she loved her, too. "I know I can't make up my mind."

Patient asks if she can go on and tell me about something else "I've got to tell you." She tells me that over the week end she watched out her window and saw a man and woman go into a tavern down the street. The woman looked older than the man, looked blowzy, and seemed pathetically grateful when the man held the tavern door open for her. Patient thought that at least she wasn't that badly off, and never would be. "But then I began to wonder that maybe I had misjudged the woman and maybe she was much better than I thought, and I felt very upset." She looks at me and says, "But that's doubting again, isn't it?" *I say it is and that she believes she killed off the woman by her magic thoughts that she was bad.* (This incident seems to be the precipitant to the nausea.)

Patient returns to talking about the girl and her need to make a decision. "I know what the decision is but I can't face it." *What would happen?* "Really nothing, I guess," and she begins to laugh with a lot of tension. *I tell patient that I must help her see what her doubting means.* "Well, I can accept that magic, but I can't see what it has to do with my mother and father." She begins to laugh nervously and gives me a significant look as *I again tell her that she felt caught between them and didn't know where to turn.* "Well, I'll have to go and look at the apartment before I decide." *I tell her that she feels frantic for an absolute answer, but there is no such thing, and we will have to help her understand why she is so riddled with doubt.* She tells me she knows she is constantly upset about this. *I tell her that she wanted an absolute answer today from me and is disappointed when I insisted that she understand what her doubts mean.*

COMMENTS ON FORTY-SECOND AND FORTY-THIRD SESSIONS: In the forty-second interview, the patient expresses considerable anxiety about her relationship with women, bringing as close to the surface as ever before her problems regarding her feminine role. Her manifest role is an envious one but behind it is a positive attraction toward women, which in turn hides her competitive and aggressive feelings toward them.

In the forty-third interview, the patient is worried about the therapist and brings into the transaction her temptation and fascination for a homosexual relationship with the potential roommate and her anxiety about it as well. In a sense the figure of the girl represents both the mother and herself, for she is a prostitute like the mother and an artist like the patient. The therapist began dealing with the patient's hostilities, which in themselves comprise an underlying implicit role in relation to women, but she dealt with this before the defensive homosexual role became clear in which the patient chooses feminine men or homosexual girls. The patient uses the method of denial in order to allay her anxiety and to indicate that other girls are worse than she. The question arises as to whether the homosexual role is a defensive maneuver or is it also based on an identification with the mother, whose prostitution probably was evidence of her own homosexual trends.

Forty-fourth Session

PATIENT BEGINS by telling me two dreams, commenting that she understands some things about the second one, but not about the first.

> I was standing up against a wall and Paul was towering over me. I could particularly recognize his head, and his shoulders were very broad. I looked up at him and said "you're a homosexual."

Patient comments that she felt very tender toward Paul all the next day and wanted to call him, but didn't. *I say that patient is attracted to Paul because he is homosexual, that she reaches out to him.* She says she too has been wondering about herself, but why do I say this? *I point out that patient had felt tender toward Paul after calling him a homosexual.* Yes, that is right. She begins to associate to the number of people she knows who are homosexuals and *I say that she is attracted to people with homosexual problems.* She is wary; Kay, for instance, is going to get married. Yes, this is right. She will have to admit it, but isn't it true that everyone has these feelings? *I ask how she feels* and she brings out fears that maybe she is homosexual but she doesn't know it if she is. *I say that patient is attracted to homosexual people.* She defends herself; "Not every one," and *I tell her that we are talking about the problems.* What about the models? She cannot see them as homosexuals. *I say that to her they are rivals whom she fears and is also attracted to and repelled by.* She agrees. Well, she knows that she is attracted to homosexual men, but is not so sure about women, though she can see something of what I mean. She relates the second dream, telling me first that she thinks it refers to me and treatment.

> It is in my apartment, only different because there is a big building directly outside the window. The light is strange, like early morning, only I don't know really what time it was. I think there was another girl there with me talking. I saw a man's brown hat outside the window (above the ground level) and I thought he must be stealing from the big building even though he wasn't near a door or a window. I went over to the window to look. It was a casement window [patient stresses this]. It was like an outside elevator on two big posts and two men were standing on the platform up at the level so their hats were even with my window ledge. They had their backs toward me. I opened the casement window so I could see. I intended to open it just a little but it swung way open and made a noise which the men heard. One of them had a camera around his neck and he put it up to his eye to take my picture. I ducked below the window sill out of sight.

Patient begins to tell me about the apartment. She did not take the apartment and the girl really gave her the opening to say no. She could see that the girl was like herself in being sure she never imposed on anyone. The apartment is in an inconvenient location. She might consider living with her in a different neighborhood. The girl told her she had expected this, because she had seen patient's apartment. Patient then begins talking about how much she had enjoyed getting to know her. They are alike in many ways and had hit it off; she is going there to dinner next week. *When I ask how they are alike,* patient indicates that they both think alike about art and describes her paintings. She is quite animated. *When I wonder what she thinks now about her friend's sexual behavior with men and women, it is as if she had never brought this up last week. I comment on this.* Patient laughs and says, "I'll tell you what really cinched the decision for me. It's strange. Her sneezes smell." She looks at me provocatively. She is very sensitive to the smell of some people's sneezes. It is an odor she can't explain and there are several other odors she can't stand; one is Dentyne gum. She went into the bathroom and could smell her sneezes. She is laughing with a lot of anxiety but can't explain further.

Patient wants to tell me about three things that happened at school. The art exhibit, a conversation with a teacher, and a conversation with the principal. In each instance she did not get the praise or recognition she wanted and felt hurt and mad, which surprised her very much. *When I ask why,* "Well, you know I always think I'm so wonderful that nothing touches me. But I've been upset all week because I didn't get more praise for the art show at school."

Forty-fifth Session

PATIENT SAYS that she is "nuts"—she got very angry during the week. She laughs somewhat anxiously as she begins to tell me what happened. When she went to the art exhibit on Tuesday night she learned that a fuse had blown out. Everyone including the director said it was her fault and patient got very angry and staged what must have been a scene. She was very upset by this the next day, was going to try to wait to talk with me, but decided that she was going to have it out with the director the following day. In the course of this all the patient's hidden resentments against the director and his treatment of her for many months came out in the open and were aired. Patient was angry but not out of control as she had been the evening before. As she details the many things that she brought up, *I point out that all of these could have been handled over many months.* She wants recognition for finally getting up the nerve to talk with him of her anger, and *I agree that this is a real step forward for her since she had been covering it up for many months. I then ask why.* She brings out a great deal of hostile depreciation of the director and then becomes uncomfortably aware of the attack for the first time. She switches to describing her anger of the previous evening, picturing it dramatically as a scene of rage. *When I ask for patient's evaluation of this,* she said that she was really mad. *I point out that to get really mad she had built up a scene where everyone had turned on her and she ended up getting punished and disliked for it.* She accepts this, and says she had some feeling of being driven to it. "Whenever things go wrong I always have to end it in a big scene." *I say that in this way she takes it out on herself; she makes people reject her.* Yes, she did make a fool of herself, "but I went back." *I say that this is good. What happened?* It is difficult for patient to describe, but each resentment she took up with Art had somehow been aired and ventilated. *I pointed out how they had been baiting each other and it had been building up for a long time.* She then expresses resentment at his preferential treatment of the other girl, who has now left. She is surprised that she still has so much feeling about it. When she told Art how he was baiting her and the girl by his remarks to each, he admitted this partly. Patient wonders what made her get out of control. *I ask if she knows what she is guilty about.* Well, she was right about all those resentments she had. *What about the night before?* Patient then brings out her feeling with some shame that she was just using Art because she wanted some place to do her work. He had asked her to stay on, offered her a sounder and fairer working agreement, and she in turn had offered to pay part of the equipment bill. She is able to admit that when she got so terribly angry Tuesday she was actually in the wrong. *I say that patient had to be angry in such a way as to make a fool of herself because of this.* Yes, it was like she couldn't stop. "But I did recover and straighten it out." *I say that this is right and it had turned out well.* Patient bridles a little at this.

She went to the opera and was disappointed and mad because, while the singing was exquisite, the acting and staging were wooden and bad. She wondered what was happening to her that she was so angry about it. Opera should be beautiful all the way through. *I say that patient was disappointed because it wasn't perfect.* "Yes, but that's what I do all the time, isn't it? I can't stand things unless they are perfect. I know it isn't right to be like that." Patient tells me that she hasn't ever been angry like this about it. *I tell her that she is closer to understanding herself because she is not covering this up so much.* Patient indicates that she understands how she pretends everything is lovely to cover up.

COMMENTS ON FORTY-FOURTH AND FORTY-FIFTH SESSIONS: In the forty-fourth session the patient's subtle manner of acting out her homosexual role is made more explicit by the therapist. The patient cannot see that the people she chooses as friends or lovers are always homosexual women or weak passive feminine men. In the second dream her voyeurism is portrayed when two girls secretly watch two men but one turns the tables and takes her picture. The dream is reversed and suggests that as a child she watched her mother in sexual relations, some of which were homosexual. Patient's own homosexual problems may be one of the elements of her behavior that stems from identification with the mother and constitutes a role available to her when she becomes frightened of her hostile and competitive heterosexual feelings and her fears of men.

In the last session the patient's hostile competitive role breaks out, displaced from the girl of the last interview to the male director, whom she views as a safer object. The therapist makes explicit that the patient is enabled to be angry by arranging for punishment at the same time. The patient describes her objections to the operatic imperfections and thus patient's boasting about her self-perfection comes out. The boastfulness evoked further anxiety which is partly allayed by the therapist.

COMMENTS ON FOURTH PHASE OF TREATMENT

THIS PHASE (ending with the forty-fifth session) by no means completes the therapy and is not considered as a terminal stage. Rather, the

Outline of Patient's Role Difficulties

MAJOR DEFENSIVE BEHAVIOR = denial of responsibility or compulsive doubts leading to a need to be cared for

HOSTILITY IN ADULT ROLES

A. *Toward men*

1. because rejected as sexual female ⎫
2. failure in masculine role ⎭ hostility → guilt → need for punishment

    → depression → eroticized as masochism

B. *Toward women*

1. competition—failure—regression to childish dependency
2. identification with mother

    → prostitution and homosexual fantasies → need for gratification → failure → anger → guilt and depression

VACILLATING ROLES IN LIFE AND EXPOSED IN THERAPEUTIC TRANSACTION

1. pretense at being a woman
2. failure as a woman—repetitively self-induced masochism
3. childish dependency
4. rejected, frustrated angry child
5. prostitution fantasies and play
6. envy of men—sadistic masculine role

sessions from 27 to 45 fit together because the contents conform to what may be viewed as a consistent pattern.

In this phase, as in the preceding two, the greatest obstacle against insight is the patient's proclivity for acting out roles which are justified by external circumstances and by the attitudes and demands of others. Thus there is little introspective inquiry into the internal source of her behavior. Yet as a person who plays the roles demanded by her internal identifications, the patient demonstrates how these role patterns function in her total psychological, neurotic functioning.

During the second phase the patient became more aware of her childish role of dependency when she asks for advice, direction, and control, and when she asks everyone to like her as she strives to please as a good girl. Although she has not abandoned this role, returning to it when life situations become a little rough for her, the patient begins to show evidences of competitive attitudes toward women for men who do not belong to her. This is a continuation of her strong erotic attachment to father and brother, both always unavailable to her. In addition to the all-pervading sense of failure in the feminine role, there are characteristics of this role which are painful. It includes the image of a sado-masochistic behavior based on the parental model and it is associated with the frightening but also fascinating model of the promiscuous mother.

Failure is always frustrating and often leads to hostility toward the rejectors, who for this role are men. These she fights, degrades, and depreciates. Failure also turns the patient to the mother, not only as a source of gratification but also as a love object to hide the competitive hostility which threatens to erupt at any time.

We can begin to understand the confusion in the patient's role behavior because no position vis-à-vis either sex is tenable for long. Where was the neurotic equilibrium before therapy? Only with Paul and back to him she is pulled when any of the unstable roles is threatened. For Paul is both male and female, mother, father, and brother. Changes in role behavior require no change in object with whom, however, the form of relationship changes rapidly and without warning. Thus Paul is stability because both patient and Paul have in their repertoire complementary roles, to match those of the other, and readily available for use.

10

The Last Phase of Therapy

THE PRECEDING CHAPTERS have included the significant contents of 45 sessions with the patient, spanning about a year of therapeutic work. After this year the seminar devoted its energies to preparing the results of its lengthy studies for publication, but the therapist continued working with her patient. At the point of final closure of this manuscript, another 18 months had passed and the therapy had reached the session 160. We think that the reader will be interested in a summary of these later proceedings and the details of one recent therapeutic session.

From sessions 46 to 52 the patient was involved with a female artist friend who served as an ideal for her. This girl was considered to be better than the therapist in many ways, although there was much vacillation between attachments to the friend and the therapist. In this phase of therapy there was an idealized homosexual relationship but behind it was an implicit feminine rivalry with increase in anxiety as this became more explicit. The positive attractions toward women constituted a strong defense against her anger toward women who control and are decisive.

Sessions 52 to 60 exposed her lonely and depressed inner feelings. She recounted memories of her childhood aggressivity from the ages of five to fourteen. She was an acting-out "brat" toward her stepmother. The patient suddenly became "sweet and nice" when she entered high school. Interposed was the memory that when she was four the father exposed his penis to her and shortly afterward she and a little boy friend undressed before each other. They were caught, and the patient was banished by the boy's mother. When the patient was in her early twenties she started drinking and experiencing sexual intercourse. This seemed to be in defiance of the mother who depreciated her relationships with boys and used to take her little boy friends away. During a current visit mother divulged her own sexual behavior which stimulated the patient's feeling that mother was a powerful sexual rival.

During sessions 60 to 77 the patient dealt with the dangers of her sexual impulses. She began to recognize that a homosexual man—one who loves another man—was a safe defense. She began to understand how the mother attempted to seduce her as a rivalrous daughter. This in turn led to her resentment of the father who rejected her and the wish for a man who would take her by force. As she became conscious of sexual feelings toward the father, she became more aggressive with insight into her mechanisms of flight.

In the next period, until session 88, the therapist was not well, suffering with dizzy spells. Although she maintained an explicit role of concern and outward innocence, patient was provocative, hostile, and anxious because of the threatened eruption of rage.

At session 89 the patient requested two sessions a week. She had begun to see mother's homosexual trends in her concern with the patient's body and curiosity about her dates. The patient had become anxious and concerned regarding her own homosexuality. She recounted a dream that indicated homosexual feelings toward the therapist. The dynamic pattern seemed to indicate flight from her incestuous feelings for the father to the mother and, as a reaction, fear of the homosexual attachment to her.

As a result of the anxiety over her forbidden sexual impulses, in session 111 the patient demonstrated in the transaction the role of a helpless and lonely child pleading for attention and direction. When the therapist did not assume complementarity, the patient suffered from depression indicating a repressed anger. She assumes this pattern regularly when regressing (fleeing) from a current problem to an old childish position, but she did not thereby get satisfaction in the therapeutic relationship as she had from her childhood mother.

The patient recalls that when living with her father she was instrumental in pushing out her first stepmother who did not gratify her needs. When the father married again, the patient deserted the father and picked up the long-lasting relationship with Paul. Then she wandered about homeless and with no stable identity. When she attempted to deal with the therapist as she had her mothers of the past, hostility was more openly expressed.

In session 122 patient learns she has really lost Paul, who has profited from his own therapy and has a stable heterosexual relationship. Patient at first expresses overt hostility, attempts to revert to an aggressive masculine identity as when she was a child "tomboy," but becomes fearful. She seems to be most indecisive as she vacillates regarding which role she should play in a heterosexual relationship, fearful of the violence of heterosexuality. Should she be the aggressive male or the masochistic female?

Change occurs gradually, until session 137 when patient is depressed, equally hostile to both men and women. She discards her friends whom she considers to be shams and who do not meet her expectations of help under her conditions of strain. Then she has a frank incestuous dream in relation to father—regressing to the level of a soiling infant from the anxiety aroused.

Beginning with session 149 patient begins to resolve her conflicts regarding male or female identity, competes with girls, and becomes "the life of the party" in her social gatherings. She fails in her masculine role and despite her contempt for weakness implies her envy of the soft, sensuous role of the female. All of her attempts at role denials and attributing her role to others are blocked by the therapist, and the patient is brought to the problems of mastery of real life situations.

One Hundred Sixtieth Session

PATIENT CAME dressed up, prepared to go to a cocktail party and feels happy. A boy friend drove her to the hospital. She had called him that morning about some art supplies, and very compliantly he drove her around all day on many errands she had to do. She told him she was going to visit a friend at the hospital, and he insisted on bringing her here. He "caught her" going down the street to the clinic, and she felt mad and nervous because she didn't want him to know where she was going. She should have been able to say she was busy. *I point out that when he began to cling she became angry and then felt guilty.* She admits that she did not handle the situation well because she got nervous and excited. She is mad at herself for this, feels like a fool, and can't look him in the face.

She discovered that mother, who was here all last week, has a way of making her feel guilty by just looking at her and playing the martyr. Mother approached her and asked, "Are you over Paul?" and patient told her it was not Paul but she herself who was mixed up and got involved with Paul in the first place. Mother blamed it all on the father; however, when she asked patient whether she had anything to do with it, patient told her directly that she had her faults but patient still knew that mother loved her. Mother is so sensitive to criticism that even one comment deflates her for hours—"I'm like that, too," "or at least I used to be," and patient told her that nobody could be perfect. She knew it was impossible for mother to tolerate really talking to her.

Patient had a man come to call, and mother wanted to "get out" so patient could entertain him "alone." The man knew mother was visiting. Patient told her not to leave, and mother was charming to man. She discovered that they had a mutual interest in health foods. *When I ask if mother took over*, patient remarks that she knows how mother used to do this. The patient did not just sit back, she actively entered into the conversation herself, and did not let mother take over. *When I comment that patient was feeling less threatened by mother and had shifted their relationship quite a bit*, she agrees. Mother collapsed pretty quickly when patient would not let her run her down. Patient knew that mother could tolerate very little, but remembers how guilty and inadequate mother had made her feel before.

Another thing happened, too. One of the three people who originally recommended treatment to her is now out of the state hospital and came to visit her. She was terribly glad to see him. He is still very depressed and just wants to stay at his mother's home and read. She told him about a job contact and invited him over often but told him not to feel he had to come, because she recognized that he was still afraid of close relationships. She describes this and asks me whether this was right. *I agree*, and patient adds that she attempted to suggest further treatment for him but dropped it when she saw he was not ready.

Another thing—she is going on a vacation with another teacher, driving and sharing expenses for about three weeks. She had decided not to take courses this summer, to schedule herself for certain hours only at the workshop, and to plan this vacation. They will stop off at about five different places and visit friends for a few days. She has never planned a vacation like this before.

She is hoping the boy friend is not hanging around outside waiting for her. She thinks she could tell him off. *I point out that she feels guilty after having said this.* Yes, she feels she let herself in for this, thinking that they could spend a friendly day while he accompanied her on errands. For a while it worked. *I say that when he began to cling and put pressure on her she got rattled and couldn't tolerate him.* She knows that he would understand about her treatment, but she didn't want him "throwing himself at her feet or checking up on her." She guesses she is responsible for letting this happen.

COMMENTS ON ONE HUNDRED SIXTIETH SESSION: The session begins with a series of lies, overt to the boy but implicit to the therapist. She could have avoided all the distortions but somehow contrived to get the boy near the therapist as if to defy her and deny dependence on her. Yet this is a passive, weak male indicating that her capacity to develop closeness to a virile male has not yet been achieved.

In the second part of the session mother reveals that she is still erotically attached to the patient by attempting to participate in her sexual life. The patient openly accuses the mother of responsibility for her confusion but then realistically and compassionately has to placate the highly sensitive mother. Patient does not let mother take over and successfully competes and asserts herself in relation to her male friend, but also protects the mother.

Later patient identifies with the mature female therapist as she takes over her role in relation to her friend, the recently discharged mental patient. The previous phase of the therapy indicated a slow and tortuous but steady progress toward female psychosexual maturity. Yet when the going gets tough the patient still has, at least partially, her old regressive pattern available as when she became rattled about meeting the boy again.

We believe that from this brief summary of sessions 45 to 160 and the outline of session 160 the reader may conclude that real progress has been made in the patient's insight and behavior in work, play, and sex. She is quieter, surer of her identity and self-esteem. What specifically in the treatment was responsible? Was it the relationship or the interpretations, the corrective emotional experience, or just the passage of time? Among these possibilities we cannot decide, any more than can any therapist using any method. One thing we can state emphatically—for psychotherapy on a once-a-week basis for our patient, we were always confident that the transactional relationship gave us a better understanding of what was going on in both therapist and patient and what transpired between them.

IV

The Transaction

11

The Development of
the Transactional Approach

IN THE FIRST SECTION of this book we sketched out a transactional framework for social work functions. In the second part we demonstrated the operations of the transactional approach applied to the traditional social work tasks of screening, information-giving and recommendations and supportive therapy. In the third part we exemplified psychotherapy by discussing a single case in treatment for more than a year. Now we shall discuss the operations of our research seminar, further develop transactional theory, and discuss its practical and technical implications.

About ten years ago when our Institute—functioning in makeshift quarters—entered its new building, we began to expand our training and research activities according to an orderly, preconceived plan. Eventually our training program encompassed the teaching of psychiatric residents, psychiatric social work students, clinical postdoctoral psychologists, graduate and undergraduate nurses, psychiatric aides, occupational therapists, as well as staff psychiatrists and nonpsychiatric physicians.

The content of didactic courses and goals of seminars were easy to plan, develop, and modify because of their "public" nature. But it was not so easy to know what went on in the "private" two-person relationship between social workers, psychiatrists, and psychologists and their patients and between supervisors and students. Staff conferences did not divulge the heart of the interviews; seminars for clinic psychiatrists and supervising psychiatrists covered generalities only. Rapid shifting of supervisors—at six-month intervals—and treatment review staffs still left us with vague ideas of what professional people actually did.

Then, too, we began to think seriously about the problems of functional differentiation among members of the so-called psychiatric team in the clinic. The psychiatrist was presumed to do psychotherapy, but so also did the social worker and eventually the psychologist. In analyses of social workers' functions and distribution of time, we still heard a great deal about casework, but increasingly more about supportive treatment and psychotherapy.

What did the social worker really do and how? We realized that he was well trained, busy, and performed valuable services to patient, clinic, and community. But the nature of his services did not seem to be what the schools described or defined as casework. We decided to start our analysis of professional psychiatric functions with the social worker.

A seminar was arranged for the members of our psychiatric social work staff by Dr. John Spiegel, then chief of the psychiatric clinic. From 1950 to 1952 the group discussed vignettes from case histories to determine what the worker did. From these meetings the first tentative definitions of functions were formulated. These are presented here in outline form to demonstrate how two unsuccessful formulations led to a final model which we subsequently adopted. In 1952 Dr. Roy R. Grinker, Sr., the Director of the Institute, carried on the work after Dr. Spiegel assumed another post. At this point the seminar organized itself into a research group and for many years met weekly, organizing and reorganizing its concepts and models. For two of these years case reports exemplifying items in our final outline were carefully studied. Many are included in this book as examples of current social service functioning according to our model.

Our transactional theory indicates that understanding of what goes on in any process requires a definition of its setting, its participants, and its goals. These will be described under the headings of: The Setting; The Patients; The Social Work Staff; and The Goals of Action.

THE SETTING

Early in 1922 a mental hygiene department was initiated in the isolated Mandel Clinic located far from Michael Reese Hospital in an extremely poor environment. Under the direction of Dr. David Levy for five years, this clinic first concentrated on the treatment of children, although collaborative treatment of parents was initiated quite early. The first annual report in 1922 indicated that casework services were classified into categories of *intensive therapy, short-term services with-*

out full responsibility and *steering functions.* By 1925 the now traditional psychiatric, psychologic, and psychiatric social service team was organized. Diagnostic, intake, and agency staff conferences were held regularly, and varying goals of therapy were planned for each case. In that same year graduate students from Smith College were accepted for training in psychiatric social work. Those were pioneering days because Michael Reese was the first general hospital in Chicago and in the Middle West to establish a special psychiatric clinic devoted to the practice and teaching of therapy for psychiatric patients. Psychiatrists who had special training and experience were in attendance, as contrasted with the usual clinic staffed by neurologists who listened (or not) for five or ten minutes to patients' complaints and then prescribed sedatives such as sodium bromide or phenobarbital.

In 1928 the Mandel Clinic was rebuilt on the Michael Reese Hospital and Medical Center campus and became more closely attached to the general hospital within a large therapeutic community. The volume of services for children increased, and a strong demand developed for adequate psychiatric care for adults who were still the responsibility of the Neurological Department. In 1933, at the hospital's request, the National Committee for Mental Hygiene surveyed its facilities and the community's needs, and recommended a staff of full-time psychiatrists. At the same time the University of Chicago School of Social Service Administration established a field work center at Michael Reese. Finally, in 1936 the recommended Department of Psychiatry staffed by full-time workers was organized, a psychological laboratory was started by Dr. Sam Beck, and several residents were accepted for training. In 1939 the first inpatient psychiatric unit with eleven beds was opened; it soon mushroomed to double its size, limited to this number because of the restrictions of available space. Individual residents were then trained in both inpatient and outpatient services. World War II interrupted for the time being the continuity of service, teaching, and expansion.

After the war the present Institute for Psychosomatic and Psychiatric Research and Training (with 80 beds) was planned, ultimately to be finished and occupied in 1951. In the meantime the psychiatric clinic, with its full-time psychiatrists, social workers, and psychologists, was expanded to occupy a newly completed psychiatric floor in the clinic building. By the time the new building was completed, the Institute had become a multidisciplinary training and research facility.

Since its beginnings in 1922, clinical psychiatry at Michael Reese has progressively emphasized psychodynamic principles and since the late 1930's has had an almost exclusively psychoanalytic staff. Year by year the training program in psychiatry graduates not only psychiatrists but also social workers and psychologists. Our staff social workers include, in their personal training, either the additional experience of a personal psychoanalysis and/or attendance at the child-care training program at the Chicago Institute for Psychoanalysis. Most of the psychiatrists graduated from residency training continue the study of psychoanalysis and become psychoanalysts as well as psychiatrists.

THE PATIENTS

Although we have considerable responsibility to the community and to other departments of the hospital and clinic, our attempts to maintain quality of service outweigh our concern for quantity. We accept only those patients who we believe can be adequately treated by the available staff of psychiatrists, residents, social workers, and psychologists. For this task we impose no time limitations, although we expect all disciplines to present their patients for staffing and recommendation after therapy has continued for six months to a year. Sometimes this results in termination, reassignment, or altered procedures. Undue prolongation of therapy (a natural tendency in all practice) is also decreased because the psychiatric residents' supervisors are shifted every six months, student social workers leave after a nine-month academic year, and residents eventually terminate their training.

Our patients come from all social classes but are not indigent as were clinic patient populations of the past. They pay from fifty cents to $10 per visit depending on their ability to pay, based on analysis of their budgets. Thus we accept patients from those unemployed to small businessmen, from the uneducated to candidates for advanced university degrees.

The diagnostic categories of our patients range over the entire psychiatric nosological classification. For example, our 1958 annual report lists: 22 per cent depressive reactions, 20 per cent personality trait disturbances (character neuroses), 10 per cent anxiety reactions, 10 per cent schizophrenics, 5 per cent psychosomatic disturbances, and the remainder consisting of various psychoneurotic syndromes. During the same year, 309 patients were treated in the clinic, utilizing 8600 hours of service from all therapists.

Our clinicians agree that today there is little difference between patients who seek clinic care and those who consult private psychiatrists. All patients seem much sicker than those who applied for treatment a decade ago, or perhaps our increased knowledge of prognosis makes us more pessimistic. The nostalgia for the classical hysteria or "easily treatable patients requiring only brief therapy" is universal, but, until better methods of therapy are available, our goals and expectations must be lowered.

Clinic patients are seen once a week, in exceptional cases twice, and in emergencies even more often. The long interval between sessions sometimes burdens the patient with anxieties, angers, and depressions which he cannot ventilate elsewhere. As a result, continuity of therapy is often jeopardized if the patient takes flight from a treatment that temporarily makes him feel worse. The once-a-week therapy requires that much time in each session must be devoted to catching up with the intervening behavior in life situations and requires from the therapist a more directive focused interview concentrating on fruitful topics.

It is often stated that one should be especially cautious against overestimating the clinic patient's capacity to endure interpretations of conflicts and attitudes below the level of conscious awareness. The result has been an overcautious attitude which often slows and handicaps adequate treatment. Clinic patients are not more chronic, do not have weaker egos, and are not less motivated than most private patients in our time. Considerable discussion with the patient and careful diagnostic evaluation of his emotional problems and ego strengths before beginning therapy are necessary for all patients to determine what may be expected during the course of treatment.

Some clinic patients are often more unsophisticated, naive, and dependent and enter therapy with a background of long-standing economic and social failures. On the other hand, many intellectually sophisticated students failing in college or in progress toward advanced degrees are even sicker with borderline states, latent or overt psychoses. For these patients it is sometimes stated that they need supportive, suppressive, or relationship instead of expressive therapy, but these terms only define the therapist's intentions. The dichotomy of supporting or uncovering treatment is not definitive, since all therapy is supportive to some degree. The essential approach is directed toward solving the patient's most significant problems by whatever means are available and effective, and within whatever time span is suitable.

Chronically ill patients with large elements of secondary gain impose special problems for treatment. Their symptoms may increase with self-devaluation after an initial improvement because too much may be expected of them by their families if they should become better. Others may take a flight into health when threatened by exposure of unacceptable attitudes, or act out their neuroses, or develop intellectual defenses. Many try to isolate the therapy from their life situations.

It should be expected that once-a-week visits for chronic patients will effect no major structural changes in personality. For both clinic and private patients, however, the profession at large and each therapist individually are gradually learning through experience the futility of setting up unrealistic goals.

THE SOCIAL WORK STAFF

The psychiatric social work staff consists of a chief and five or six caseworkers, all of whom supervise students to some degree and participate in casework themselves. They are thus both teachers and therapists. In addition, they all participate in some of the clinical research programs, such as the research on motivation for treatment in child psychiatry and the research formulated in this book. Thus, each psychiatric caseworker is not limited to a specific function.

Included in the actual service functions of the caseworker is the handling of psychiatric emergencies in the admitting department when some professional person is needed to help in an admission or immediate referral elsewhere. Often this means planning for the care of children or making financial arrangements for dependent members of the family. The psychiatric social worker acts as a liaison between the psychiatrist who sees the patient in an emergency and the social agency referring the patient to the clinic.

Social workers participate heavily in intake and exploratory services. All applicants for acceptance in psychiatry are given an "intake interview" to determine the suitability of the patient for services, the adequacy of his motivation for treatment, and his present social matrix. The results of this interview are presented to a screening staff at which decisions are made regarding further procedures. If the patient is rejected, the social worker is responsible for steering service, disposition, and referral elsewhere. If the patient is accepted, he is studied diagnostically by the psychiatrist and psychologist, both of whom may require further social work exploration with relatives and other informants. Often information about community resources is desired or some details must be procured from doctors or agencies who have treated the patient in the past. The final diagnostic study is presented at an interdisciplinary staff meeting at which the social worker takes an active role, presenting his social study or social history. He also acts as staff recorder, making notes which remain in the chart as a record of the case conference.

The social worker is assigned the task of treating the patient as primary therapist when the staff so advises, or he treats the patient as a secondary collaborative, or adjunctive, therapist. The cases for which he acts as primary therapist generally do not include suicidal or psychosomatic cases, acute disturbances, or panic reactions. Many of the patients treated by the social workers are those in special need of a female therapist (on our staff, however, are several skilled male social workers). As far as diagnostic prediction is feasible, they are assigned patients whose level of difficulty corresponds to their skill and interest.

The social worker may be used at any time as a consultant on social service matters for any of the ongoing cases under treatment by any therapist in the Psychiatry Department. He may interpret a specific social reality to the psychiatrist who may need this information to understand better the patient's distortions. The psychiatrist may need consultation about community activities, agency functions, housekeeping services, etc. He may seek out the social worker for help in considering further social implications of the illness, planning for children, appointments, convalescent care, and special needs such as recreation.

The social worker functions in liaison with the community social agencies when they are jointly active on a case, thus decreasing difficulties in communication between the psychiatrist and the agency. The social worker may have an adjunctive contact with the patient, seeing him in relation to such specific areas as job seeking, job training, recreational planning, housing, etc. Often this requires interviews with the patient and consultations with the psychiatrist.

Social workers may see relatives in collaborative treatment, sometimes to get information, secure more history, or clarify roles of responsibility. In addition, they may communicate with relatives for ongoing collaborative treatment aimed at restoring equilibrium between the patient and members of the family or, on the other hand, toward loosening the ties between them. Ongoing collaborative treatment may attempt to engage the relatives in a more constructive relationship with the patient or to help the relatives, especially the mothers of children, more directly. Sometimes a relative will enter active therapy with a social worker. Thus the role of a social worker may range from giving advice to supportive treatment or in special circumstances acting as primary therapist for a relative who then becomes a "patient" in his own right.

Our studies were concerned with the functions of the psychiatric social worker in a clinic (outpatient) service. We were not troubled by his confusion of functions in the inpatient setting, because there is little overlap between what the worker and psychiatrist do in the hospital. The problems are more concerned with utilizing the full and adequate services of the worker by psychiatrists whose education and practice for such cooperation have been neglected. For the purpose of completeness, however, the social worker attached to the inpatient service functions as follows:

1. Incorporates the social service function into the admission procedure. The social worker is available to meet with relatives of newly admitted patients, to interpret hospital procedures and facilities to the relatives, to answer questions and to help, if indicated, with the anxieties aroused in a relative who is placing a patient in the hospital. This interview is fairly brief, to be conducted without referral and essentially an additional step in the admission procedure.

2. Provides social histories as supplemental material to the psychiatric history as secured by the resident. This and subsequent functions are on a referral basis.

3. Assists relatives of patients with their own particular problems,

such assistance to be concurrent with the therapy given to the patient by his physician.

4. When indicated by the doctor, assists the inpatient who might need direction or support as he progresses in the hospital toward healthier functioning and prepares for discharge.

5. Participates with the doctor in discharge plans for patients in relation to the resources in the community, and establishes liaison between the hospital and the family and social agencies to which he is being returned.

6. Participates in nursing unit conferences and in policy committee discussions.

THE GOALS OF ACTION

In our seminar we first considered the social worker's functions as falling into two categories: planning and treatment. Our initial study attempted to clarify the function of the worker in intake and diagnostic surveys of the patient, in treatment activities with patients, and in collaborative contacts with parents and relatives. As a result, an outline of levels of functioning was developed (*see* Table 2).

TABLE 2

LEVELS OF SOCIAL SERVICE FUNCTIONING IN PSYCHIATRIC CLINIC

I STEERING The giving of information, not heretofore made available to the patient, when no particular modification of attitudes is involved.
   A. Common sources of request for such services
      1. Admitting office—when patient is ineligible for clinic.
      2. Cases already in therapy with a psychiatrist in the clinic or hospital.
      3. Lay people, community agencies, and schools requesting specific information.
      4. Letters and telephone calls from potential patients requesting information.
   B. Types of services given
      1. Referral to and information about community resources.
      2. Information about clinic and psychiatry clinic procedures.
      3. Recommendations for handling of a given situation when information only is needed.
      4. Letters.

II HISTORY-TAKING AND EXPLORATION PROCESSES

III MODIFICATION OF EXTERNAL ATTITUDES Limited goals, and directed toward relieving-action.
   A. With community people or agencies with the objective of integration of services and points of view. Example: Recommendations for treatment or handling of case.
   B. With patient and/or family and surrogates. This type of case is re-

ferred to social service by the staff person who has principal contact with the patient, after he has determined or tested the need for modification of external attitudes, has himself given the initial interpretation or recommendation to the patient and/or family and finds that the patient needs and can use further help in accepting this.

Examples

1. Hospitalization (psychiatric, etc.).
2. Placement (school, camp, etc.).
3. Reorientation regarding the specific need for psychiatric service.
   a. Working with patients who cannot benefit from therapy from this point as:
      (1) Patients who lack sufficient motivation and need further testing of this.
      (2) Patients with whom therapy is not possible unless the home situation is changed.
   b. Working with patients not accepted for treatment because of clinic limitations (waiting list closed, frequency of interviews needed not possible in clinic settings, etc.) when the patient needs further help in accepting this.
4. Stabilization of external environment.
   a. Neutralization of anxious or unrealistic attitudes of parents or relatives.
   b. Development of appropriate, reality-adjusted attitudes in parents or relatives; *i.e.*, cultural differences in background.
      (1) Mother in collaborative treatment, not primarily for her own needs but to facilitate treatment of child.
      (2) Relatives of adult patients in treatment, especially in hospital.

IV MODIFICATION OF INTERNAL ATTITUDES

   A. Therapist acts in role of parent-substitute in corrective relationship characterized by permitting of considerable dependence, allaying anxiety, acceptance of patient in nonchallenging fashion, and working mostly with current life situations.
   1. Reality interpretation (focus is patient's ego).
   2. Authoritative interpretation (focus is patient's superego).
   3. Safety valve (abreaction).
   4. Primary interpersonal relationships in otherwise isolated individuals.
   B. Direct treatment relationships.
   1. Clarification of need for therapy.
   2. Clarification of steps and goals in therapy.
   3. Working through conflictual defenses: *i.e.*, derivatives of the nuclear conflict.
   4. Working through the nuclear conflict.

Detailed discussions of these "goals of action" revealed considerable dissatisfaction, for they added nothing to the admonitions of standard texts with their directives of "must" and "should." The classification was one-sided because it contained only *a priori* notions of what the worker should do without defining the patient and his needs. Nor was the "how" of action indicated. Therefore, a shift was made, and the outline was reformulated by paralleling the functions of the worker with the needs of the patient (*see* Table 3).

TABLE 3

AREAS OF SOCIAL SERVICE FUNCTIONINGS IN PSYCHIATRIC CLINIC

Needs (Patient and Situation)	*Function (of Clinic Social Service)*
1. Undefined help from clinic	1. Exploration and anamnesis
2. Information	2. Direct information and steering service
3. Modification of specific external situation (*i.e.*, placement, hospitalization)	3. Goal specific relationship
a. Modification of patient's attitude *re:* this specific need	a. Orientation of patient *re:* specific need
b. Modification of collateral's attitude *re:* this specific need	b. Orientation of collateral *re:* specific need
4. Stabilization of external situation	4. Role playing and replacement therapy (conscious assumption of parental attitudes with patient)
a. Stabilization of patient's external situation	a. Reality interpretation
b. Stabilization of collateral's attitudes	b. Authoritative interpretation
	c. Safety-valve therapy
	d. Primary interpersonal relationship
5. Modification and reintegration of internal attitudes	5. Role-constant and uncovering treatment
	a. Clarification of the nature of treatment
	b. Dealing with defenses against the nuclear conflict
	c. Working through nuclear conflict
6. Separation	6. Termination of relationship

We were again dissatisfied with the outline. True, it listed in parallel columns the needs of the patient and the functions of the worker. What was lacking seemed to lie in the empty spaces between the columns, representing the relationships between the needful patient and the helping worker within the specific setting of the clinic. Within the changing relationships are communications that contain the essence of reverberating transactions between the two persons involved. This required a dynamic model from which an operational theory of human relationships could be derived. This is contained in Table 1 (pp. 22–25).

The reader should not be unduly alarmed by the apparent complicated statements in the columns headed *Patient Roles, Clinic (Worker) Roles,* and the column between with the heading of *Transactional System.* The first and third columns simply indicate, when known, the explicitly and implicitly assigned and assumed roles. The Transactional System indicates the reciprocal, reverberating cyclic processes going on between patient and therapist and several possible resolutions.

The details of each system numerically labeled as areas have been discussed in separate chapters: Area 1 in Chapter 2; Areas 2 and 3 in Chapter 3; Area 4 in Chapter 4; and Area 5 in Chapters 6 through 10.

12

Transactional Theory

Although not clearly specified, the three tables outlining social service functions are derived from rather sharply defined theories. What the social worker does is still often thought to be an operation or a function performed by the worker *for* or *to* the patient. He does something to the person in need or suffering from an illness in order to help him, to ameliorate his illness, or hopefully to cure him. From this point of view the social worker has traditionally assigned functions which he should learn to perform, and these can be outlined in detailed and lengthy lists (*see* Table 2).

This is essentially a theory of adjustment requiring an *a priori* knowledge of "mental health," "adaptive behavior," and what society asks from "well-adjusted" people. It presumes that there is a "normality" or, according to Jahoda,[1] a positive state of mental health. There is a faint reminder from this approach of the "friendly visitor" who knew what the indigent should do, and told them so.

Unfortunately, words such as normality, adaptation, adjustment, health, etc., are, as Szasz[2] points out, panchrestons that attempt to explain all and accomplish nothing. Indeed, the doing something to a person for his health through the medium of words is little different from prescribing medicine for him or performing an operation on him. This doing or giving not only is a magical concept of "cure" but also is strictly an imitation of the medical model. Unfortunately the magic of the right words spoken at the right time is still hoped for by many therapists of all disciplines. Szasz states, furthermore, that our nosological classification also is based on the medical model, containing only

292

few words to designate problems of interpersonal relations within a social matrix.

The second theoretical concept exemplified in Table 3 is more realistic in that it attempts to match the needs of the patient with the functions of the worker. Parallel lists are presented as if patient and worker existed for a single purpose in a vacuum, each one acting in stereotyped and fairly steady explicit roles. This conforms with a theory of interaction in which one person, the therapist, influences another person, the patient, after determining his needs.

Such a system takes little cognizance of the total field of either one or the other participant. It ignores the changing implicit roles of each, and it does not consider the real essence of the encounter between them. This consists of the back-and-forth communications of messages, the clarification of implicit roles, and the learning process. In truth, the essence of learning for both patient and therapist is contained in the content and form of what in Table 3 is seen only as white spaces between the parallel lines.

Table 1 is a summary of transactional theory applied to social workers' operations. It leans heavily on a changing mutual and reciprocal system of communications between the two participants of the transaction. Within the context of communications expressed verbally, nonverbally by gestures and expressions, and paralingually by grunts, ahs, ughs, and pauses, meanings are expressed and concealed.

Such communications reveal not only explicit roles of each participant of the two-person group but also a variety of their implicit roles as indices of past transactions which have led to identifications. In the transactional system there is a two-way communication which can be expressed in behavior by each person enacting an explicitly assumed role more or less concealing and revealing a variety of implicitly assumed roles. At the same time, the partner assigns to the other what we call an explicitly assigned role, but again more or less implicitly assigning other roles at the same time.

All this is enacted within a specified field or setting which influences the transaction and is influenced by it. The more information received and elicited regarding the life field of the patient, which is often designated his "social matrix," the easier his implicit roles are to decipher. The more analogous patterns of behavior in life are available, the more confidence can be placed on the significance of current here-and-now transactions.

Although the essence of communications reverberates between patient and therapist as they enact their various roles, the impact on each is within them. Words and sentences meaning one thing explicitly may evoke quite different meanings within the perceptor, a phenomenon that can be determined only by his responses. These may be explicit or implicit but are usually characterized by some apparent emotional tone which permeates the transaction.

Psychoanalysis has termed the emotional reaction of patient to therapist as transference and of therapist to patient as countertransference. These have been considered to be new editions of old emotional patterns and desirable from the patient as an index of his patterned behaviors and their source. On the other hand, countertransference has been considered as a pollution of the analyst's objectivity, highly undesirable, and hopefully to be vitiated by his personal analysis.

Lately the "blank screen" completely unemotional and unperturbable characteristic of the analyst stemming from Freud's early formulation has become weakened. Analysts are real people with personalities, emotions, problems, and disturbances (perhaps lessened by their own analyses) who are reacted to and react like other human beings. In fact it is now recognized that the patient's emotional responses may not be entirely transferences from the past but reactions to the real current communications.[3]

We should like to go a step further and exploit the so-called countertransference as the function of the psychotherapist's main tool; in other words, the process whereby he understands and appreciates the patient's implicit communications by observing his own emotional reactions to them. Naturally we would hope that the therapist is freed from severe or interfering neurotic processes, that he is sensitive to others' communications, and that he is capable of freely communicating internally within his own mind and knowing his feeling states. Then he can utilize these as signals of the meaning and impact of the patient's implicit communications and respond in proper time with accurate statements.

Finally, Table 1 is based on transactional theory because there transpires between patient and therapist a moving system of *processes* in which reverberating communications indicate understandings and distortions of messages capable of being corrected and leading to learning, growth, and change. These we have exemplified in Part II, Chapters 2 through 4, and in Part III, Chapters 6 through 10. Theory and technique have been discussed in relation to clinical examples under special headings. We shall review the techniques in the next chapter, but first we shall consider more fully theory in relation to psychotherapy.

We have used the phrase "modifying complementary relationships" to designate a form of psychotherapy that implies the goal of change within the patient. Because alterations of psychological processes are inferred by the patient's reports of his feelings and concerns, his self-esteem, and his inner "comfort," they are not easy to verify. In truth, the only objective criteria of dynamic equilibrium, growth, and change are represented by behaviors, including verbal behavior, in a variety of life situations and in the therapeutic transaction.

The term homeostasis, originally applied to stability and equilibrium within the internal milieu of the body, has recently been applied to psychological functions. The ego or boundary processes may be considered as the essential regulators of multiple internal forces in transaction with and within the environmental field. As Hartmann puts it, the ego serves the function of adaptation.[4]

Grinker states:

Homeostasis in biological systems is concerned with attempts at maintenance of a range of equilibrium or (and at the same time) efforts to regain the environment that can re-establish a past equilibrium. This is a general principle which categorizes those psychomotor activities that are vital and self-preservative and lead to *goal-seeking* activities. They change in modes of expression by maturation of special human functions and by conditioned and symbolic learning derived from the human and physical environment which stimulates or restricts the available mechanisms.

Just as homeostatic principles have been applied to ego functions, so is there usefulness in applying to psychology the principles of growth and change as potentiating forces activating *goal-changing* devices.[5] Development and differentiation of the psychological system, although probably dependent to a greater degree than somatic systems on external stimulation, are also probably under the control of organizing processes.

Although physical growth is self-limited, we have as yet observed no limits to psychological growth except those set by the aging of somatic organs, and no limits to social and cultural change. Human individuals seek new experiences, new challenges, and new concepts. They seem involved with growth, development, and change independently of self-preservation, although new devices of internal regulation and homeostasis closely follow each change.

Man, more than any other animal, is excessively and for long periods of time dependent on parental figures. Because of excessive dependency or external restrictions on growth or because of the lack of sufficient stimulation or satisfaction, individual inertia against personal growth often increases. For one of many reasons the organism becomes fixed or held in a more or less dependent position and is not capable of utilizing its growth potential. If it is able to develop to any degree, the inertia or longing for its previous dependent relationships makes it vulnerable in times of stress or disappointment to regress to the old states of dependency.

The healthy or so-called normal individual has passed through a reasonably satisfactory period of gratification appropriate to various phases of growth and has been able to utilize his particular growth potential to a considerable degree. The always present need for equilibrium and stability and its never satisfactory fulfillment is represented by the individual's participation as an integral and dependent part of a whole group. There are many possible permutations of utilization of growth potential and dependency, but in all types of personalities there are combinations of both. It seems that psychological growth expresses change as the person develops newer organizations for the expression and satisfaction of primary needs and for security. Changing goals accompany a utilization of other systems capable of operating through longer time-spans and greater distances for the purpose of obtaining the same basic satisfactions. These systems develop as assemblages around the retained primary core of personality.

The difference between homeostatic goal-seeking and growth may be expressed in another way. Growth may be measured by the number of goals which an organism can attain. As growth increases, the organism can deal with more environments without repetitively searching for the same ones. The ability to reorganize, to seek new stimuli, and then to make appropriate response patterns part of one's stable internal organization may be a measure of growth. Such transformations of environment and of self occur without loss of internal cohesion or organization. Growth involves an efficiency of integrated goal-seeking, goal-setting, and goal-changing. Neurotic inefficiency is exemplified by the repetition-compulsion of goal-seeking, the compulsive goal-setting, and the phobias against goal-changing.[6]

Buhler [7] puts these concepts in somewhat different language. She speaks of four basic life tendencies: (1) need satisfactions, (2) upholding of internal order or maintenance, (3) adaptation, and (4) creativity. Personal "fulfillment" can be reached when these four basic tendencies approach their goals in good balance and are integrated.

Perhaps now it is clearer that change and growth can be validated not only by knowledge of private modes of life (according to Sullivan) [8] or so-called "insight" but more clearly by behavior within the transactions. In fact, it is from behavior within the therapeutic transaction that understanding and change arise. The implicit shifting role functions are made explicit in the reverberating transaction, enter into awareness, and then are modified or controlled. Likewise, behavior in this two-person transaction portrays the progressive changes characteristic of movement toward more healthy relationships with a wider variety of people and in a large number of environments. Sullivan describes it well: "*Personality*, I now define in the particular sense as the *relatively enduring pattern of recurrent interpersonal situations which characterize a human life*."

It was stated earlier that psychoanalytic psychodynamics constitutes the most fruitful theory in modern psychiatry. It gives satisfaction because of its relative completeness and sense of closure. Probably most important, it has an analogical fit with its borderlands of sociology and biology. In fact, as a theory it is useful in setting up hypotheses in many other fields of science. The basic core of modern psychiatry is the psychodynamics of Freudian psychoanalysis.[9]

We also indicated that psychoanalytic theory, fruitful as it may be for viewing the psychological processes of humans, places a heavy load on the operations of psychotherapy. Many aspects of psychoanalytic theory have no representations even in psychoanalytic technique. These include the theory of instincts, the libido theory, and the theory of aggression (death instincts). On the other hand, the dynamic, topological, economic, and structural points of view, now amplified to include the genetic and adaptational, are important frames of reference which are helpful in "locating" various aspects of communication. Certainly, theories of the origin and effects of anxiety are of practical importance in understanding the dynamics of transactions.[10]

The reader may have noticed that in the comments concerning each transactional session and in the review of treatment phases psychoanalytic psychodynamics furnished the skeleton on which the living flesh of the two-person transactions was modeled. In fact, some originally psychoanalytic words such as "defenses," "regression," "narcissism," and "sado-masochism" were used. There is no replacement for them, nor need there be, because they, and many others, belong in the "public domain" of psychiatry.[11] Mental mechanisms and functional allocations for named mental processes are necessary for any orderly conception in normal or abnormal psychology. Certainly a vast amount of psychoanalytic theory serves as the best conceptual system for the functional interplay *within* the mental apparatus.

For the living dynamic meaning of reverberating communication between two persons, however, the transactional approach is closer to the informational data. Furthermore, it combines without distortion the dimensions of time (Freud) and those of space (Sullivan) in a first order of information. Interpretations in accordance with any theory constitute a second or third order of information that satisfies the needs of the observer (in the observer-participant therapist) for continuity and abstract generalities which are applicable to more or less extended categories of people. Plainly speaking, abstract theory is satisfying and often fruitful for research, but therapy is a down-to-people process that does better when it is based on theories of operation.[12] Students express this well when they cry for help in "doing" even though during and after training they know much theory, but only know "how" after many more years of practical supervision and practice.

Sullivan's operational concepts may be epitomized by his statement: "A personality can never be isolated from the complex of interpersonal relationships in which the person lives and has his being." He characterized the therapist as a participant-observer who maintains role flexibility, and also as a real person who exists as a contrast to the fictionalized person that the patient tries to make him. In this tactic he corrects the patient's parataxic distortions. There is no doubt that Sullivan's "interpersonal therapy" has had a salutary influence on psychotherapy.

All this leads to the recognition that psychotherapy could fruitfully be considered within the theoretical framework of operationalism. Anatol Rapoport [13] points out that knowing and action are inseparable. In a recent book on operational philosophy he states that the fundamental problem of relationship is: "Two people who have not shared a common experience cannot favorably communicate with each other. The meanings of words are not in the words themselves, but in the experiences behind them." Operational philosophy seeks acceptable criteria of reality. "A theory of reality follows from the operations performed and resides in the invariants observed."

Psychotherapy deals with operations in that behaviors are elicited in a field within which two people strive for understandable communications. In the here-and-now transaction they share common experiences which accelerate communications and improve the accuracy of information received. The field, the roles, and the communications are the invariants that define the quality of the behaviors which not only are shared in participation but also are observable by therapist first and, after precise interpretation, by patient second. The distortions of the latter then become meaningless and sooner or later must be abandoned in favor of the disclosed reality. Through this process, learning, growth, and change may be effected and neurotic behaviors diminished.

In no way do we deny the internal dynamics of psychological patterns. However, whether conceived of as "internal" or portrayed through action, no knowledge and change can be effected except through the understanding of action in verbal or nonverbal behaviors. Although phrased in different technical language, resistances, transference, or any other psychodynamic processes cannot be known unless they are expressed in a behavior of the patient in the presence of the therapist. Reified egos, ids, ego ideals, and superegos do not behave or speak.

What is expressed through the operations involved in communication of shared experiences are the memory images of identifications that are residues of past transactions. These filter through ego boundaries, escaping the locked-in state of suppression, regression, and various types of distortion. They take allocated positions in relation to each other, reminiscent of past two-person transactions, and may be ascribed to various structural aspects of the mental apparatus. But no matter where they may be placed in dynamic, economic, or structural aspects of metapsychological theory, operationally they appear in action.

For these reasons we prefer the transactional approach, at least for psychotherapy, which is operationally understandable by *communications* through role-relations within a designated and defined *field*. It is essentially an action theory.

How does one differentiate the transactional approach, or for that matter any dynamic psychotherapy, from psychoanalysis? This question is not involved with psychoanalytic theory, concerning which there is considerable disagreement and even controversy so bitter that the formation of separate societies and periodicals has resulted. It is not clear whether these divergencies have influenced technical operations.

As a broad definition of psychoanalysis, Rangell [14] has proposed that it is a treatment *whereby* conditions favorable for the development of a transference are created *in order that* through a systematic interpretative attack on resistances there occurs a resolution of the neurosis *to the end* of bringing about structural changes in the mental apparatus of the patient in order to make him capable of an optimum adaptation to life.

In the panel discussion at which the above definition was proposed, presentations by several leading analysts indicated considerable overlapping of agreement and disagreement which showed that Rangell's definition of psychoanalysis is not unanimously held. Assuming his definition is fairly accurate, let us contrast it with our transactional approach as a form of dynamic psychotherapy.

1. We avoid conditions favorable for the regression inherent in the development of a transference neurosis.

2. We attempt to interfere with a transference neurosis by such techniques as limited frequency of interviews, face-to-face position, focusing on the here and now rather than on the past there and then, rapid generalization from an interpretation of implicit transactional role, no interpretation of latent content of dreams apart from the current role relationship.

3. Satisfaction with resolution of current "derivative conflicts" and unconcern with so-called "primary conflicts," lifting "infantile amnesias," and meticulous "working through."

4. Less ambition for "structural change" and "optimum adaptation" which practically amounts to a delusion that "complete personality reorganization" and "cure" could be achieved by any psychotherapy.

On the other hand, our psychotherapy deals with transference manifestations in implicit roles and with resistances in relationship. It utilizes transference and countertransference impacts as indices of meanings of communications understandable by the emotional effects of both participants on each other in the transaction.

One of us (R.R.G.) has been conducting continuous case seminars for psychiatric residents and has supervised individual residents using the transactional approach. In all of these experiences there has been a struggle against the deep impressions made by the psychoanalytic model on neophytes barely beginning their training in psychiatry. It was easily observed that their goals included uncovering significant dynamic processes during long-term treatment with the desire for cure or so-called "complete reorganization of the personality" which they held out for themselves in their future personal analyses. In the young therapist this involved long periods of passivity and listening to the patient, hoping that at some time a significant dynamic process would pop up and be recognized. The passivity and length of relationship often induced a serious regression on the part of the patient, the development of a transference neurosis, and serious countertransference problems. In imitation of the psychoanalytic model these beginners called for and encouraged the recounting of dreams which they could not understand or interpret. Lack of understanding forced them to defend themselves against anxieties stimulated by communications from their patients and by frustrations of their failures to understand or to make progress, thereby further handicapping their therapeutic effectiveness. They tried to imitate the analytic imperturbability but instead only achieved attitudes of coldness and "objectivity," concentrating entirely on the content of the patient's productions. Without attempting to understand the patient's needs of the moment, some of them developed the notion of furnishing a "corrective emotional experience" by playing artificial roles which were easily penetrated as play-acting by anyone with a modicum of intelligence.

Some of these difficulties were apparent in working with and in teaching psychiatric social workers, as evidenced by the comments after each session of Case 20. Failures in the transactional approach were apparent from the statements made by the therapist. But the language used is only a reflection of the experiences and thinking of the speaker. As Rioch [15] stated: "A person trained to orient himself productively and communicate in a conceptual frame of reference cannot adequately use another without training in the general attitudes as well as in the precise words."

In Chapter 13 we shall discuss the operations in the transactional approach; in other words, the tactics. These are by no means complete or perfected, but only a beginning rough sketch of the techniques that we have found useful.

REFERENCES

1. Jahoda, M.: *Current Concepts of Positive Mental Health.* New York: Basic Books, 1958.
2. Szasz, T. S.: The classification of "mental illness." *Amer. J. Psych., 114:* 405, 1957; *Psychiatric Quarterly,* Jan., 1959.
3. Frosch, J., and Ross, N. (Eds.): *The Annual Survey of Psychoanalysis 1954.* New York: Internat. Univ. Press, 1959, Chap. VII, Sec. II.

4. Hartmann, H.: *Ego Psychology and the Problem of Adaptation*. David Rapaport, Tr. New York: Internat. Univ. Press, 1958.
5. Deutsch, K.: "Autonomy and Boundaries According to Communications Theory." In Grinker, R. R. (Ed.), *Toward a Unified Theory of Human Behavior*. New York: Basic Books, 1956.
6. Grinker, R. R.: Growth inertia and shame: their therapeutic implications and dangers, *Int. J. Psycho-Anal.*, 36:1, 1955.
7. Buhler, C.: Theoretical observations about life's basic tendencies. *Amer. J. Psychotherapy*, 13:561, 1959.
8. Sullivan, H. S.: *Conceptions of Modern Psychiatry*. Washington, D.C.: William Alanson White Foundation, 1945.
9. Freud, S.: *Collected Papers*. New York: Basic Books, 1959.
10. Hendrick, I.: *Facts and Theories of Psychoanalysis* (3rd ed.). New York: Knopf, 1958.
11. Fenichel, O.: *The Psychoanalytic Theory of Neurosis*. New York: Norton, 1945.
12. Glad, D. D.: *Operational Values in Psychotherapy*. New York: Oxford Univ. Press, 1959.
13. Rapoport, A.: *Operational Philosophy*. New York: Harper, 1954.
14. Rangell, L.: Similarities and differences between psychoanalysis and dynamic psychotherapy. *J. Amer. Psychoanalyt. Assoc.*, 2:734, 1954.
15. Rioch, D. McK.: "Theories of Psychotherapy." In Dennis, W. (Ed.), *Current Trends in Psychological Theory*. Pittsburgh: Univ. Pittsburgh Press, 1951.

13

Techniques of the Transactional Approach

A GREAT SOURCE OF CONFUSION and anxiety for students of psychiatric practices is the lack of structure, of tactics, or "rules of the game." Individual psychotherapy permits no "other" therapist, and even group psychotherapy is usually conducted by only one professional. Psychiatric interviews for any purpose are essentially two-person private affairs. There are no "umpires" to explain the rules or to call the errors.

For the most part, learning is achieved by supervision "after the act" through discussions of what went on during the interviews or therapeutic sessions. Forgetting, omissions, distortions, and discounting of nonverbal communications, etc., by the student therapist seriously handicap the supervisor. Even the experienced psychiatrist cannot or does not remember or reveal many facets of the patient-therapist transactions, especially the nuances and subtle connotations of the relationship. Nonparticipant observers, although somewhat disturbing to the transaction, are necessary for objective descriptions, and they are now being used in almost all research studies.

The essence of a therapeutic relationship—the reverberating emotional impact of two personalities on each other—is really not taught, it is learned. What can be taught are the general strategies and a few of the detailed tactics, to serve not as rigid rules but as bases from which flexible derivations or parameters are to be utilized wherever necessary. Some of these we shall discuss now.

302

VARIETIES OF TRANSACTIONAL SYSTEMS

Between worker and patient a wide variety of transactional roles and systems may develop, depending on many changing parameters. Psychiatric clinics and their professional personnel may classify these systems according to their personal preferences for categories or areas of functions. Our classification conforms fairly well to that usually employed in most psychiatric clinics. It includes exploration, information, recommendation, experiencing complementary relationships (supportive psychotherapy), and modifying complementary relationships (intensive or uncovering psychotherapy).

These areas are defined from the frame of reference of the *intentions* of the worker who has been assigned a special task, the accomplishment of which requires a specific explicit role. With the task defined it would be expected that the worker would always be in control of his role structure, the processes of communication, and the degree of permitted regression. This is not always so, and we have indicated (in Table 1, in the column headed *Transactional System,* and in the chapters devoted to separate areas) that transactional systems develop and stabilize, or fade out, or move forward or backward into other areas. Sometimes these movements are progressive and helpful; at other times they present serious complications.

Thus, knowing full well that transactional systems are unstable and have little respect for one participant's (worker) intentions, we may summarize the tactics usually employed for the tasks inherent in Areas 1 through 4 from the details recounted in previous chapters devoted to these areas.

The area termed exploration (described and exemplified in Chapter 2) is characterized by a brief transactional system. It is essentially an area of investigation in which only the explicit roles are known. The patient is assigned the role of expressing his needs; the worker assumes the role of investigating the patient's problems with the goal of determining his motivation for help. Thus the transactional system is relatively simple because it rapidly develops and terminates, requiring complementarity of roles so that there may be a free exchange of information.

The skills of the worker reside in the capacity to (1) overcome the patient's resistance and know how to achieve complementarity, and (2) know when the end point has been reached and when either termination of the interview is indicated or another session is necessary.

The worker's skill in establishing communication and overcoming resistance is dependent on his learning—as he and patient present small arcs of their total life spaces to each other—how to recognize the form and content of the patient's manner of communication so that complementarity may be facilitated. Thus we may visualize such a successful maneuver as resulting in the two convex arcs shifting and becoming concave and forming a small temporary circle around which communications reverberate. This is achieved by the worker's skill in understanding and recognizing the patient's implicit role assumptions and accepting complementarity. Here *a priori* biases and not listening carefully are handicaps.

The end point is recognized by the repetitiveness of the kind of information traversing the transactional system and by a shift in the patient's role from a giver of information to that of a questioner. Probably the most important sign of completion is a sense of closure within the worker associated with a feeling of satisfaction as if the declarative sentence were spoken internally: "I know," or what scientists call the "aha" reaction. It may require more or less time, one or more interviews, but, once reached, the transaction should be terminated to avoid complications within the subsequent transactional areas even though the patient remains under some endurable tension.

Information-giving and recommendations are two transactional systems that are usually combined into one. (These are described and illustrated by case reports in Chapter 3.) In most clinics the social worker or psychiatrist assigned to the task of transmitting recommendations to a particular patient with whom he has been involved during intake or diagnostic studies usually accepts the assignment as a boring task. To the contrary, the task is highly important for several reasons: (1) Rejection should be accomplished without hurting the patient. (2) Recommendations and steering to extramural sources of help should be made so that the patient reasonably accepts what has been decided for his best interests. (3) Alertness should be maintained so that the patient may be rescued from an erroneous decision for rejection by understanding the patient's communications of new information. (4) The accepted patient should be prepared for his subsequent treatment or for the tension of being on a waiting list without the transaction slipping into a therapeutic relationship.

The tactical considerations involved require that the worker assume a double role of both giving and receiving information. The first aspect of the transaction is a subtle and delicate delaying maneuver through which the worker determines what form his painful message of rejection should be given, if this is the recommendation. Once this is apparently ascertained, it may still require change depending on the patient's reactions; hence, flexibility is a prime requirement. Logical and reasonably truthful reasons should be available for both the rejection and the recommendation of alternative plans.

The second tactical consideration is the use of a listening role, even as one is giving information, to hear indications of erroneous recommendations. Rejection may in itself be a significant stress stimulus which elicits responses that indicate reconsideration or even immediate on-the-spot acceptance. For this to be valid and effective for both the patient and the clinic, the worker requires considerable understanding of his own transactions with his staff colleagues, his own biases for or against certain personality types, and his own reaction formations against rejections. He should maintain his explicit role assignment as much as possible, being sensitive to the patient's implicit roles but not assuming complementarity with them.

Finally, for the accepted patient, who usually asks many questions, answers must be found which are informative enough but not too anxiety-producing or distorted so that subsequent therapy with another person will not be unduly complicated. Despite the narcissistic gratification of the patient's pleading for the information-giver to become the therapist, the worker should resist permitting the transaction to slip into therapy, not only because teaching clinics require management and assignment of therapists according to plan but also because succumbing to such maneuvering is technically inadvisable. It signifies acceptance of an implicitly assigned role and for the patient a success which will lead him to expect more of the same.

The fourth area, labeled as experiencing complementary relationships, is really supportive therapy. (Its details are discussed and exemplified in Chapter 4.) Since all relationships and all forms of therapy are to some degree supportive, the structure of a special transactional system should be defined in terms of its role relations which are essentially complementary for both explicit and implicit roles. This means that the system, once established, becomes relatively stable and dangerously interminable even though its goal is a temporary "tiding over" or a preliminary stage prior to a therapy oriented toward modification.

The main tactical problems, therefore, are: (1) the recognition of the patient's needs for implicit role complementarity; (2) the re-establishment of re-equilibrium when the system breaks down prematurely; (3) the testing of the patient's capacity to move on to modifying therapy; and (4) the avoidance of interminable support.

Recognition of the patient's needs is dependent upon the therapist's ability to discern his leading and essential role patterning in life underneath reaction formations and other defenses and pride-saving devices. For this a sound knowledge of psychodynamics is necessary. We stress the fact that this role pattern has been either life-enduring overtly or existing covertly, exposed only by a breakdown in defenses due to a wide variety of possible internal or external conditions. It is here that important sound decisions are required, depending upon the patient's pride on the one hand or shame on the other. Should the role complementarity become engaged with the implicit dependent roles entirely, or at first, or should they become involved with the overcompensating, denying, or reaction-formation functions of the ego? Of course, this is not an either/or question but rather a how much and when question.

Once the complementary implicit role relations have been established, accidental external factors or processes occurring in the transaction may disturb the equilibrium of the system. The patient may not be ready to leave the system, and efforts at establishing equilibrium, or what Spiegel calls "requilibrium," may be necessary. In Chapter 1 some general principles concerning this process are quoted from Spiegel. In general, the therapeutic situation may be out of focus or even seem chaotic. When this is recognized with an attitude of "let's see what happened," the events preceding the disequilibrium should be recapitulated. Misunderstandings may be exposed, meaningful implicit attitudes on the part of the therapist may have been caught by the patient, the therapist may have missed some cues from the patient concerning implicit needs, and a wide variety of external conditions may each or all tend to disrupt the equilibrium of the transaction. For this system the therapist's tactic is to get at the strain quickly, expose the cause, indicate openly and explicitly his share in the problem, and endure the humility of obeying the implicit command of the childlike patient who demands, "Say you're sorry." This should be in the context of "I didn't understand" or hear or recognize or "I'm sorry, I failed to be clear" or definite or understandable, "Hence, you misunderstood me."

To test the patient's ability to move on to Area 5, gentle verbalization of the patient's implicit roles that are being satisfied should be attempted. The result may be flight, disequilibrium requiring requilibrium tactics, or movement into modifying psychotherapy. Escape hatches should be prepared so that the testing devices do not result in worsening the patient's condition.

Avoidance of interminable support requires tactics such as manipulating time of appointments, decrease in their frequency, interruptions, suggestions of external human objects with whom similar transactions can be enacted in real-life situations, urging toward attempts at independence and graduated trials of performance in which success can be predicted. Finally, setting of a termination date with strong indications of confidence may successfully end the supportive therapy. If the need for support has developed from severe stress and is not based on a life pattern of childlike dependency in an infantile character, then the chances of successful termination are greater.

We shall now consider the general techniques and some specific tactics appropriate to Area 5 (elucidated by a single case report in Part III). The comments after each session should be scrutinized with great care, because they implicitly indicate many tactical considerations through their critique of the therapist's activities.

THE PLAN AND GOALS OF THERAPY

The first step in selecting patients for psychotherapy is the screening for suitability and motivation. This saves considerable time because patients often are misdirected and misinformed regarding their needs. For our purposes, strong preliminary motivation is highly important for therapeutic success, although later the motivation may be revealed to be not for change but for gratification of some implicit needs. Recent published studies by Lichtenberg, Kohrman and MacGregor [1] indicate that the least motivated persons often need therapy most. It may be possible to intensify weak motivation through "social boosters" or, if professional time ever becomes more plentiful, to develop pretreatment techniques for clarification of needs for treatment. Almost all our patients have some degree of motivation or they would not be accepted for treatment.

The next step in selecting patients for psychotherapy is the *diagnostic evaluation* and diagnostic staffing which is concerned not only with classification but also with making a preliminary formulation of the psychodynamics on which the tentative treatment plan is based. Current trends in psychotherapy do not separate diagnostic evaluation from therapy; yet, in practice, we preliminarily elicit information that permits choice of patient, method of treatment, and possibly planning for the opening tactics. Diagnosis is a necessary step in selecting patients for treatment, especially when the setting is part of a teaching center.

The determining of goals and the planning for treatment are explicitly spelled out in formulating the case in the traditional approach for the benefit of the student. Each trained therapist goes through the same process in his own mind, often automatically. Helpful though this may be, there are certain disadvantages. Primarily these are: (1) The diagnostic decision and psychodynamic formulation are often inaccurate. (2) The plan of therapy should be changeable, depending on the current transactional process. (3) The goals of therapy cannot be set without constantly testing the patient's capacities to learn, grow, endure anxiety, and experiment with new behavior.

In making plans for treatment and setting goals, we establish a bias which, unfortunately, may influence our therapy of the patient. Innovations are made to fit into a preconceived theoretical plan. Information is skewed to coincide with the psychodynamic formulations distilled from the diagnostic study.

To offset the rigidity resulting from fixed plans and set goals, we attempt to delineate a focus on which we can concentrate for as long as necessary. Then, decisions to stop, continue, or change the focus are based on the transactional process so that flexibility is enhanced. In this we maintain continuity of activity so that the patient and therapist do not stray from the therapeutic work. Nor do we let the patient set the focus for consideration by waiting for his "free associations." In this sense our therapy is directive, but only in effecting concentration and in avoiding defensive flight from a significant therapeutic focus. But first we have to find the appropriate focus at the beginning of treatment and, although easier, for each successive step.

Probably the most effective teaching device for learning that a pre-conceived plan frequently founders on the rocks of the patient's control is a review of the first few sessions at the beginning of treatment. After the patient is told that he may start where he chooses and speak openly and frankly regarding anything he wishes, chaos seems to dominate for a while. Around the listening therapist's head swirl countless bits of information regarding past and current life events, feelings and concerns, and names of vaguely identified relatives, friends, and enemies. Where does the therapist enter? The answer is simple—he doesn't!

CASE 21

A SOCIAL WORKER treating (under supervision) an intelligent female college student attempted to respond to questions and discussions for the first few interviews as if, by so doing, complementarity of explicit roles could be achieved. The social worker also responded nonverbally by facial gestures to indicate her involvement in a "relationship." Her supervisor suggested that for the next few sessions she remain impassively as a listener, only giving encouragement to "go on." The result was a quick realization by the patient that the therapist had changed. "Are you trying to be nondirective?" Then ensued a crescendo of demands, threats, and denials: "I don't need you, I can be successful without you, I can treat myself." With deep feeling she then told how lonely she felt with no friends at her first college. There was no one even to eat with, and finally, when some girls approached her with friendly invitations, she didn't care and refused to join them.

Here the patient exposed her implicit role relationship because the worker would no longer adopt complementarity with the defensive sophisticated banter. The therapeutic focus of the beginning phase of therapy became clear, chaos was now superseded by order, and progress could be made. Psychodynamic formulations could not furnish an appropriate plan; it had to be developed as the transaction started.

THE FIELD

We mentioned previously that field theory is a necessary background for psychotherapy even though its operations are focused sharply on two persons. It seems clear that a vast number of behaviors, values, and attitudes (both past and present) directly or indirectly influence what goes on in the interviewing room. This background is a vital changing "surround," influencing and being influenced by the therapy. Too frequently psychotherapy is considered to be something apart from the total field and somehow detached from an "outside" life.

The therapist has some advance knowledge of the patient's life and background obtained from the pretreatment studies. The psychosocial matrix in which his present troubles are embedded should be elicited by adequate social service investigation. The more that is known about the patient's significant past experiences, the better can his present be understood and the clearer can his expectations be defined.

But this is not enough. The field changes constantly, and a continuous stream of current information is necessary to understand the occurrence of these changes and how they are produced by and affect transactions with people within the patient's family and wider social worlds. For instance, relatives have considerable significance for the present troubles and certainly will play important roles in the future. They may seek out the therapist to give him their attitudes, distorted or undistorted information. At suitable times they may furnish a check on the patient's communications. At other times it may be necessary to invite key figures for a conference.

By his understanding of the broad transactional field the therapist may assist his patient in better understanding reality as represented by the social groups within which his adaptation is expected. Primary, however, is the therapist's need to know what past transactional equilibriums were satisfactory, what precipitating factors disturbed it, the nature of the patient's regressions, defenses, and flights, and what reequilibriums are possible in transactions with significant persons.

In sum, the ambulating patient participates in the therapeutic transaction for a fraction of his time. For the remainder he struggles along in real life. It is necessary for the therapist to know as much of this current life field as he can if he wishes to help the patient to the fullest degree. When a patient is seen only once or twice a week, obviously it is more difficult to keep up with changes and happenings in the intervals between visits. When in doubt about shifts in the patient's attitudes or communications, the therapist should ask about what happened between interviews. Unfortunately, physicians who become psychotherapists often forget this, relinquish their role of doctor, and isolate themselves from life. Of all people, the social worker, by virtue of his knowledge of the meaning of social processes, should avoid this error.

THE EXPLICIT ROLES

The explicit therapeutic roles are conscious, reportable, and observable as clearly as if the person in need of help had a sign around his neck reading, "I am the patient," and the helper's one reading, "I am the therapist." There is, of course, little danger of confusing these roles except when the therapist is also in treatment elsewhere or is a student or a resident. These explicit roles are highly structured—each one has publicly agreed functions and is complementary to corresponding roles in others. Although there are a limited number of explicit roles available for assignment and assumption, they have quantitative ranges.

The degree to which the patient assumes the role of patient depends upon his suffering, the extent of his failure in real life, and his acceptance of responsibility for his trouble and for his recovery. From the phase of experiencing to that of modifying complementary relationship is a transition that describes the change from wishing or demanding satisfaction to participating and working for recovery as a patient. Psychotherapy requires a basic willingness to cooperate and to work mutually with the therapist and the abandonment of expectations to be given to materially or told what to do. The patient is uncomfortable and thus motivated for change. His explicit role is that of a person who comes for help, although, as is frequently the case in all forms of therapy, when he begins to know more clearly what his implicit feelings really mean, he resists help, clarification, insight, or change quite forcibly and wishes to maintain his old role relationships. Through the diagnostic evaluation, however, it has already been indicated that there is sufficient motivation for the patient to withstand the exigencies of treatment.

The therapist explicitly has a desire to help people who are suffering and has a particular attitude by virtue of the role that he has chosen for his professional life. This attitude cuts across all theoretical orientation. The therapist feels that his patient is a human being, is worthwhile working with, and has the optimism that *respect* for another human being would instill in him. He hopes and believes that his patient will change, will feel better or perform better, and that the patient's inherent capacities for being different or for growing will be realized. This positive feeling is the first maneuver which helps the patient begin to override his nuclear core-feeling of badness. This applies to all persons who eventually are able to understand, after giving up their security operations, that much of their anxiety is based on their self-concept of badness.

There are, however, liabilities inherent in positive feelings in the therapist's role when they reach an intense quantity. It has been said that results from therapy of any type are proportional to the therapist's enthusiasm in his method. Unfortunately this does not insure more than temporary effects. The overenthusiastic "I love all my patients" attitude creates for both patient and therapist expectations that may not be achieved, and ultimate disappointment. Strongly hopeful and confident feelings may stimulate magical notions of cure or personality reconstruction that create serious blows to pride when they are not achieved. Far from being an asset, the young therapist's overenthusiastic missionary concept of *self* as a curative agent may become a serious liability. Unfortunately this difficulty is corrected only by the experiences obtained through time.

THE BEGINNING OF THE TRANSACTION

As the patient and the therapist approach each other, it is as if each is represented by convex arcs of two incomplete circles across which distorted, misunderstood, and incomplete messages traverse in both directions. In this preliminary meeting or engagement both therapist and patient strive to learn each other's language and test out its trustworthiness as an honest medium of communication. The therapist pays special attention and attempts to learn the verbal, nonverbal, paralingual language of the patient, including the meaning of pauses, change in speed, kinds of distortions, delaying ejaculations, gestures, eye movements, blushing, neck pulsations, etc. As the therapist and patient come closer together, after a variable period of time, complementarity of *explicit* roles is achieved. Then there is no gap in the explicit roles, and messages are not distorted. Information reverberates rapidly in a circular plane ultimately spiraling until a peak is reached. In this last phase mutual understanding (complementarity) is achieved for this stage of therapy, and patient and therapist have a feeling of well-being. At this point patterns of information about this particular therapeutic problem become repetitive although the contents include present, and recent and distant past.

In the therapeutic process we start out with the here and now; that is, the current real life which involves the communications between patient and therapist about their relationship. Although the time element is not restricted to the immediate relationship but will always bring in memories and communications about the recent or distant past, we do not emphasize the so-called genetic processes or the past experience of childhood, nor do we attempt to evoke early memories or feel particularly successful when we have been able to recapture childhood feelings. The patient himself will bring into communication as much of the past as is significant for the particular focus under discussion. Granted a modicum of intelligence, he will see, when he understands the implicit nature of the current transaction, that other experiences in different periods of his life conform and correspond to a category. We work in the transaction with what the psychoanalyst calls derivative conflicts and are not specially interested in his uncovering the so-called primary conflicts as a specific aim.

DEALING WITH ANXIETY

Since so many aspects of the person's difficulties are symptoms derived from defenses or security operations against anxiety, it is only logical to assume that in every therapeutic relationship anxiety will occur. The patient will require much time before he has confidence that strength to master anxiety increases with growth, that the anxiety of the past is now endurable, and that the therapist is a staunch agent for support. The therapist has the task of estimating the degree of disorganization in the patient's communications that his anxiety produces. Although he wishes to understand the nature and cause of the anxiety, he recognizes that this cannot be done as if one were demolishing a building with a bulldozer. He must be prepared, therefore, to gauge the degree of anxiety and to issue supportive and reassuring statements indicating that he understands, and he must learn how to remove or sometimes to avoid anxiety-producing pressures.

In our experience, psychiatrists have a tendency to permit or encourage excessive quantities of anxiety which disturb cognitive and conative functions and throw the therapeutic transaction out of its optimum equilibrium. This seems to be based on the old concept that emotional expression, even to the point of abreaction, is therapeutic. On the other hand, social workers are fearful of anxiety as if it portends an imminent breakthrough of a psychosis. They have become masters of anxiety-allaying clichés. Somewhere there is an optimum degree of expression, since reasonable degrees of anxiety are significant in facilitating mental work, recall, and understanding. Therapeutic progress does not occur without free anxiety as a sign that significant defenses are weakening. But the therapist needs to learn the "ego

capacity" of each of his patients to endure affects. The problem of dealing with anxiety after knowing through testing the patient's ego capacity to endure this affect is not to choose between avoidance or
allaying on one hand or stirring and facilitating on the other hand. The
goal is to determine what implicit roles are associated with anxiety
and communicate this fact within the current situation before the
patient becomes involved in panic or defensive maneuvers. The most
effective way to gain relief from anxiety is to know its cognitive corre-
lations, and that is the principle of interpretation at the right time.

CASE **22**

A PRETTY TWENTY-YEAR-OLD Catholic female entered therapy because of unhappiness over excessive parental controls. She had
been educated in the dance, acting, etc., but recently upon registering
at a dramatic school her parents became alarmed at the possibility of
promiscuity, rape, early marriage, etc. Her attachment to father was
intense although he frequently showed his affection by violent physical
action. Mother was inconsistent, confused, and dishonest in that she
attempted to get her way by pretending collapse and physical illness.
The patient had experienced brief supportive therapy by a social
worker in another agency, and transfer was made to our clinic because
of fear that patient would impulsively act out some self-destructive behavior. Following is the third interview with a young female psychiatrist.

Patient on time. Pretty, more feminine. Dressed very smartly, with
heels. Went to playroom. *I explained we were meeting there because
the other rooms all were occupied.* She entered, looked around, and
picked up a baby doll.

"I forgot we were to meet this Monday so that is why I wished you
a Merry Christmas last week—so silly."

"A terrible thing happened last Saturday." Told how she called home
from Jack's apartment to say she would be late, and father's response,
"You know what I have told you about going to men's apartments."
Made them come home and have a talk. Jack informed father that he
loved patient and felt responsible for her welfare and would take care

of her. This surprised father. She had told mother that Jack said he loved her but she hadn't told father.

Then mother said I must have been born into the wrong family.

That must have hurt you.

"Funny but when I was small I always thought that I was adopted. When twelve, I asked my mother and she said of course not. Now that I'm older I can now see my resemblance to my father." (Ignored the idea of being hurt.)

I went back to the issue of the incident with father and asked her whether her father had told her something about going to men's apartments.

"Yes, it wasn't Christian."

You must have known that he would disapprove of your calling from there. Did he ask or did you tell him?

She told him. "I had nothing to hide."

Did you feel a need to tell him about your being there?

"I guess I must have. I think the idea is silly and I don't agree with it at all."

Could this have been your way of telling him that you disagree with him? It reminds me of the way you told him about getting an apartment by leaving the letter for him to see.

"Maybe so. My father is funny. After they got through, he and Jack talked about the steel strike and how it affected each of their businesses. My father said he hated for things to be like that but he still regarded me as a child and they couldn't be uneasy about what happened to me. They shook hands and we left. They are always worried about whether I have been killed or hurt or raped when I am out after dark. I can't stand to live with that."

What?

"Fears like that. I don't like to think about things like that all the time." Pause. "Did you see that movie on TV last night?"

What was it?

The "Snake Pit." Talked about it with great concern, Particularly struck by Hester who didn't talk and was lonely and had no friends and who held up her fists before her face when people came near and was afraid. Didn't feel sorry for the main character. Didn't think she was really sick at all. Describes interaction between main character and Hester in which she made friends and first time Hester spoke was when other girl left. At that time main character said, "I know you will get well now because you have talked." It sounded silly or lame.

Sometimes it is hard to communicate entirely in words.

"Yes. After movie I felt I would like to go to a state hospital. My family thought this was silly."

I wonder why Hester impressed you so much. Could it be that you are trying to tell me something about your own feelings or ask me a question about yourself?

"At the time I didn't think about it that way but I guess I do feel like that, misunderstood and all."

"My family just doesn't appreciate the things I do. Mother is right, I just don't belong in the family. They say it is abnormal for someone my age to enjoy classical music, that should come only after years of maturing. They make fun of WFMT and said 90 per cent of people like popular music, why should I be different? They say I'm trying to grow up too soon."

How do you see your parents' attitude toward you?

"They don't want me to have my independence. They want to keep me a baby and under their wing."

And how do you think they really feel about you?

"They must hate me now. So much has happened. I don't see how they could still care."

You must feel hurt when you think they don't care.

"No, I don't care if they care, if they would just leave me alone."

"Mother says I'm 'normal,' why do I have to go around making myself depressed? I don't make myself depressed. Nobody likes to be depressed. They don't understand how anyone in their family could ever need a psychiatrist. I guess I really don't belong in the family after all."

You haven't always felt that way.

"I thought maybe Mrs. Marshall could make them understand." Turns out she told her parents that Mrs. Marshall wanted to see them. This was her idea and not Mrs. Marshall's. They went grudgingly and for a while she "got her freedom" but it didn't last long. (Mrs. Marshall is the former social worker-therapist.)

Some way to communicate with your family?

"But it didn't work."

The indirect way isn't too successful, is it?

Long pause. "Are all nurses so mean?"

What do you think about that?

Told incident of nurse luring patient out of locked room (in movie) by telling her that husband was there. She came out of her own accord. "Think that was very bad, to fool her like that."

Pause. "This week end I just withdrew to my room and didn't come out except for meals." Pause. "I don't know what he was trying to prove, but my father told me about a man he knew who came back from the war and wouldn't come out of his room or anything and he eventually was hopeless and in a mental hospital for life."

Sounds as if he was trying to frighten you.

Not consciously.

*I wonder if you are asking me, through the movie and telling me
your father's attitude, how sick you are and what my ideas about this
are.*

"I think I'm O.K. (*with some assurance*). I just wish things were
different with my family."

Long pause. Looks over room. Eyes light on doll house, flicker of
pleasure.

The doll house?

"Yes. I had one just like that. It was always falling down. I liked
the bathroom best." Pause.

Any particular reason?

"No, it was just nice. It was so small and there were so many things
that had to be fitted in. Playing with glass in the alley."

Long pause. "That was really a terrible thing my father did last
Saturday night but he had to do it."

Did you have a choice of where to call him from?

"No, where we were going didn't have a phone. (*Long pause.*) And
that is bad too because I don't like the thing with Jean." *Stopped her
to have her tell me who she was talking about. How do you feel about
her?* "Oh, she's just horrible. No, she's not really horrible but I don't
like what she is doing." Talked about her wanting to sleep with two
fellows at once.

*I was visibly surprised and anxious. Made communication inter-
pretation. You mean she was going to sleep with both men?*

"She goes from one guy to another."

Why do you think she is doing this?

"She is looking for something I suppose."

Do you think she is successful in finding it?

"No, she is just mixing herself up even more."

*Do you think you may have some of these same feelings about your-
self?*

Surprise. "What do you mean?"

I mean from your family's point of view.

"No, I'm trying to straighten myself out, that's the reason I'm coming for therapy. My family expects so many things. They want me to
do my own washing and ironing. I hate ironing and I have a big bag
in my room. They say I don't do anything creative. I can't tell you
exactly how I feel."

"I feel like I am in a tunnel and I keep going but I don't see the
way out."

A tunnel always has two openings.

Surprise. "Well, I guess I just want to be free. Why am I in a tunnel
anyway?"

Well, to take it away from the symbols, everyone has this kind of problem to a greater or lesser extent depending on his own life circumstances. It seems that your tunnel may just be longer than average—your problem is more complicated.

"I just want to break out and be free, but my parents won't let me."

Do you see the solution to the problem as necessarily involving some change in your parents?

"You know, I guess if I really wanted to be free from them I wouldn't care what they think or how they feel."

Pause. "I just hope I don't do something silly. I'm so impulsive. It's as if waves come up over me, and it starts at the feet and right now it is about up to my neck."

You seem to be describing an emotion by using the symbol of the wave. Do you know what the emotion is you feel at these times? Let's see if we understand.

"Well, I don't know but it just wells up."

Is it anger—fear—some other feeling?

"It was stronger than my fear of pain."

Are you aware of the quality of the feeling?

"No, I guess not."

Felt that she brought up this subject at this point to see if I would extend the hour. I didn't. Made arrangements for next week.

Got up and at the door she said thank you.

Wished her Merry Christmas.

COMMENT: The unfortunate accidental setting of this interview facilitated regressive attitudes, since it was a child therapy playroom. Patient tells how she acted out the impulse to communicate her sexual relationship with her boy friend to father implicitly to create trouble and win the father to herself. She says it was terrible, yet there was no affect to this contrived scene. She brings out the "adoption fantasy," indicating the wish not to belong to father's family and hence not be restricted by taboos. As the therapist brings out the "indirect message" technique, however, the patient becomes increasingly uncomfortable as evidenced by her metaphorical allusions to the psychotic patient in the movie "Snake Pit." She reacts to the tunnel symbolism and the therapist's supposedly optimistic promise of an opening with mounting anxiety of impending disintegration as a wave coming over her. This could lead her to flee from insight and symbolic openings for understanding into impulsive acting out. The therapist focused correctly on the patient's content; namely, her implicit attachment to the father, the wish not to leave him, and missed the anxiety as it mounted and threatened to break through into her habitual acting-out pattern.

Its recognition in view of the patient's history would have led the therapist to slow down the threatened insight and deal realistically with the threats to behavior which could be self-destructive.

ACTIVITY

In our treatment we are considerably more active than those individuals who model their therapy after the psychoanalytic pattern. Strupp has shown that the most experienced therapists are much more active, whereas the younger, less experienced ones are passive as if they await the patient's insight and his communication to the therapist of what should be interpreted. We are active in that we narrow the transaction to a specific therapeutic focus; we communicate adequately with the patient, avoiding long silences and the continued impassivity of a nonparticipant. Not only do we narrow the transaction to a specific therapeutic focus for the subject of communication but, when we perceive that this specific transaction has been satisfactorily understood, we also shift the transactional focus to a new therapeutic problem.

As the transaction develops, the therapist chooses the therapeutic unit and is then often under pressure by the patient to leave the field and talk about "anything else" or the patient may insist "there is nothing more to say." Maintaining the focus should be clearly one of the therapist's responsibilities. Likewise, the therapist decides when to move on and choose a new focus not passively in terms of "let's see what comes next," but by a considered decision based on questions remaining unanswered in the previous therapeutic unit.

As a general rule psychiatrists, just as they permit more anxiety, tend to be more active in therapy than social workers and often control the transactions somewhat roughly. Following is an example of such a procedure in contrast to the technique elucidated in Case 20.

CASE **23**

PATIENT is an unmarried nineteen-year-old doctor's office assistant, formerly a student nurse, who has been in treatment for eight months because of uncontrolled crying and dissociative episodes after beginning her second year of nurse's training. These were precipitated by calls from a boy friend whom the patient did not want to see but who was the choice of her parents. She stated that her problem involved a struggle between her needs to become independent versus doing what her parents wished. She was the second of three siblings (others were male) of a Midwestern Presbyterian family. The father was a civil engineer, a critical person with all of his family, but one whom patient saw as depreciating to mother and all women generally. Mother was an attractive, aggressive woman who treated patient as a potential competitor, who made patient feel that she should not grow up (*e.g.*, censored patient's reading material), and implicitly presented to patient the maxim: Do as I say, not as I do.

Sixty-second Session

ON THE PREVIOUS WEEK END the patient's parents had visited her, and father had criticized her for not getting a job where she could get ahead; mother had agreed with father; patient had gotten angry at them because she had just asked for a pay raise and felt proud about getting it.

Patient (*after short silence*): I'm still a little upset by something about my parents' visit (*short silence*).

Therapist Did you ask them to come visit you?

Patient Yes, I asked them up; I just wanted to have them come see me. Why do they have to be so contrary? It seems as if they can never agree with me. (*Silence.*) Oh! I've been thinking—I want to move away from where I'm living now. The woman I live with is kind of balmy. She's always asking me to come and watch TV with her; to find out what I'm doing. I tell her "right away" but I'm not interested in talking to her. She tells me about her sons-in-law, whom she doesn't like. I have my own things to think about. I would like to move into an apartment with a girl friend. She's coming to school in Chicago this fall.

Therapist Seems as if your concern about your parents' visit and your desire to move are related.

Patient My parents might make a fuss or they might not, but it wouldn't make me change my mind.

Therapist Your concern about their visit might be related to what happened Saturday (when patient asked for and got raise in pay).

Patient What? Oh! (*smiling*) about the job—surprised by that myself.

Therapist And then father comes along and says it's not enough, and suggests a change that might not even interest you. Nothing can please him.

Patient What did you say? (*Long silence.*) I think my father might be the way he is because he was never around much—he missed the boat about having children and now wants his children to be like they were when he was gone. Do you think that might be right?

Therapist   Do you think that your father wants to relive what he missed previously in relation to you and your brothers?

Patient   Yes.

Therapist   In the past you were angry at your father for not being around when he was needed and because when he was around all he did was criticize. He asked more than you were able to give, and things that you might not have wanted for yourself. Now he comes up on Sunday and is critical and demanding again. You're angry again, but I wonder if part of this is because you wonder what my response will be to your moving—whether I will ask too much or be critical.

Patient   (*silence*): not sure if right or wrong in the past.

Therapist   About what?

Patient   Well, last year I wanted to move, but could not afford it financially. Remember? But you said it was running away. (Therapist's actual interpretation at that time now thrown back at him.)

Therapist   And now?

Patient   I don't think so. Then I thought you were criticizing me.

Therapist   I asked you to think before you acted—so you would know what you're doing. It seems as if you've thought this move through.

Patient   Oh! (*smiling*) yes, (*silence*). You know, I'm not sure that I can say it—how I feel; but now I can see for the first time that I can be happy about living—that I can enjoy things.

Sixty-third Session

Patient   Maybe it's a phase I'm going through. Not meeting any young men—well, not the right kind.

Therapist   Are you looking?

Patient   Don't know.

Therapist   I don't understand.

Patient   Well, I've been thinking of Dr. A. again, and I would like to have him return my feelings. He has a number of fine qualities. I know that he doesn't go out with anyone else.

Therapist   Is this the Dr. A. that you told me of going out with once before?

Patient   Yes. He seems to be burying himself in his work. (*Short silence.*) I guess I don't have the stuff. Then there's a pharmacist who works upstairs in the building where I am. He told B. (the other young woman who works with patient in doctor's office) that he was going to ask me out—about a week ago—said something about it recently too. He probably won't because maybe he doesn't see anything in me.

Guess part of it is my fault—I don't smile—don't respond to greetings by young men—always seem to be thinking.

Therapist   About what?

Patient   Things I have to do—have done—have not done. But the good part of this is that it protects me.

Therapist   From what?

Patient   (*sighing—brings hands up to face—tearful—silence*).

Therapist   Both of us know this is an old pattern of yours—falling back or not knowing; being helpless as a child. You really do know what you need to protect yourself from.

Patient   I feel like a failure (*tears*) and I have to protect myself against this feeling of being a failure. I don't want to be hurt.

Therapist   You failed once (*meaning with father*)—so do all girls. What do you expect now?

Patient   All right, so I failed once, twice, three, or four times; but I feel that I can do nothing but fail all of the time.

Therapist   What if you had succeeded?

Patient   I'd be surprised. I couldn't believe it.

Therapist   Maybe you have more concern with success than you think?

Patient (*silence*): You make me so angry—you act as if you don't know what I'm telling you.

Therapist   Yes, what?

Patient   I want to have a man return my feelings for him (*exasperated*).

Therapist   You've been talking about wanting to be accepted as a woman. You've made some moves in that direction. I think you're concerned now whether I will accept that—whether I will like you and accept you as a woman.

Patient   I haven't been aware of that.

Therapist   I wonder what makes you feel that I don't accept you?

Patient   I feel that you think of me as a failure. That I am not moving toward being a woman fast enough.

Therapist   Last week you spoke of your father being critical of you; of your not being good enough for him, and his criticizing whatever progress you made. You seem to interpret what I say or don't say as criticism of your being a woman as if your father were saying it.

Patient   Guess it happens that sometimes I confuse you with my father.

COMMENT: In these two sessions, which are typical of the patient's transactions with the therapist, her explicit role is that of a young adult working and striving toward independence from controlling and directing parents and current parental figures. Implicitly she longs for the childlike dependent role with its praise and affection from father, easily collapsing with tears and helplessness at criticism, and conversely bubbling with joy and happiness at praise and approval. Implicit in the transaction is her fascination with the therapist and its accompanying guilt with the expectation that with him, as with father and all men, she is doomed to fail.

The therapist explicitly wants his patient to move away from her dependence, but at first his implicit role is pushing and ambitious for her while at the same time controlling. He wants her to be independent but accuses her of running away, making her more ashamed and helpless. Correcting this results in the patient's temporary joy. Then, feeling less a child, her sexual feelings for the therapist increase and she expects rejection and failure. At once the therapist dissociates himself from the father and makes clear the difference between himself and the patient's expectation that he will be like her father. The transaction, however, is being *pushed vigorously* by the therapist's therapeutic ambitions and his implicit acceptance of her affection, despite his words, as specific and personal, for his own gratification. This dooms the patient to another future failure. Thus, around the axes of both dependency and sexuality, the therapist is sending contradictory messages. As a result there is a rapid movement by the patient, oscillating between the two axes, which has to be resolved to avoid her giving up hope completely and becoming deeply depressed and/or substituting her own fantasy solutions for a contradictory reality.

Understanding and interpreting implicit roles

When mutual understanding has been achieved within the explicit roles of patient and therapist, much information is communicated by the patient. This eventually becomes repetitive, even though the contents vary, since the pattern is clearly understood.

At this point, or "set," the therapist communicates his understanding of the patient's *implicit* role and the role the patient is attempting to ascribe or induce in him, but rejects it and avoids complementarity. By recognizing and rejecting these implicit role relations, the therapist turns the patient toward the reality of the transaction and exerts pressure for understanding and the search for meaning. There may be resentment, anger, or rage at frustration, anxiety may mount, subterfuges develop, and manipulations occur, but, if the therapist is firm, new solutions are sought. Some of these ways may be equally unrealistic, but finally a fit between implicit and explicit roles is achieved, repeated in form with different contents in "working through," and learning is consolidated. The therapist then has a sense of closure and knows that the therapeutic unit has been concluded.

In the process of communication the therapist becomes an instrument. He has knowledge of the three forms of language of communication—the verbal, nonverbal, and paralingual. He is aware of the effects of the patient's communications on himself and observes the patient's responses for indications of what effect his communications have had on the patient. Thus the therapist is engaged, as he *participates* with the patient in a back-and-forth series of communications, in observing responses both in the patient and in himself. In that sense he becomes an *observer*. The effective nature of his communications on the patient is determined by the patient's responses. The implicit aspects of the patient's responses are revealed by the impact on the therapist. Obviously this instrument is never completely *accurate*. Supervision in training as well as personal analysis broaden the range of the therapist's awareness. This never becomes complete but expands step by step as he becomes more skilled in sensing implicit roles in the patient and in himself. Furthermore, as supervision occurs, the therapist gradually learns to alter his way of thinking so that he may become more sensitive to the implicit roles of both himself and his patient.

The therapist and patient characteristically approach each other with awareness of their explicit roles and come together repeatedly with messages which are explicitly clear, but those that are not clear emanate from the implicit roles of each one of the participants. It is the implicit roles that carry with them the emotional, the expressive, and the neurotic behavior. The therapist should not assume complete complementarity with the patient's implicit roles; instead, his function is to make explicit by communication to the patient what his implicit roles really are. Thus the therapist primarily searches for information, and the interventions consist of making clear to the patient the information he has obtained about his implicit roles.

We do not invite dreams, nor, when they are recounted, do we interpret them except when indicated in the focus of the current transaction. Dreams are communicated to us as messages in their manifest content, which we use along with other information. Because of the lack of emphasis on dream material, the patient soon learns not to use the dream as a means of avoiding direct communication. He does not practice remembering them, nor does he assume that without them communication is not possible.

We attempt to avoid a transference neurosis and are helped by the fact that psychotherapeutic interviews are not conducted with greater frequency than once or twice a week. We thereby avoid regression and the development of highly infantile dependent relationships with the therapist. We do not call for free associations, but ask for responses within the form of our communications. Nevertheless, without the invitation, we find that patients spontaneously communicate freely and in doing so are often able to relinquish conscious controls and liberate their preconscious processes of thinking, thereby exposing the distorted and repetitive unconscious controls. When a transference neurosis seems to be developing, we counteract the process by making as quick and as broad a generalization from the personal communication as possible.

Although we do not invite—and we certainly avoid—the transference neurosis whenever possible, we are obviously still dealing with transference phenomena, which is another way of saying that we are dealing with back-and-forth implicit communications between therapist and patient in which the present is colored by the past. The patient, by virtue of his role, develops a dependent feeling, for he needs help. And we as therapists, once we have committed ourselves to him, have a positive helping attitude. In our wish to help him, we express a respect for his capacity to grow and to develop. We assume the role of a supporting figure which, however, has within it the price of renunciation of immature forms of communication when they no longer are necessary or helpful.

Respect for the patient also involves honesty on the part of the therapist in admitting his positive and negative feelings as they are recognized within the therapeutic transaction. Particularly is this true in schizophrenics who are able to observe the slightest cues in paralingual and motor behavior indicating annoyances and irritations on the part of their therapists. To deny the existence of these, if the therapist has sufficient insight into himself, is to block or distort the communication process.

The therapist successfully communicates permissiveness which encourages his patient to achieve his desire to return and belong to the group. He helps the patient communicate about himself by substituting verbalizations for neurotic acting out or visceral language. Since the patient cannot achieve insight into his own neurotic processes, he depends upon information from the therapist in the two-person system as to how he seeks out stimuli to elicit old learned responses and hence perpetuate his neurotic behavior.

The therapist's implicit roles often represent his own failures in consciously understanding and in communication. These, too, are understood only by observing their effects on his patient which are different from his expectations. These misunderstandings are what Rioch believes have been termed "countertransference difficulties." Otherwise, the therapist must rely on his supervisor or some nonparticipant observer to understand what disturbs communication with his patient. With experience and supervision he may begin to recognize more and more of his distorted implicit responses, but never entirely. However, this is a learning process for the therapist resulting in more accurate perceptions of the patient's communications and less distortion in his own. His instrument becomes more refined.

DIRECTIVE TACTICS

In psychotherapy there is considerably more direction and control than, for example, in psychoanalysis. This does not mean that the psychoanalyst does not select what he considers to be most meaningful in associations, does not choose interpretations, or impart judgments and values. These are all true, but to lesser degree and in more subtle forms.

In the transactional approach "acting out" instead of communicating verbally may be directly interdicted. Value judgments regarding the patient's antecedent behavior in terms of what was good for him may be explicitly stated. Value judgments concerning future behavior and expectations are expressed for the benefit of the patient. Approval or disapproval, including justified anger at behaviors in the transaction, are salutary expressions of reality. It is not necessary in psychotherapy to maintain an exclusive or continuous positive relationship.

We attempt to avoid as much as possible what has been called the symmetrical relationship which especially occurs in treating schizophrenics, whose loss of self-esteem prevents them from daring to relate in complementarity. They avoid knowing themselves by assuming various roles as if they were someone else, or defend themselves by learning by imitation or by becoming like the therapist. Thus we try to avoid permitting the patient to become anonymous, intellectualizing, or talking persistently about others. We persist in expecting that the patient will accept our attitude of respect and consider himself fitting to enter a complementary relationship with us.

In relation to the real life of the patient, we encourage him to experiment in relationships outside of the therapeutic situation, accepting whatever failures or successes may be reported as part of the learning process. In this context we refer the reader to the operational concept that knowing and action are inseparable. As others have stated: knowledge without action is futile. Trial action is necessary for confidence. This requires that which many deterministic therapies deny—the existence of a psychological function of "will power." Perhaps this is one of the autonomous functions of the ego, but without it therapy may drag on endlessly and dependency may be prolonged. Knowledge is necessary, but "will power" and action must follow.

THE THERAPIST AS INSTRUMENT

The only tool or instrument used in psychotherapy is the personality of the therapist. The transactional approach makes special use of the reverberating feedback effects of conversations between therapist and patient. The patient utilizes his expressive roles to indicate the emotional impact of the therapist's messages. The therapist *feels* the impact of the patient's messages. For this function he needs a great deal of understanding of self, achieved by an ability to communicate with his internal psychological process.

Psychoanalysts emphasize the interfering role of countertransferences because of the original Freudian concept that the therapist should be a blank screen on which the patient projects his feelings. At the same time transference communications are considered to be valid manifestations of the patient's feelings.

The "blank-screen concept" has only slowly dissolved, and countertransference is still considered as a problem. Granted that the therapist should be as healthy mentally as possible, this is a desideration now infrequently achieved and not likely ever to result after many trips to the analytic couch. The patient is expected to develop a transference neurosis but, as Wolstein[2] says, that of the analyst is denied or hidden. He points out that analysis is an experiential field in which roles are frequently reversed; in other words, the patient may also become a participant-observer.

Wolstein enumerates five qualities in a classification of analysts' countertransference: the over-protective nurturing; the aggressive dependent; the overtly modally adjusted; the obsessional critical; and the detached. These are general and descriptive categories and do not take into account the myriad live and changing emotional attitudes in the therapist that arise in response to the patient's messages and are specific to the transactions of the moment.

Adequate emotional responses to the patient's messages are indicators of meanings implicitly conveyed by the patient. These in turn lead the therapist to feed back his understanding to the patient. In other words, transference and countertransference attitudes and feelings are fully utilized as recognitions of implicit meanings in the transactional communications. When, however, the emotional responses of therapist or patient are inadequate, the subsequent communication to the patient indicates misunderstanding which causes the beginning of disequilibrium in the transactional focus and disruption of the progress toward closure. The therapist's feelings are the only sensitive instrument that he has available. This tool needs great care, frequent calibration, and many practice readings. Eventually it can become a trustworthy instrument.

Since the therapist is an instrument through which the therapeutic influences emanate, his personality needs to be freed from its compulsive rigidities and restrictions. Often for this purpose he requires insight that can be achieved only by personal therapy or psychoanalysis.

Freedom of his personality, imagination, capacity for empathy and identification—all signs of creativity—are necessary for the adequate receipt of communications from his patient. A sense of timing for the proper messages to be given to his patient and the recognition of implicit aspects of these messages constitute the art of psychotherapy. Based on the capacity for self-communication and on the release of creativity, the therapist learns, develops, and improves his art. These are elements that are emotionally learned—they cannot be taught by rote.

There are many more technical, tactical, and theoretical problems to be resolved for the transactional approach. We have stressed repeatedly that we are experimenting with an approach for better understanding of what goes on between therapist and patient. We have applied the transactional approach to five demarcated areas of social work functions, but we do not present it as a novel, separate form of therapy nor do we propose a school, movement, or cult based on its approaches. The transactional approach may be applied to the analysis of system relationships, concept relationships, and personal relationships. For the two-person system of psychiatric interviewing and treatment it promises better understanding as well.

For what kind of patients is it applicable? What kind of therapist is best able to use it? For what purposes is it best suited? What therapeutic results does it achieve? How much permanent, and how extensive, personality reorganization, growth, and change does it initiate? These are questions that remain to be answered from ongoing and new researches hopefully to begin in a large number of clinics.

At the present time the teaching of the transactional approach requires corrective techniques to help the therapist alter his previous semipsychoanalytic methods which represent attempts to apply theories of analysis directly to psychotherapy. This is why the comments after each session of Case 20 point out more erroneous than correct communications. Supervisors should consistently use the transactional approach in discussions. For example, what is divulged in the session is not "material" or substance that the patient should "face" as if he had to be turned to view a disagreeable scene or physical structure, i.e., "Look at the dirt you have made." But the essence of the transaction is always a series of reverberating communications indicating role processes in which both patient and therapist as well as student and supervisor are currently and vitally involved.

One of us (R.R.G.) has used the transactional approach in the teaching not only of social workers but also of psychiatrists, psychologists, social scientists, and even biologists. Many problems develop in such attempts. First and most important is the vocabulary which is somewhat different from other technical usage, although it is easier and more related to ordinary language. But the correct use of language is based on corresponding logic and syntax of internal thinking and speech. This requires change from other systems and at first evokes resistance and confusion. We believe these difficulties are worth enduring.

Thus, only the rudiments of technique or tactics of psychotherapy utilizing the transactional approach have been outlined in this chapter. Further observations, descriptions, and experimentations are necessary to extract more rigorous definitions from the vast reservoir of the art of treatment. This is necessarily a continuous and never-ending process in all psychotherapies.

REFERENCES

1. Lichtenberg, P., Kohrman, R., and MacGregor, H.: *Motivation for Child Psychiatry Treatment.* New York: Russell & Russell, 1960.
2. Wolstein, B.: *Countertransference.* New York: Grune, 1959; *Transference: Its Meaning and Function in Psychoanalytic Therapy.* New York: Grune, 1954.

Précis

W<small>E HAVE OUTLINED</small> the present-day dilemma of the caseworker-
psychotherapist and have developed a method of analysis of social
work functions and a theoretical framework which led to a transactional approach. This was exemplified in four areas of functioning and
illustrated with selected case examples. We then redefined transactional theory and its operational techniques.

As theory and technique developed hand in hand, they were utilized
for teaching and supervising psychiatric residents and clinical psychologists. The concomitant methods of thinking and vocabulary have
"caught on" in our clinic and hospital despite the still overwhelming
influences of the psychoanalytical model. We have been wary of
promulgating our ideas as a "system of therapy" because we are not
ready to attempt the development of criteria for its choice and for
evaluating its results. This is a task for the future. Until then we make
only minor claims: The transactional approach minimizes the impeding
effects of the psychoanalytical or "internal dynamic" model on psychotherapy. The transactional approach is an effective way to further
understanding by therapist—and hence by patient—of contemporary
real-life problems and how to solve them, and of facilitating "change"
within the patient.

Index

abreaction, 101, 113; defined, 121
achieved role, 15
Ackerman, N., 116
acting out, 9, 96, 142, 159, 167, 193, 245, 249, 255, 271, 317
activity, in transaction, 318
adaptation, 296
adaptational psychotherapy, 121
adjustment, as goal of social casework, 4
affect, 169, 172, 204
affective response, 139
aggression, 149, 158, 161, 175; child-hood, 273; frustration and, 163; murder and, 40; projected, 89; sexuality and, 245; theory of, 297
"aha" reaction, in closure, 304
alcoholism, 48, 50, 79
Alexander, F., 17, 110, 112, 122
alter (ego), in role theory, 15
ambivalence, 179
American culture, framework of, 5
amnesia, 53, 56
analysis, distributive, 119–120; among social workers, 130
analyst, "blank-screen" characteristic of, 294, 326; see also psychoanaly-sis; psychoanalyst

anamnesis, 119
anger, 50, 201–202, 248, 251, 269–270
"anniversary syndrome," 76
anxiety, 77–78, 90, 99, 111, 154–155, 175, 203, 267; as factor in recom-mendations, 66; handling of, in transaction, 312–313; theories of, 297; of therapist, 149, 152, 167; transaction and, 41
approval, need for, 168
armed services, 5; see also World War II
ascribed role, 15, 36, 322
assigned role, 88, 141, 175, 200
associations, blocking of, 45
assumed role, 15, 36, 94, 138
Austin, L. N., 111, 116
authoritative interpretation, 98–100
authoritative role, 149; rejection of, 141
authority, revolt against, 142

Bales, R. F., 19
Bateson, G., 11–12
Beck, S., 283
behavior, language phenomena and, 13; verbal and nonverbal, 11; see also communication; role(s)